Children's Literature for Dramatization

Under the Advisory Editorship
of
J. Jeffery Auer

Children's Literature for Dramatization:

An Anthology

GERALDINE BRAIN SIKS
Associate Professor, University of Washington

HARPER & ROW, PUBLISHERS
NEW YORK, EVANSTON, AND LONDON

Library of Congress catalog card number: 64-18491

To Charles, Jan, and Mark and
my mother, Alice Pearl Brain, a rare storyteller

Contents

vii

THREE—POETRY MOTIVATING CONFLICT   44

FOUR—STORIES FOR YOUNG CHILDREN   82

Preface

This book has been written in response to requests from teachers and youth leaders for easily available dramatic stories and verse for children. It is intended to be used in conjunction with my text *Creative Dramatics: An Art For Children* (Harper & Row, 1958) which emphasizes philosophy and techniques. This anthology came into being as a result of creative dramatics teaching in elementary and junior high schools, in community programs, in universities, in children's observation classes, and in workshops for teachers and youth leaders. The collection grew slowly, like a stream that steadily etches its way downward from a hillside spring and is not particularly evident until some years later, when its presence becomes clear.

This is the way the anthology developed. While teaching creative dramatics over the past twenty years, a variety of children's literature was explored and shared with children for dramatic interpretation. Some of the selections were recognized, at once, as sure-fire dramatic material. When this recognition was evident the selections were shared, frequently with different groups of children. Teachers and leaders requested copies of these particular selections from time to time so that they, in turn, might share them with their children. In some instances a poem was not always available for reprinting, or a story was not always written down in the form in which it had been told.

On many occasions children asked if they might "play" a particular tale or a certain kind of story, such as a legend, a fable, a story they had seen on television, or an episode from a book which a child had enjoyed particularly and had brought to class to share. In many instances these stories were in narrative form, often with plots which digressed in rambling, related episodes. When these stories were told or read to children for dramatization it was evident that the children and teachers alike found difficulty in clarifying the dramatic line of action. Groups bogged down consistently when they attempted to analyze and reconstruct narrative story form into dramatic form. It was evident, also, that children responded consistently to the challenge of character analysis and original interpretation in scenes of conflict. For these reasons dramatic adaptations were made of stories which appealed to children but were extremely narrative in form. Plots were strengthened by tightening episodes and placing story events into fewer places of action, and characterizations, when needed, were given fuller development. After an adapted story had been told to children and interpreted by them through creative dramatics, further revisions were made whenever it appeared advisable. Thus, by a continuous process of developing dramatic materials this collection of stories and verse evolved.

Colleagues, classroom teachers, youth leaders, and students throughout the country participated in similar searches for dramatic materials for children. During the past decade particularly, thanks to the Children's Theatre Conference Division of the American Educational Theatre Association and to leading educational associations concerned with children and youth, there has been a noticeable exchange of dramatic materials by teachers and leaders. Some of the outstanding "findings" of others are, also, included here.

As a result of research over a long period of time this anthology brings together more than eighty poems and fifty stories, each of which has been dramatized by children with zest and belief. Like life itself, the dramatic situations represented here span the gamut of human feelings from awe to awfulness and from great good sense to great good nonsense.

Poetry includes dramatic nursery rhymes and many favorite poems of children by well-known poets as well as popular new, dramatic poems by new poets. Brief dramatic interpretations may be motivated quite readily by poetry. It has been found that the vividness of the sensory image in a poem affects a child's emotional response in turn frequently stimulating a spontaneous and original dramatic interpretation. Poetry has not been categorized according to age level appeal but rather according to dramatic content, for it has been shown that poetry with its various moods reflects generally the universal wonderings of children.

Stories include original tales by children, original stories and adaptations by adults who understand and enjoy children and who have guided them in creative dramatics; folk and fairy tales from fourteen different lands; tales from Greek and Norse mythology; episodes from biblical literature; true tales and modern realistic and fantasy tales by well-known authors who hold strong favor with children and youth. Stories for younger children are those whose themes reflect the very elements of the struggles in real life dramas for fours, fives and sixes—searching, exploring, surviving, learning, listening, thinking, loving, obeying.

Stories for older children reveal the imaginative and heroic world which is their life. What heroes! What exemplars!—Robin Hood and his merry company of right with might men; gods and goddesses with majesty, wrath, and magic equal only to faithful Noah's encounter with the first bow of light; noble princes enchanted as ugly beasts and toads; fun-loving Tom and Huck with wary eyes alert for Injun Joe; loveable Jo, Meg, Amy, and Beth and a hundred more heroes who *are* the real "stuff of life" for red-blooded boys and girls who cry out for action, excitement and adventure.

The anthology has been organized to facilitate its use. All art is orderly; beneath every man's search for beauty in expression there is profound order. If children are to enjoy the spontaneous freedom of believable expression in story dramatization they need to be introduced to the basic elements of drama in a step-by-step procedure over a period of time. There is no other way to build a secure foundation for dramatic expression except by orderly experiences which begin with expression in the simplest forms and lead gradually to the complex form of story dramatization. In this collection the poetry and stories are categorized according to dramatic content, in order of simplicity. Contents are arranged as follows: First an Introduction by Gregory A. Falls; Chapter One—Poetry Inviting Action; Chapter Two—Poetry

Inviting Characterization; Chapter Three—Poetry Motivating Conflict; Chapter Four—Stories for Young Children; and Chapter Five—Stories for Older Children.

A suggestion precedes each selection to strengthen its usefulness for adults who have had little or no training in creative dramatics. These suggestions are questions or comments intended to pique interest and offer ideas for imaginative or dramatic interpretation.

Although the poems and stories are intended chiefly for use in creative dramatics, they have been shared often with children for listening enjoyment. Many of the selections have been told or read by classroom teachers, children's drama leaders, nurses, librarians, occupational therapists, puppeteers, social workers, recreational leaders, mothers, fathers, grandmothers, and grandfathers. Good dramatic literature always entertains because drama, like life, has heart.

Many people have helped with this anthology. I am grateful to Gregory A. Falls for his perceptive Introduction, and to each one who contributed poetry, stories, and suggestions. Their specific contributions have been acknowledged individually throughout the book. I am appreciative as well to those who suggested dramatic materials which could not be included.

My thanks go, also, to many others: to various members of the Children's Theatre Conference of the American Educational Theatre Association, particularly Winifred Ward and Agnes Haaga; to teachers and school administrators, including Helen Olson and Louise Markert, Seattle Public Schools, and Adah Miner, Shoreline Public Schools; to the Seattle Public Library, especially the University Branch and Helen Skahill, Children's Librarian; to the Seattle Girl Scouts and Seattle Campfire Girls' Associations; to the Seattle Council of Churches; and to colleagues in the School of Drama, College of Education and Division of Evening and Extension Classes at the University of Washington.

My deepest appreciation is to the many children whose enjoyment of stories, poetry, and creative dramatics has been the catalyst which brought this particular collection into being.

GERALDINE BRAIN SIKS

Children's Literature
for Dramatization

Introduction

by **GREGORY A. FALLS***

There was a child went forth every day;
And the first object he looked upon and received with wonder, pity, love, or dread,
that object he became.

          WALT WHITMAN, *There Was a Child Went Forth*

    Recently after a public lecture on creative dramatics, a stage director commented to me, "Children discovered and practiced creative dramatics long before adults and teachers." And it is true that the fascinating mind of a young child finds much to explore and devise. This sheer joy of exploring the possibilities of a situation is one of the strongest recollections of my childhood. I can recall my mother remarking to me after a two-hour play session with another boy, that we had spent so much time preparing for a make-believe game of adventure, that we had no time left to actually play the events we had imagined. Although I thought my mother a very wise person, I was puzzled by her inability to see that the activity and imagination of "getting ready" was greater fun than ultimately acting out the whole story-game. Our greatest pleasure came from the unlimited possibilities of imagination, rather than taking time to enact only some parts of the game.

    This freedom of imagination that characterizes child-thought is both the envy and terror of the adult. The wild colorful painting, the antic dancing in infinite gyrations, and the complete acceptance of personification are but some of the freedoms shared by all children

---

* Dr. Falls is Executive Director of the School of Drama at the University of Washington.

1

and a few adults. A purple cow with two legs and no eyes can be perfectly acceptable—to the child artist, although similar freedom and abstraction by an adult artist antagonizes many of his peers.

In general, our process of education is a gradual disciplining of this free-wheeling child-mind into controlled intellectual, and logical experiences to the end that knowledge and judgment are acquired. This is a more efficient way of learning than trial and error which is the natural method of complete freedom. Channeling this free-wheeling imagination in the early disciplines of language, thought, and art begins the process of preparing it to recognize the order of what we know. Obviously the best education will demand this discipline and order, while still retaining and encouraging productive imagnation. Like many other methods of teaching, creative dramatics does encourage free imagination, while channeling it into more conceptual knowledge.

Three characteristics of early youth learning lend especial value to creative dramatics as a school discipline: imitation, direct confrontation, and free imagination. As a discipline it teaches the arts of the theatre, while in methodology it often directs children into corollary study of geography, social behavior, science, and the like.

Consider *imitation* first. At one level it is quite obvious that children learn many things such as language, walking, or games, by imitating adults and siblings. At a deeper level imitation is a basic human trait with profound implications. Mimesis, if not instinctive, is primal in man. From Frazer's classic study to the latest anthropological reports, research reveals how basic to primitive man are the laws of homeopathic magic. Whether the Osiris rites along the Nile, or the imitation of the kangaroo totem among the stone age primitives of present day Australia, we note that man has always imitated physical phenomena around him. From this imitation he has evolved imaginative stories, explanations, myths, and religions to explain the deeper meanings of these imitations. Thus, children and men imitate (mimesis), and in imitation find meaning. The arts of dance, theatre, painting, and music have both their origins and their profundity in imitation. They are at once a physical doing, and in the doing an understanding and a pleasure to man. It is not chance that the first drama critic began defining tragedy by saying it is an *imitation* of an action. Thus, creative dramatics with its first principles of imitation, or acting out, touches what may be an instinctive thinking process. In using imitation, creative dramatics begins with one natural method of the human mind and uses techniques of explanation found in every civilization. Through imitation it stimulates knowledge and perception in a way capable of beginning with the first simple understandings and progressing to man's most sublime thoughts. In brief, it teaches art.

The need for children to directly experiment with or confront new things is also obvious. Things must be touched, tasted, shaken, thrown. No new toy is real until the child has touched and personally manipulated it. The experience must be a direct confrontation. How else can it be really understood? Gift certificates are for adults. In creative dramatics the child is permitted to experiment or directly confront a number of human relations, emotions, and activities. Just as some adults learn much about psychology and human relationships from seeing plays or reading novels, so children can learn by imitation and acting out (direct confrontation). The meaning (the knowledge) comes first to children through the action, the doing, and only later in vicarious or reflective experiences. One understands the story when one can *do* it.

The third trait, free imagination, stands very close to a quality greatly respected by society: creativity. Children in their own way are highly creative because of their innate freedom of imagination. Although serious studies of creativity have been under way for about ten years at the University of California at Berkeley, too little is yet understood about it except that it is a priceless commodity in science, business, or art. Creative dramatics utilizes and challenges the imagination of the child. Although we cannot be sure what correlations there are between such challenges and later creative imagination, it does seem logical to assume that this "exercising" of the imaginaton is useful, if only to balance the rote or very disciplined study of other subjects such as spelling and penmanship. One suspects that creative dramatics' challenge to the child's imagination increases his capacity for imaginative thought and behavior. At the least it is a rich pleasure and perhaps at the most, a development of latent talents and appreciation.

From a more scholastic point of view, educators have established the value in elementary education of painting, music, and literature. Study and practice in these arts are considered important in child learning. Creative dramatics offers a similar value in the study of theatre arts. Just as the mature study of theatre teaches both *art* and *literature*, so does creative dramatics. In all arts there are two ways of study: doing (performing) and receiving (being an audience). Certainly for the youthful beginner the doing or performing of the art is fundamental to its study, whether it be painting, music, dance, or theatre. For children to perform as actors, playwrights and designers is for them to study the art in a direct, productive way.

Since theatre (or creative dramatics) is also a way of studying literature, it has an additional educational value. In some creative dramatics situations, the children create their own play, their own literature. They then work directly in the art of literature. In others, as this anthology will attest, they begin with formal literature. The first or primary experience in this case will be the reading (or the hearing of the reading) of the story or poem. If this direct reading experience is to be most meaningful, it will be followed by reflection, criticism and relation. This same sequence can be observed in any adult literary study, because it is fundamental to an appreciation of literature. Creative dramatics is an instrument for helping the young discover this formal, mature approach to literature. By dramatizing the story, the child is led through the techniques of reflection, criticism, and relation in ways that appeal directly to his understanding and perception.

For some years now, creative dramatics has been taught in public schools and many envision greater acceptance of it in curricula. This valuable and enlightened work is enhanced by additional formal literature for use in classes. Professor Siks has collected this anthology of literature from creative dramatics teachers in this country and from her own experiments with creative dramatics classes. Because the stories and poems have proved their appeal to children and have the seeds of interesting dramatic activity, this anthology is a contribution both to the art and to education.

CHAPTER ONE

Poetry inviting action

Let me laugh and dance and sing,
Youth is such a lovely thing.
ALINE WECHSLER, *Creative Power*, Hughes Mearns

What is art? . . . It's anything . . . you look at particularly, anything you see
particularly, anything you make particularly, anything you isolate particularly
. . . anything made by nature or by man deserves to be looked at particularly.
WILLIAM SAROYAN

A child and a poet are both aware; they look at life particularly. The poems that follow reflect universal delights of children. They invite *a child to do something particularly.*

Poems are arranged in order of simplicity. A teacher who is aware of his children's particular moods may recognize a poem which is "right" for dramatic enjoyment for a particular group on a particular day. When children are ready to express, a teacher's key words become: "Do it in your own way so long as you make us believe it is real and is truly happening to you."

Young children delight in rhythm and rhymes which invite immediate response in make-believe play. Children enjoy chanting or singing rhymes while others play that they are doing something particular.

PAT-A-CAKE

Cake-baking time holds appeal for children of all ages. Little children enjoy the pantomime of making a cake for Tommy or for one of

5

their friends' birthdays. To decorate a cake in one special way offers individual thought and delight.

> Pat-a-cake, pat-a-cake, baker's man
> Bake me a cake as fast as you can;
> Pat it and prick it, and mark it with T,
> Put it in the oven for Tommy and me.

TO MARKET

Everyone enjoys shopping. Children like to make believe they take turns going to market to buy a surprise for dinner or lunch. On other days they enjoy the make-believe of shopping for a toy, a present, something new to wear, or something needed.

> To market, to market,
>   To buy a fat pig.
> Home again, home again
>   Jiggety-jig.
> To market, to market,
>   To buy a fat hog,
> Home again, home again,
>   Jiggety-jog.

SPRING IS SHOWERY

Children enjoy charades. This rhyme lends itself to seasonal activities of both work and play, with children organized into four distinct groups for playing and guessing.

> Spring is showery, flowery, bowery;
> Summer: hoppy, croppy, poppy;
> Autumn: wheezy, sneezy, freezy;
> Winter: slippy, drippy, nippy.

YANKEE DOODLE

The rhythm of riding appeals to almost every child. A little child enjoys the make-believe of riding an imaginary pony, and pretending that he, too, rides to town to be in a parade with other children on their ponies. Original ideas come when each one decides what one thing he might put in his hat to dress for a parade. Some children enjoy thinking of a funny name to call whatever they wear in their hats.

> *Yankee Doodle went to town*
> *Riding on a pony,*
> *Stuck a feather in his hat*
> *And called it Macaroni.*

HAPPY BIRTHDAY

A birthday is a happy day. To sing the birthday song and panto-mime the giving of presents holds strong appeal. "Who would like to show the present he would like best to give to Jim on his birthday?" This kind of question generally invites immediate individual thought and expression.

> *Happy Birthday to you, Happy Birthday to You*
> *Happy Birthday, Happy Birthday*
> *Happy Birthday to You!*

SING A SONG OF SEASONS
by Alice Ellison[1]

Rhythms change with seasons and weather. Each arouses a different individual rhythm. Children are particularly alert to enjoyable

[1] By permission of the author. Miss Ellison lives in Thorp, Washington, and writes for local club groups, etc.

rhythms in seasonal games, sports, and activities. Children delight in considering seasonal activities at any time of year. They enjoy the make-believe which is motivated by a single verse or an entire poem such as the following.

> It's spring!
> Such a hippity, happity, hoppity
> First spring day.
> Let's play! Let's play! Let's play!
>
> It's summer!
> Such a swingy, swazy, lazy
> First hot day.
> Let's play! Let's play! Let's play!
>
> It's fall!
> Such a brisky, frisky, crispy,
> First fall day.
> Let's play! Let's play! Let's play!
>
> It's winter!
> Such a blowy, snowy, joy
> First winter day.
> Let's play! Let's play! Let's play!

AT THE SEASIDE

by Robert Louis Stevenson[2]

Playing on a shore arouses curiosity as shown in the following verse. Children like to make believe they are playing in the sand, which is what they enjoy the most at the seashore. They like to play in water when the tide comes in. Some children like to walk along a make-believe shore until they find a surprise washed in from the sea.

[2] From Robert Louis Stevenson, A Child's Garden of Verses, Charles Scribner's Sons, 1905.

When I was down beside the sea
A wooden spade they gave to me
To dig the sandy shore.
My holes were empty like a cup,
In every hole the sea came up.
Till it could come no more.

MERRY-GO-ROUND

by Geraldine Brain Siks

Because almost every child enjoys the rhythm of a merry-go-round, this verse invites enjoyment in rhythmic and dramatic play. Originality occurs when a child describes his pony and a particular view he sees as he rides, and shows how he rides.

I'm merry-go-erry—
    Whenever I ride
On a shiny pony with stirrups at his side.
I'm merry-go-erry—
    When around I go
With merry music, down-and-up, high-and-low.
I'm merry-go-erry—
    When I ride around
On a merry pony on a merry-go-round.

AFTERNOON ON A HILL

by Edna St. Vincent Millay[3]

Children experience beauty in individual ways. This poem invites a discussion of children's experiences. Discussion often leads to a desire for dramatic play by the group in which each child pantomimes his

[3] From *Collected Poems*, Harper & Row. Copyright 1917–1956 by Edna St. Vincent Millay. By permission of Norma Millay Ellis.

enjoyment of a hill. Frances Hufford[4] suggests using Grieg's "Morning" from *The Peer Gynt Suite* to heighten the mood.

> I will be the gladdest thing
> Under the sun!
> I will touch a hundred flowers
> And not pick one.
>
> I will look at cliffs and clouds
> With quiet eyes,
> Watch the wind bow down the grass,
> And the grass rise.
>
> And when lights begin to show
> Up from the town,
> I will mark which must be mine,
> And then start down.

MARCHING SONG

by Robert Louis Stevenson[5]

Children find curious delight in making music with combs. When their music becomes rhythmic they enjoy marching to it. Children like to take turns leading the march. What might a Commander do with his hands to lead marchers to make believe they make drum or trumpet music? What might a Commander do with his feet to command a march that is beautiful?

> Bring the comb and play upon it!
> Marching, here we come!
> Willie cocks his highland bonnet,
> Johnnie beats the drum.

[4] Frances Hufford teaches at Dale Mabry School, Tampa, Florida.
[5] From Robert Louis Stevenson, *op. cit.*

Mary Jane commands the party,
 Peter leads the rear;
Feet in time, alert and hearty,
 Each a Grenadier!

All in the most martial manner
 Marching double-quick;
While the napkin like a banner
 Waves upon the stick!

Here's enough of fame and pillage,
 Great commander Jane!
Now that we've been round the village,
 Let's go home again.

✓ GALOSHES

by Rhoda Bacmeister[6]

Galoshes and boots hold fascination for most children. They like to
walk and tramp in them. This verse invites discussion and an immediate desire to play. After walking rhythmically in make-believe galoshes
children enjoy the challenge of creating designs. A single question
often focuses thinking: "What is the prettiest slush picture your
galoshes might make as you slish and slosh?"

Susie's galoshes
Make splishes and sploshes
And slooshes and sloshes,
As Susie steps slowly
Along in the slush.

They stamp and they tramp
On the ice and concrete,
They get stuck in the muck and the mud;
But Susie likes much best to hear

[6] From the book *Stories to Begin On* by Rhoda W. Bacmeister. Copyright,
1940, by E. P. Dutton & Co., Inc. Reprinted by permission of the publishers.

The slippery slush
As it slooshes and sloshes
And splishes and sploshes,
All round her galoshes!

✓   MUD
by Polly Chase Boyden[7]

Mud has always intrigued children. They like to make mud pies and other creations as well as to feel mud with their toes. Recalling experiences with mud arouses empathy. This verse invites make-believe play which centers first in the delicious feel of mud. It may lead then to wading in mud to make a "mud picture or design." And, at last, to make a special mud thing.

Mud is very nice to feel
All squishy-squash between the toes!
I'd rather wade in wiggly mud
Than smell a yellow rose.

Nobody else but the rosebush knows
How nice mud feels
Between the toes!

PICNICKING
by Phyllis Lee Baird[8]

Picnics are happy occasions. Recalling picnics awakens children's enjoyment of playing and eating out-of-doors. This verse invites active dramatic play which may center in outdoor activities followed by pantomimes, as each picnicker in turn shows the food he most enjoys from a make-believe picnic table.

[7] From *Child Life* Magazine, Copyright 1930 by Rand McNally & Company.
[8] By permission of the author. Miss Baird, a nurse in Bellingham, Washington, writes poetry for her own and her patients' enjoyment.

Hooray! Hooray! Hooray!
We're off to the woods
For a picknicky day!
Hooray!

THE SWING

by Robert Louis Stevenson[9]

The rhythm of swinging has appealed to children for centuries. Children also find delight in the rhythm of making believe they swing. This verse is an old favorite. Swinging for enjoyment is heightened when children are invited to swing high enough in the air to see a most beautiful thing they want to tell others about.

How do you like to go up in a swing,
    Up in the air so blue?
Oh, I do think it the pleasantest thing
    Ever a child can do!

Up in the air and over the wall,
    Till I can see so wide,
Rivers and trees and cattle and all
    Over the countryside—

Till I look down on the garden green,
    Down on the roof so brown—
Up in the air I go flying again,
    Up in the air and down!

HAPPY THOUGHT

by Robert Louis Stevenson[10]

Happiness is individual. Children respond to discussions of happiness and to dramatizations of moments of happiness. A child likes to

[9] From Robert Louis Stevenson, *op. cit.*
[10] *Ibid.*

look ahead and make believe he does the one thing he most enjoys seeing an adult do for pleasure or what he will do for his life's work when he is grown up.

> The world is so full of a number of things,
> I'm sure we should all be as happy as kings.

✓ MY SHADOW
by Robert Louis Stevenson[11]

Shadows interest children. This poem invites creative shadow play. Children delight in teaching a shadow how to play. Questions, such as these, focus thinking for variety in rhythmic play: "What is the most interesting game you might teach your shadow to play by using your hands? by using your head? by using your whole self? by dancing with your shadow?"

> I have a little shadow that goes in and out with me,
> And what can be the use of him is more than I can see,
> He is very, very like me from the heels up to the head;
> And I can see him jump before me, when I jump into my bed.

> The funniest thing about him is the way he likes to grow—
> Not at all like proper children, which is always very slow;
> For he sometimes shoots up taller like an india-rubber ball,
> And he sometimes gets so little that there's none of him at all.

> He hasn't got the notion of how children ought to play,
> And can only make a fool of me in every sort of way.
> He stays so close beside me, he's a coward you can see;
> I'd think shame to stick to nursie as that shadow sticks to me!

> One morning, very early, before the sun was up,
> I rose and found the shining dew on every buttercup;
> But my lazy little shadow, like an errant sleepy-head,
> Had stayed at home behind me and was fast asleep in bed.

[11] Ibid.

IF ONCE YOU HAVE SLEPT ON AN ISLAND
by Rachel Field[12]

To retreat to an island appeals strongly to almost every child. This verse arouses deep feeling which invites discussion and dramatic play. It may center on the activity each child most enjoys as he vacations on an island. Daytime and night-time activities are enjoyed in different moods and expression.

> If once you have slept on an island,
>   You'll never be quite the same;
> You may look as you looked the day before
>   And go by the same old name.
>
> You may bustle about in street and shop;
>   You may sit at home and sew,
> But you'll see blue water and wheeling gulls
>   Wherever your feet may go.
>
> You may chat with the neighbors of this and that
>   And close to your fire keep,
> But you'll hear ship whistle and lighthouse bell
>   And tides beat through your sleep.
>
> Oh, you won't know why, and you can't say how
>   Such change upon you came,
> But—once you have slept on an island
>   You'll never be quite the same!

SKATING
by Herbert Asquith[13]

There's no rhythm exactly like the joyous rhythm of ice skating.

[12] From *Taxis and Toadstools* by Rachel Field. Copyright 1926 by Rachel Field. Reprinted by permission of Doubleday & Company, Inc.
[13] Reprinted with permission of the Macmillan Company from *Pillicock Hill* by Herbert Asquith. First printed in Great Britain in 1926.

After children hear this verse they enjoy the play of learning to skate. They then enjoy making believe it is five years later when each one skates like Mary. Questions such as the following focus thinking and invite individual expression: "In what one way might you do some unusual skating on a single foot? on two feet in a most beautiful design? with another skater as champions in the Olympics Games? with a group of six in ice follies? How might all the skaters enjoy a skating party on a mountain pond for sheer enjoyment?"

✓

When I try to skate,
My feet are so wary
They grit and they grate:
And then I watch Mary
Easily gliding,
Like an ice-fairy:
Skimming and curving,
Out and in,
With a turn of her head,
And a lift of her chin,
And a gleam of her eye,
And a twirl and a spin;
Sailing under
The breathless hush
Of the willows, and back
To the frozen rush;
Out to the island
And round the edge,
Skirting the rim
Of the crackling sedge,
Swerving close
To the poplar root,
And round the lake
On a single foot,
With a three, and an eight,
And a loop and a ring;
Where Mary glides,
The Lake will sing!

Out in the mist
I hear her now
Under the frost
Of the willow-bough
Easily sailing,
Light and fleet,
With the song of the lake
Beneath her feet.

AN OLD CHRISTMAS GREETING

Author unknown

As Christmas approaches children like to talk about plans and preparations. After a general discussion this poem focuses thinking upon customs and friendship. While some of the children sing appropriate Christmas songs others may pantomime favorite customs or make believe they enjoy a Christmas present each would like to give or receive. Suggestions similar to these may serve as guides: "Show how you decorate your Christmas tree in the way you think is most beautiful." "Tell about the custom you enjoy best of all with your family." "Tell about the present you look forward to giving most this year." "If you could send a toy to a boy in France to surprise him, what would you like to send best of all?" "If you could send a surprise package to a girl in Japan which included a gift she could use every day, what gift would you send?" "If you could send a gift which represented our country to a person your age in Russia, what would you send?"

Sing hey! Sing hey!
For Christmas Day;
Twine mistletoe and holly,
For friendship glows
In winter snows,
And so let's all be jolly.

FOR HANUKKAH

by H. N. Bialik[14]

This poem was suggested by Mrs. Esther Wykell,[15] who has found that children enjoy the dramatic play which centers around the customs of Hanukkah after they hear this verse. They particularly like to make believe they rub and grind potatoes to make pancakes, and then to eat them; become spinning tops; light or become candles while others open and show a present they would like most to give to another child in honor of Hanukkah.

Father lighted candles for me
Like a torch the Shamash shone.
In whose honor, for whose glory?
For Hanukkah alone.

Teacher bought a big top for me,
Solid lead, the finest known.
In whose honor, for whose glory?
For Hanukkah alone.

Mother made a pancake for me,
Hot and sweet and sugar-strewn.
In whose honor, for whose glory?
For Hanukkah alone.

Uncle had a present for me,
An old penny, for my own.
In whose honor, for whose glory?
For Hanukkah alone.

[14] Reprinted from *Far Over the Sea*, by H. N. Bialik, translated from the Hebrew by Jessie Sampter, by permission of the Union of American Hebrew Congregations. Copyright 1939 by the Union of American Hebrew Congregations.
[15] Esther Wykell is a dramatics teacher and author for the Board of Jewish Education, Chicago, Illinois.

A SONG OF GREATNESS (A Chippewa Indian Song)
Transcribed by Mary Austin[16]

Every child dreams of achievement. Older children respond to this verse and enjoy discussing and dramatizing it. Most groups prefer to make believe they are ten or twenty years older and have earned individual esteem. A child likes to decide where he will be and what he will do that merits honor. One group developed individual pantomimes into a make-believe television program in which television cameras were set up across the land to honor six men and women of achievement. As a camera focused on a single person he pantomimed an activity which represented most clearly his esteemed life's work. The children chose a narrator to weave the program together. They set the opening mood by having a group chant the Indian Song to reveal the country's theme of greatness in its individual pursuits.

When I hear the old men
Telling of heroes,
Telling of great deeds
Of ancient days,
When I hear them telling,
Then I think within me
I too am one of these.

When I hear the people
Praising great ones,
Then I know that I too
Shall be esteemed,
I too when my time comes
Shall do mightily.

[16] From *Children Sing in the Far West*, by Mary Austin, by permission of Houghton Mifflin Company. Copyright 1928 by Mary Austin.

CHAPTER TWO

Poetry inviting characterization

Children are rich with all they do not own, rich with the potential wonders of their universe. Making believe is not only one of their earliest pleasures, it is their vital spark, the token of their liberty.

PAUL HAZARD

A poet is a man who sees unusual things (or sees usual things very clearly) and then describes them very accurately.

SIR HERBERT READ

A child and a poet see people and things "very clearly." In each of the following poems a poet has seen a person or thing doing something particularly. Each poem invites a child *to become* someone different from himself in an interesting situation.

These poems are arranged in order of simplicity. A teacher's key words in guiding children to interpret through characterization are: "*Make believe you are* this particular character in your own way, doing what he does particularly so he comes alive with true belief."

Children enjoy the simplicity of characterization offered in this form of charades. Focus needs to be centered upon characterizations of particular appeal, such as forest animals, zoo animals, community helpers, machines for transportation, machines for work, kitchen utensils, heroes, and television personalities.

Riddle-dee-dee, Riddle-dee-dee
See if you know who I'd like to be.

After children play this riddle in the nature of a charade, they may be motivated to become a star shining so brightly as to penetrate deep within the ocean to discover one beautiful or unusual thing down there. Others may become stars that shine on a mountain in search of a secret.

I have a little sister, they call her Peep, Peep;
She makes the waters deep, deep, deep;
She climbs the mountains high, high, high;
Poor little creature, she has but one eye.   (A star)

After playing this riddle children enjoy characterizing candles in situations they think of, such as lighting a birthday cake or lighting the night of Christmas Eve while carolers sing.

Little Nancy Etticoat,
With a white petticoat,
And a red nose;
She has no feet or hands,
The longer she stands
The shorter she grows.   (A candle)

THE WIND

by Robert Louis Stevenson[1]

A windy day arouses wonder which is heightened by this verse. A child likes to characterize the wind when he makes believe he blows in his own windy way for a particular purpose.

[1] From Robert Louis Stevenson, *A Child's Garden of Verses*, Charles Scribner's Sons, 1905.

I saw you toss the kites on high
And blow the birds about the sky;
And all around I heard you pass,
Like ladies' skirts across the grass—
    O wind, a-blowing all day long!
    O wind, that sings so loud a song!

I saw the different things you did,
But always you yourself you hid.
I felt you push, I heard you call,
I could not see yourself at all—
    O wind, a-blowing all day long,
    O wind, that sings so loud a song!

O you that are so strong and cold,
O blower, are you young or old?
Are you a beast of field and tree,
Or just a stronger child than me?
    O wind, a-blowing all day long,
    O wind, that sings so loud a song!

BABY SEEDS

Author unknown

Opening a milkweed pod and discovering how Mother Nature has protected seeds motivates appreciation for this poem. Children like to create Mr. Wind with the particular purpose of sending baby seeds flying through the sky. Becoming a seed flying quietly and looking for a new home invites individual thought and free expression.

In a milkweed cradle,
Snug and warm,
Baby seeds are hiding,
Safe from harm.
Open wide the cradle,
Hold it high!
Come, Mr. Wind,
Help them fly.

RAIN

by Robert Louis Stevenson[2]

A rainy day invites awareness of rain and its rhythmic patterns. This verse motivates characterizations of rain which falls for purpose on a particular place.

> The rain is raining all around,
> It falls on field and tree,
> It rains on the umbrellas here,
> And on the ships at sea.

FALLING SNOW

by Author unknown

On a day when it snows this poem will be particularly enjoyed by young children. In his dramatic play each child likes to create his own idea of a snowflake. Original expression comes when each snowflake decides for itself how it will come down from the sky and where it will come to rest to make a particular place white and fresh. "Morning" and "Anitra's Dance" from Grieg's *Peer Gynt Suite* provide appropriate accompaniment in two different moods.

> See the pretty snowflakes
> Falling from the sky;
> On the walk and housetop
> Soft and thick they lie.
>
> On the window-ledges
> On the branches bare;
> Now how fast they gather,
> Filling all the air.

[2] *Ibid.*

TRAINS
by James S. Tippett[3]

After a unit on transportation this verse will be appreciated by young children. They will enjoy *playing* train by beginning with a simple pattern of becoming engines and cars and gradually adding a conductor, signals, tunnels, and other creative characterizations. Children often enjoy chanting this verse with its chugging train rhythm.

> *Over the mountains,*
> *Over the plains,*
> *Over the rivers,*
> *Here come the trains.*
>
> *Carrying passengers,*
> *Carrying mail,*
> *Bringing their precious loads*
> *In without fail.*
>
> *Thousands of freight cars*
> *All rushing on*
> *Through day and darkness*
> *Through dusk and dawn.*
>
> *Over the mountains,*
> *Over the plains,*
> *Over the rivers,*
> *Here come the trains.*

UP IN THE AIR
by James S. Tippett[4]

When a discussion of planes and air flights arises this verse heightens wonder and generally motivates young children into dramatic play.

---

[3] Reprinted from *I Go A-Traveling* by James S. Tippett. Copyright 1929, Harper & Row, Publishers, Incorporated.
[4] *Ibid.*

A child who expresses from experience enjoys the make-believe of being a plane that takes off, flies, and lands. In the mood of play, a teacher, from a control tower, often sends each plane into flight, and radios to pilots to ask questions concerning sensory aspects of the flight.

Zooming across the sky
Like a great bird you fly,
    Airplane,
    Silvery white
    In the light.

Turning and twisting in air,
When shall I ever be there,
    Airplane,
    Piloting you
    Far in the blue?

√ THE LITTLE PLANT
by Kate Louise Brown[5]

Suggested by Kathryn Kayser[6] who explains: "This may be shared during a nature study unit designed for spring when children learn about the sun, rain, seeds, and soil. Children enjoy dramatizing the content of the poem to the accompaniment of improvised music in three-quarter tempo. A large group of children becomes the seeds, each curled up on the floor with his face hidden. One child becomes the sun, and a number of children are raindrops. After the seeds have become plants above the ground, I ask each one to tell what wonderful thing he sees. Sometimes I have a group give the poem in choral reading while another group plays. The choir likes to watch and then guess what plants and flowers the seeds have become."

[5] From *One Thousand Poems for Children*, by Elizabeth Sechrist, by permission of Macrae Smith Company. Copyright 1946 by Macrae Smith Company.
[6] Kathryn Kayser teaches at University of Denver, Denver, Colorado.

In the heart of a seed
Buried deep, so deep,
A dear little plant
Lay fast asleep.

"Wake!" said the sunshine
"And creep to the light,"
"Wake!" said the voice
Of the raindrops bright.

The little plant heard,
And it rose to see
What the wonderful
Outside world might be.

BABY SEED SONG

by Evelyn Nesbit[7]

A sunflower in full bloom and a red poppy have aroused children's wonder about sizes, shapes, heights, and colors of plants, flowers, and seeds. After children have played "The Little Plant," this verse offers a further experience in dramatization where a child may weave newly found knowledge into his interpretation. Larks and bees invite new characterizations with distinctive rhythmic purposes.

Little brown seed, oh! little brown brother,
Are you awake in the dark?
Here we lie cozily, close to each other:
Hark to the song of the lark—
"Waken!" the lark says, "waken and dress you,
Put on your green coats and gay;
Blue sky will shine on you, sunshine caress you,
Waken! 'tis morning—'tis May!"

[7] From *For A Child,* by Wilma McFarland, Westminster Press, 1947, by permission of John Farquharson Ltd. Copyright by John Farquharson Ltd.

Little brown seed, oh! little brown brother,
  What kind of flower will you be?
I'll be a poppy—all white, like my mother;
  Do be a poppy like me.
What! You're a sunflower? How I shall miss you
  When you're grown golden and high!
But I shall send all the bees up to kiss you;
  Little brown brother, good-by!

ESKIMO LAND

by Vivian Mackey[8]

After a study of cold lands, this verse holds strong appeal. Children dramatize the content in pantomime with pleasant satisfaction to express newly found knowledge. Most groups have improvised by having two children make believe they go by boat or plane to visit an Eskimo boy and his family. After they are welcomed and dressed appropriately, each member of the family shares a different custom with the visitors, including a ride by dog team to see and feed animals.

O happy little Eskimo
In your land of ice and snow,
You have so many things to do
You make me wish that I were you.

I'd like to feel your soft warm clothes
With boots all furry on my toes.
I think your igloo must be nice
All chiseled out of blocks of ice.

I might not call your food a treat,
But if I'm hungry, I can eat!
I'd like to ride on your big sled
With Husky dogs spread out ahead.

[8] By permission of the author. Mrs. Mackey, a classroom teacher, Seattle Public Schools, has contributed several poems to children's magazines.

Your whole outdoors is one big zoo
Where Polar bears do tricks for you,
While funny walruses and seals
Flop on ice and wait for meals.

Someday I'll take a boat or plane
(Although I do prefer the train),
And travel to the land of snow
To meet a frosty Eskimo.

MEXICO

by Vivian Mackey[9]

Here is another verse by the same poet for children who study about Mexico and wish they might visit it. This verse invites dramatization of the content with an opportunity for Spanish dialogue for groups who speak the language. Most groups have created improvisations in which two children fly by plane to Mexico to visit a senorita and her family. The visitors are entertained by each member of the family who shares a different custom, including shopping in a market, visiting a church, and dancing and singing in a fiesta.

I really think I'd like to go
To visit sunny Mexico.

It is a land of happy hours
With markets full of fruits and flowers.
They count in Spanish, "Uno, dos,"
And when they leave say, "Adios."

Their mamacitas pat and pat
To make tortillas round and flat,
While papacitos go to town
With little burros loaded down.

[9] By permission of the author. (See note 8.)

They love a time to dance and sing
A big sombrero in the ring,
Yet they remember God each day
And often go to church to pray.

Maybe—"mañana"—I can go
To see the land of Mexico.

FISH

by William Jay Smith[10]

Children are often fascinated by fish—their colors, sizes, rhythms, and individualities. This verse is appreciated when a discussion of fish arises. Younger children enjoy *playing* they are fish in a bowl, a stream, an ocean, or an aquarium. Older children prefer to work in groups to create fish improvisations in unusual settings. This poem lends itself to verse speaking synchronized with fish improvisations.

Look at the fish!
Look at the fish!

Look at the fish that is blue and green,
Look at the fish that is tangerine!
Look at the fish that is gold and black
With monocled eye and big humpback!
Look at the fish with the ring in his nose,
And a mouth he cannot open or close!
Look at the fish with lavender stripes
And long front teeth like organ pipes,
And fins that are finer than Irish lace.
Look at that funny grin on his face,
Look at him swimming all over the place!

[10] Reprinted from *Laughing Time* by William Jay Smith, by permission of Little, Brown and Company—Atlantic Monthly Press, Copyright 1955 by William Jay Smith.

Look at the fish!
Look at the fish!
Look at the fish!
They're so beautiful!

FOG

by Carl Sandburg[11]

This verse is made for a foggy day. Each child is encouraged to interpret his characterization in his own way, which is often different from a cat or "a silent white stallion."

The fog comes
on little cat feet.

It sits looking
over harbor and city
on silent haunches
and then moves on.

THE SECRET

Author Unknown

To children the word "secret" is almost magic. It never fails to create a responsive mood. Miss Ann Kimball[12] introduces this poem by asking: "What is a secret? Who has a secret?" After discussion the first two verses of the poem are told and the secret guessed. Children then want to tell and to show their awareness of birds in a variety of activities, including nest-building, hatching, feeding, flying, singing. Miss Kimball finds that young children like to make believe they

[11] From *Chicago Poems* by Carl Sandburg. Copyright 1916 by Holt, Rinehart and Winston, Inc. Copyright renewed 1944 by Carl Sandburg. Reprinted by permission of Holt, Rinehart and Winston, Inc.

[12] Miss Ann Kimball is a kindergarten teacher in the Shoreline Schools, Seattle, Washington.

are little birds hatching; looking from a nest "to see the most beautiful thing from high up in the cherry tree"; listening for the most beautiful sound in daytime and at night when it grows dark"; "flying to find one delicious thing for breakfast"; and, "singing a song to the cherry tree about the most beautiful thing you see when you fly out in the world and back to your nest."

> We have a secret, just we three,
> The robin, and I, and the sweet cherry-tree;
> The bird told the tree, and the tree told me,
> And nobody knows it but just us three.
>
> But of course the robin knows it best,
> Because he built the—I shan't tell the rest;
> And laid the four little—something in it—
> I'm afraid I shall tell it every minute.
>
> But if the tree and the robin don't peep,
> I'll try my best the secret to keep;
> Though I know when the little birds fly about
> Then the whole secret will be out.

A VALENTINE

by Eleanor Hammond[13]

It is a new experience for most children to create an outdoor valentine. This verse appeals on Valentine's Day. Each child likes to decide the particular character he will create to add to the beauty of the whole valentine. To animate the valentine with rhythmic movement to greet this special day offers an active purpose.

> Frost flowers on the window glass
> Hopping chickadees that pass,
> Bare old elms that bend and sway,
> Pussy willows, soft and gray,

[13] From *Child Life* Magazine, Copyright 1927 by Rand McNally & Company.

Silver clouds across the sky,
Lacy snowflakes flitting by,
Icicles like fringe in line—
That is Outdoor's valentine!

JACK FROST

by Geraldine Brain Siks

Young children enjoy this verse on a day when they have awakened to find frost. Children have interpreted in groups of five or six to become Jack Frost and his sprites who fly quietly through the make-believe world to "paint a lovely frost picture in a special place." Sprites like to describe their pictures to Jack Frost.

Jolly Jack Frost is a light, little elf
He lives in a mountain all by himself
He mixes frost in hollow log kettles
To make it ready for leaves and petals.
When autumn nights grow cold and bright
Jack Frost calls for his frosty sprites
All together away they go . . . .
To brighten the world with frosty glow!
With brushes of silver they fly like a song
To paint lovely patterns all night long.

✓   HALLOWEEN

by Geraldine Brain Siks

A quiet mood of mystery is presented here. Children enjoy improvisations with witches, ghosts and jack-o-lanterns in an eerie mood.

Sh! Hst!
Hssst! Sssssh!
It's Hallowe-e-e-e-n.
Eerie creatures now are seen.

Black, bent witches fly
Like ugly shadows through the sky.
White, stiff ghosts do float
Silently, like mystery smoke.
Lighted pumpkins glow
With crooked eyes and grins to show
It's Hallowe-e-e-e-e-n.
Hsssst! Sssssh!
Sh! Hst!

A FAIRY

by William Shakespeare[14]

When children are in a mood for fantasy, this beautiful verse stimulates their imaginations. To create a characterization convincing enough to serve the fairy queen provides strong individual motivation to interpret fairies and elves. Comments such as the following motivate purposeful action: "Suppose you are invited to attend the fairy queen's party at midnight tonight. Fly over hills and dales to find the most beautiful clothes to wear to honor this occasion. Return then to this pond—the fairies' secret looking-glass—to show what you've found. Now that your clothes are ready, search through floods, through fire—everywhere to find a most beautiful gift to present to her majesty."

Over hill, over dale,
Through bush, through brier,
Over park, over pale,
Through flood, through fire,
I do wander every where,
Swifter than the moon's sphere;
And I serve the fairy queen,
To dew her orbs upon the green,
The cowslips tall her pensioners be:

[14] From A Midsummer-Night's Dream, Act II, Scene i.

In their gold coats spots you see;
Those be rubies, fairy favours,
In those freckles live their savours:
I must go to seek some dewdrops here
And hang a pearl in every cowslip's ear.

PSALM 150[15]

This beautiful psalm is appreciated when older children become aware of the beauty of nature in a particular season. Groups have created in different ways when guided with questions similar to these: "Perhaps a group gathers to praise on a make-believe hillside, in a grove of trees, a church, a temple. Who might the persons be in such a group? What time of year and time of day might it be? How might individuals praise with make-believe musical instruments while others chant the psalm? How might a bird join in to praise? What other 'thing that hath breath' might also praise the Lord? How, specifically, may this be done so that it is in keeping with the mood?"

Praise ye the Lord.
Praise God in his sanctuary;
Praise him in the firmament of his power.

Praise him for his mighty acts;
Praise him according to his excellent greatness.

Praise him with the sound of the trumpet;
Praise him with the psaltery and harp.

Praise him with the timbrel and dance;
Praise him with stringed instruments and organs.

Praise him upon the loud cymbals;
Praise him upon the high sounding cymbals.

Let every thing that hath breath praise the Lord.
Praise ye the Lord.

[15] From *The Holy Bible*, King James version.

LINES FROM "THE SONG OF SOLOMON"[16]

A beautiful spring day invites awareness and discussion of the beauty of nature. These selections motivate characterizations from nature of a particular creature or thing a child would like to become to awaken with the rising sun. Children have organized verse choirs to chant the selections while others improvise nature's awakening at sunrise. Other groups have improvised to a symphonic recording of *The Battle Hymn of the Republic*.

> For, lo, the winter is past,
>   the rain is over and gone;
> The flowers appear on the earth;
>   the time of the singing of birds is come.

THE YEAR'S AT THE SPRING
by Robert Browning[17]

> The year's at the spring,
> And day's at the morn;
> Morning's at seven;
> The hillside's dew-pearled;
> The lark's on the wing;
> The snail's on the thorn;
> God's in his heaven—
> All's right with the world.

MORNING
by Emily Dickinson[18]

Older children often enjoy this unusual verse after they have created

[16] *Ibid.*
[17] From *Pippa Passes.*
[18] From *The Complete Poems of Emily Dickinson*, Little, Brown and Company.

from Browning's "The Year's at the Spring." Experienced groups who have dramatized this verse enjoy the unusual characterizations of pilgrim, scholar, sailor and "a wise man from the skies." As the pilgrim inquires from each character in turn, his answer is revealed through a pantomimed improvisation. These have been planned in advance by the character and five or six children to surprise the pilgrim as well as the audience.

Will there really be a morning?
Is there such a thing as day?
Could I see it from the mountains
If I were as tall as they?

Has it feet like water-lilies?
Has it feathers like a bird?
Is it brought from famous countries
Of which I have never heard?

Oh, some scholar! Oh, some sailor!
Oh, some wise man from the skies!
Please to tell a little pilgrim
Where the place called morning lies!

CIRCUS

by Eleanor Farjeon[19]

This poem invites the excitement of creating a colossal circus. Children's thinking may be focused by questions such as: "If you could be the loveliest thing performing in a circus ring, who would you choose to be? the funniest thing? the biggest thing? the littlest thing? the bravest thing? the wildest animal from the jungle trained for the circus? What would your circus character do for his finest entertaining act? How might the circus acts be organized? How might the acts be announced?"

[19] Reprinted from *Poems for Children*, by Eleanor Farjeon. Copyright 1926–1954 by Eleanor Farjeon. Published by J. B. Lippincott Company.

The brass band blares,
The naptha flares,
The sawdust smells,
Showmen ring bells,
And oh! right into the circus-ring
Comes such a lovely, lovely thing,
A milk-white pony with flying tress,
And a beautiful lady,
A beautiful lady,
A beautiful lady in a pink dress!
The red-and-white clown
For joy tumbles down,
Like a pink rose
Round she goes
On her tip-toes
With the pony under—
And then, oh, wonder!
The pony his milk-white tresses droops,
And the beautiful lady,
The beautiful lady,
Flies like a bird through the paper hoops!
The red-and-white clown for joy falls dead.
Then he waggles his feet and stands on his head,
And the little boys on the twopenny seats
Scream with laughter and suck their sweets.

THE MYSTERIOUS CAT

by Vachel Lindsay[20]

Children who enjoy this poem are generally ready to dramatize it. Older children like to create animated characterizations in group improvisations. Some groups have created several curious cats who watch and wonder when the mysterious cat reacts as she does to mice, gold-

[20] Reprinted with permission of the publisher from *Collected Poems* by Vachel Lindsay. Copyright 1914 by The Macmillan Company. Copyright 1942 by Elizabeth C. Lindsay.

fish, and a handsomely dressed slave. This poem asks to be chanted by a speaking choir as the characters create mysteriously and in fun.

I saw a proud, mysterious cat,
I saw a proud, mysterious cat
Too proud to catch a mouse or rat—
Mew, mew, mew.

But catnip she would eat, and purr,
But catnip she would eat, and purr,
And goldfish she did much prefer—
Mew, mew, mew.

I saw a cat—'twas but a dream,
I saw a cat—'twas but a dream
Who scorned the slave that brought her cream—
Mew, mew, mew.

Unless the slave were dressed in style,
Unless the slave were dressed in style,
And knelt before her all the while—
Mew, mew, mew.

Did you ever hear of a thing like that?
Did you ever hear of a thing like that?
Did you ever hear of a thing like that?
Oh, what a proud mysterious cat.
Oh, what a proud mysterious cat.
Oh, what a proud mysterious cat.
Mew . . . mew . . . mew.

DANCE OF DEATH

by Henri Cazalis[21]

Children are curious about the unknown. They like to play with ideas about things they may fear. Having fun with Death seems to be an ancient and honorable sport. This poem inspired Camille Saint-

[21] Henry Cazalis (pseudonym Jean Lahors; 1840–1909) was a French poet.

Saens' *Dance Macabre, Opus 40.* When older children become interested in the music and listen closely this poem leads readily to an interpretative "dance of death" at midnight. Children's imaginations lead to original characterizations of death, skeletons, ghosts and other spirits that revel until the cock crows.

> *Click, click, click . . .*
> *Death is prancing;*
> *Death, at midnight, goes a-dancing*
> *Tapping on a tomb with talon thin,*
> *Click, click, click,*
> *Goes the grisly violin.*

THANKSGIVING DAY
by Lydia Maria Child[22]

Families and Thanksgiving go together. This verse provokes discussion and often a desire to dramatize a holiday in the country. Questions similar to these focus individual thinking and lead to group improvisations: "How might you make believe you are a member of a family enjoying a sleigh ride through the woods to grandfather's house? Specifically, what might you do to show enjoyment of the ride and the snow? After you arrive and are seated around a make-believe table, how might a sincere feeling of thanksgiving be most effectively expressed before the delight of food pantomimes begins?"

> *Over the river and through the wood,*
> *To grandfather's house we go;*
> *The horse knows the way*
> *To carry the sleigh*
> *Through the white and drifted snow.*
>
> *Over the river and through the wood—*
> *Oh, how the wind does blow!*

[22] Lydia Maria Child (1802–1880) was an American poet and prose writer.

It stings the toes
And bites the nose,
As over the ground we go.

Over the river and through the wood,
To have a first-rate play.
    Hear the bells ring,
    "Ting-a-ling-ding!"
Hurrah for Thanksgiving Day!

Over the river and through the wood,
Trot fast, my dapple-gray!
    Spring over the ground,
    Like a hunting-hound!
For this is Thanksgiving Day.

Over the river and through the wood,
And straight through the barnyard gate.
    We seem to go
    Extremely slow,
It is so hard to wait!

Over the river and through the wood—
Now grandmother's cap I spy!
    Hurrah for the fun!
    Is the pudding done?
Hurrah for the pumpkin pie!

FROM "SNOWBOUND"

by John Greenleaf Whittier

On a snowy day, older children respond to these lines from "Snowbound." After discussion, characterizations of snow and wind have been developed to transform "old familiar sights" into new "marvelous shapes." Groups have imagined creatively from recordings of "The Storm" from Rossini's *William Tell Overture* and from "Infernal Dance of King Kastchei" from Stravinsky's *Firebird Suite*.

Unwarmed by any sunset light
The grey day darkened into night,
A night made hoary with the swarm
And whirlwind of the blinding storm,
As zigzag, wavering to and fro,
Crossed and recrossed the winged snow.
And ere the early bed-time came
The white drift piled the window frame,
And through the dark the clothes-line posts
Looked in like tall and sheeted ghosts.

The old familiar sights of ours
Took marvellous shapes; strange domes and towers
Rose up where sty or corn-crib stood,
Or garden wall, or belt of wood;
A smooth white mound the brush pile showed,
A fenceless drift what once was road;
The bridle-post an old man sat
With loose-flung coat and high cocked hat;
The well-curb had a Chinese roof;
And even the long sweep, high aloof,
In its slant splendor, seemed to tell
Of Pisa's leaning miracle.

THE BAGPIPE MAN

by Nancy Byrd Turner[23]

After children listen to bagpipes or a recording of their piping, this verse is enjoyed. The Bagpipe Man offers a unique characterization for interpretation. A further challenge for original characterization comes when the Bagpipe Man asks the "scamperers" to *show* rather than tell what they hear as he plays. Improvisations in groups of six have worked out best.

The bagpipe man came over our hill
  When no one knew he was anywhere round,
With a whirl and a skirl, a toot and a trill;
  And we all went, scampering after the sound.
We cried, "Oh, tell us, what do you play?
  What do you play so queer, so queer?"
And he skipped a couple of notes to say,
  "But tell me, what do ye hear?"

Then one of us heard a trumpet sweet,
  And the tramp, tramp, tramp of marching men;
And one of us heard the dancing feet
  Of fairies down in a dusky glen;
And one of us called it a bird in June,
  And one a river that ran and ran.
But he never would tell us the name of his tune,
  That funny old bagpipe man!

MEG MERRILIES
by John Keats

This poem was suggested by Hazel Dunnington.[24] Mrs. Dunnington says: "Children who become interested in the lure of gypsy life have responded to this poem with unusual appreciation. 'Old Meg' offers one of the finest opportunities in literature for character interpretation for children. Groups have created 'Old Meg' as she lives through a day to enjoy her Brothers, Sisters, Book and Cottagers. Others have climaxed her day with an unexpected visit from a band of gypsies who come with violins to entertain Old Meg, and to ask her to tell their fortunes. Brahm's 'Hungarian Dance No. 1' provides a near perfect musical background for pantomimed interpretations."

Old Meg she was a Gypsy
And liv'd upon the Moors:

[24] Hazel Dunnington is Assistant Professor of Speech and Drama at Central Washington State College, Ellensburg, Washington.

Her bed it was the brown heath turf,
And her house was out of doors.

Her apples were swart blackberries,
Her currants pods o'broom;
Her wine was dew of the wild white rose,
Her book a churchyard tomb.

Her Brothers were the craggy hills,
Her Sisters larchen trees—
Alone with her great family
She liv'd as she did please.

No breakfast had she many a morn,
No dinner many a noon,
And 'stead of supper she would stare
Full hard against the Moon.

But every morn of woodbine fresh
She made her garlanding,
And every night the dark glen Yew
She wove, and she would sing.

And with her fingers old and brown
She plaited Mats o'Rushes,
And gave them to the Cottagers
She met among the Bushes.

Old Meg was brave as Margaret Queen
And tall as Amazon;
An old red blanket cloak she wore;
A chip hat had she on.
God rest her aged bones somewhere—
She died full long agone!

CHAPTER THREE

Poetry motivating conflict

What is a play? . . . Many things. But what it always is, as well as many other things, is people in trouble.

WILLIAM SAROYAN

A child, like a poet, soon recognizes that the course of life never does "run smooth." In each of the following poems a poet has seen a person or thing in a moment of particular trouble or sudden change of mood. These poems may be thought of as little dramas in a nutshell or "tempests in a teapot." Some of the poems present trouble clearly. Others present unexpected moments of surprise, delight, disappointment, bravery, fear, or a sudden feeling experienced often as strongly in life as in literature.

These poems are arranged, in sequence, in order of simplicity. They offer brief plots for younger children to "play a poem" or for older children to create their first plays. Poems at the beginning of the section appeal to younger children and appeal frequently to older children for beginning plot experiences. However, later selections are not understood by younger children and are not intended for them.

A teacher's key words to guide children in conflict situations are: "Make believe you are this character, feeling as he feels in this particular moment. You will then know what to do in your own way that will be right for you and true to the character."

THE NORTH WIND DOTH BLOW

A poignant little drama of survival from unexpected, bitter weather. Young children seem to understand the theme and sense the drama of the situation. Characterizations become birds against the elements. Pantomimed improvisations with sounds for wind and birds seem most satisfactory for beginning groups. Some groups have introduced a farmer or family to feed the birds.

> The north wind doth blow,
> And we shall have snow,
> And what will the robin do then?
> Poor thing!

> He will sit in a barn,
> And to keep himself warm,
> Will hide his head under his wing,
> Poor thing!

FIVE LITTLE SQUIRRELS

A quick dramatic conflict of survival is presented here from the point of view of the animals. Children understand the situation of squirrels versus man, the hunter. Characterizations motivate spontaneous dialogue.

> Five little squirrels sat up in a tree,
> The first one said, "What do I see?"
> The second one said, "A man with a gun."
> The third one said, "Then we'd better run."
> The fourth one said, "Let's hide in the shade."
> The fifth one said, "I'm not afraid."
> BANG went the gun, and how they did run!

RIDE A COCK HORSE

This situation provides surprise in the realm of fantasy. Characterizations are village folk who ride to the crossroads at Banbury to see a "fair lady." When children discuss questions similar to these, ideas are stimulated for creative playing: "Who is the fair lady? Why do villagers ride to see her? What magical power may be in her rare music? Why? What may have happened during her visit to Banbury which caused it to be put into a rhyme?"

> Ride a cock horse
> To Banbury Cross
> To see a fair lady upon a white horse;
> With rings on her fingers,
> And bells on her toes,
> She shall have music wherever she goes.

HUMPTY DUMPTY

This is a fast-moving drama of surprise in the realm of fantasy. Children like to figure out who Humpty Dumpty was and what change came over him after his "fall." If he were a character in the nature of an egg, what happened, particularly when he broke the shell that had grown around him? Children's wonderings about Humpty generally lead to a surprise drama which ends in joyous excitement.

> Humpty Dumpty sat on a wall,
> Humpty Dumpty had a great fall;
> All the King's horses and all the King's men
> Couldn't put Humpty together again.

TOM, TOM, THE PIPER'S SON

Theft and punishment provide the force of drama here. Children enjoy its dramatization as they recognize its universal theme. Questions such as the following arouse discussions, which generally lead to lively play: "Why do you think Tom stole the pig? What do you think the Piper was doing? How old do you believe Tom is? Why do you think the pig got loose? Why do you think the pig stole a goose? How do you think Tom got put in the calaboose?"

Tom, Tom, the Piper's son
Stole a pig and away he run;
    The pig got loose
    And stole a goose!
And Tom got put in the calaboose.

HEY, DIDDLE, DIDDLE

This is a lively drama which centers in victorious achievement. Interest in adult pursuits to reach the moon cause this fantasy to be timely. Children have enjoyed the humor in creating a variety of fantasy animals and object characterizations to attend a "countdown" ceremony in which a "cow" attempts to reach the moon. The cow's unexpected triumph causes a celebration, the likes of which have not yet been seen except, perhaps, in wonderland.

Hey, diddle, diddle!
The cat and the fiddle.
The cow jumped over the moon;
The little dog laughed
To see such sport,
And the dish ran away with the spoon.

THREE YOUNG RATS

The saving grace in a social situation is the humorous, dramatic conflict presented here. When fancily-dressed animals react to a sudden shower of rain, humor and empathy are strong. Children like to decide what occasion motivates such an animal walk.

Three young rats with black felt hats,
Three young ducks with white straw flats,
Three young dogs with curling tails,
Three young cats with demi-veils,
Went out to walk with two young pigs

In satin vests and sorrel wigs;
But suddenly it changed to rain
And so they all went home again.

I HAD A LITTLE NUT TREE

Here is a fantasy drama of extreme joy caused by a rare visitor. The tree character motivates original creation.

I had a little nut tree
  Nothing would it bear
But a silver nutmeg
  And a golden pear;
The king of Spain's daughter
  Came to visit me,
And all for the sake
  Of my little nut tree.
I skipped over water
  I danced over sea,
And all the birds in the air
  Couldn't catch me.

LITTLE ROBIN REDBREAST

Author unknown

Survival from an enemy attack is presented here from the robin's point of view. Children have worked in pairs to create convincing suspense, action and reaction. Children recognize the need for sharp awareness.

Little Robin Redbreast sat upon a tree;
Up went pussy cat, and down went he.
Down came the pussy cat, and away Robin ran;
Said little Robin Redbreast, "Catch me if you can."

Little Robin Redbreast jumped upon a wall;
Pussy cat jumped after him, and almost got a fall.
Little Robin chirped and sang, and what did pussy say?
Pussy cat said naught but "Mew" and Robin flew away.

BOATS IN FOG

by Vivian Mackey[1]

This verse holds particular appeal on a foggy day for children who live near oceans or lakes and hear the warning sounds of fog horns. The verse presents a dramatic focus on the possible danger of a boat accident during fog. The difference in attitude toward the situations of the big boat and the little boats provides strong rhythmic action and reaction in characterization. Some groups improvise freely in pantomime from this. Other groups have dramatized the content of the verse while some children chanted the verse. One group heightened the mood by including an additional speech choir to provide sound effects in rhythmic patterns of boat whistles, fog horns and engine motors.

The big boat calls,
"Wh o o o o o o o o o—*where are you?*" (Deep voice)
The little boat answers,
"Tw e e e e e e e e e—*here I am.*" (High voice)
"Wh o o o o o o o o o o—*where?*" (Deep voice)
"Tw e e e e e e e e e—*here.*" (High voice)
"Wh o o o o o o o o o—*where?*" (Deep voice)
The little boats love hide and seek—
They run about and play.
The big boats nearly lose their minds
On every foggy day.

[1] By permission of the author. Mrs. Mackey, a classroom teacher, Seattle Public Schools, has contributed several poems to children's magazines.

CRAB-APPLE
by Ethel Talbot[2]

Suggested by Barbara Salisbury.[3] Mrs. Salisbury says: "This is a favorite to play on a birthday for as little or long a time as is available. While it does not present a clear drama, it does depict universal feeling of longing to do something but yet being afraid. The fairies help to overcome this fear by dramatic transformation and a whole new world is revealed! Children love to create a fairy world with special games, dances, entertainment, refreshments and surprises."

I dreamed the Fairies wanted me
   To spend my birth-night with them all;
And I said, "Oh, but you're so wee
   And I am so tremendous tall,
What could we do?"
   "Crab-apple stem!"
Said they, and I was just like them.

And then, when we were all the same,
   The party and the fun began;
They said they'd teach me a new game
   Of "Dew-ponds." "I don't think I can
Play that," I said.
   "Crab-apple blue!"
Said they, and I could play it too.

And then, when we had played and played,
   The fairies said that we would dance;
And I said, "Oh, but I'm afraid
   That I've no shoes." I gave a glance
At my bare toes.
   "Crab-apple sweet!"
Said they, and shoes were on my feet.

[2] Reprinted from *Oh, What a Dream* by Ethel Talbot. (C) PUNCH, London.
[3] Mrs. Salisbury is in the School of Drama, University of Washington, Seattle, Washington.

And then we danced away, away,
    Until my birth-night all was done;
And I said, "I'll go home today;
    And thank you for my lovely fun,
I'll come again."
    "Crab-apple red!"
Said they, and I woke up in bed.

COME LITTLE LEAVES

by George Cooper[4]

Many children's groups have responded with zest to improvisations from this fantasy. When children become aware of the rhythms and color of autumn this verse arouses imaginative response. Children's interpretations of Wind, Leaves, Crickets, Brooks, and Snowflakes are original. Drama begins with joy, changes momentarily to sadness in farewells, arises to heightened joy and ends in awe and contentment. Children seem to prefer to interpret their rhythmic characterizations freely to music. "Air Gai" from Christoph Gluck's *Iphigenie in Aulis* has been used frequently.

Come little leaves said the wind one day.
Come over the meadow with me to play.
Put on your dresses of red and of gold
For summer is gone and the days grow cold.

As soon as the leaves heard the wind's loud call
Down they came fluttering one and all.
Over the brown fields they danced and they flew
Singing the sweet little songs they knew.

"Cricket goodbye, we've been friends so long.
Little brook sing us your farewell song.
Say you are sorry to see us go.
Ah! You will miss us right well we know."

[4] George Cooper (1840-1927), a children's poet, contributed many poems (particularly those concerned with nature) to children's magazines.

Dancing and whirling the little leaves went.
Winter had called them and they were content.
Soon fast asleep in their earthy beds
The snow laid a coverlid over their heads.

✓ HUNTING FOR A HALLOWEEN CAT

by Vivian Mackey[5]

This poem provides a Halloween drama which appeals to almost all groups of children. It is concerned with universal interest in good and evil, symbolized in an evil witch and in gentle kittens. The drama is presented from the point of view of the witch. It is her experience which centers in a search for evil by evil. Suspense is heightened when characters are sufficiently developed to create rhythmic contrasts in personality attitudes of good and evil. Mr. Owl, Mrs. Cat and each little kitten stimulate an opportunity for originality.

"Old Mr. Owl," said a witch one day
"Do you know a cat? Mine has gone astray.
I want a cat with a terrible howl,
With emerald eyes, and a mean old growl.
I want a cat with sharpened claws
That'll pop right out of her padded paws.
I want a cat that is big and black
With ragged fur and hunched-up back.
I want a cat who will scratch and bite.
I'm getting ready for Halloween night!"

"I know a tabby," said old Mr. Owl
"With a family of five just ready to prowl!"
So off they whizzed from the old oak tree
To find Mrs. Cat and her family.

[5] By permission of the author. (See note 1.)

But the first little cat had a musical purr
All wrapped up in his pretty gray fur.

The second little cat was trim and neat
And his claws stayed in his snowy, white feet.

The third little cat had eyes of blue
And a growl so tiny it would never do.

The fourth little cat could hunch his back
But his fur was smooth and a silky black.

The fifth little cat refused to bite
And wouldn't go out on Halloween night.

The ugly old witch flew off in a rage
As mad as a tiger locked in a cage.
The wise old owl glided back saying, "Whooooooo
Could find a Halloween cat for you?"

WOMEN IN MOSS

by Geraldine Brain Siks

This fantasy arouses curiosity and provides clear contrast in three distinct areas of characterization: Dan, Moss Women, and the mother. The action moves quickly and does not require dialogue for interpretation. The drama centers in anxiety, which changes to surprise and finally to unexpected joy.

Over the hills and far away
A bit o' good luck happened one day.
It was early morn when the bright sun burst through
And shone on the poor hut of Danny O'Hugh.
In haste the good lad ran out to the hill
Searching for food—his mother was ill.
Fresh berries he found and filled his jug
When deep in the trees sounded a rustly-thug.

Then out of the thickets, dressed in golden moss,
Came a wee, withered woman calling "Foss, foss, foss."
Danny O'Hugh leaped up with a start
And like an arrow was ready to dart
When wee Moss Women from everywhere came
Chanting and scolding and calling his name.
Dan offered them berries—from his jug they ate
Around him they danced—then off in a gait.
Again Dan picked berries in haste—
He ran down the hill not a minute to waste.
His mother was waiting—his story he told.
And lo! when they looked the berries were gold!
Good luck? Foss? Foss? Foss?
You never quite know when you meet Women in Moss.

✳ FROGS AT SCHOOL

by George Cooper[6]

After a nature study experience with frogs and polliwogs children respond with delight to this verse. To improvise frogs in a school situation appeals to almost all groups who are interested in the unique nature of a frog. Children have originated "school programs for frogs" to include lessons in learning the skills of singing, leaping, jumping, diving, and swimming. Drama is introduced when a boy enters the scene to provide action causing frogs to react for survival.

Twenty froggies went to school
Down beside a rushy pool;
Twenty little coats of green
Twenty vests all white and clean.

"We must be in time," said they,
"First we study, then we play;
That is how we keep the rule,
When we froggies go to school."

6 See note 4.

Master Bullfrog, grave and stern,
Called the classes in their turn;
Taught them how to nobly strive,
Likewise how to leap and dive.

From his seat upon a log,
Showed them how to say, "Ker-chog!"
Also how to dodge a blow
From the sticks which bad boys throw.

Twenty froggies grew up fast;
Bullfrogs they became at last.
Not one dunce was in the lot,
Not one lesson they forgot.

Polished in a high degree,
As each froggy ought to be,
Now they sit on other logs,
Teaching other little frogs.

LONG, LONG AGO

Author unknown

When children have learned the song written for this beautiful verse they generally respond creatively to dramatizations of it during the Christmas season. The drama is experienced from the shepherds' point of view. The scene begins on the hillside where shepherds and sheep react to a mood of weather as wind blows gracefully through the olive trees. The mood changes suddenly to surprise and fear as shepherds, sheep and trees react to the unexpected arrival of magnificent angels. As the angels sing or chant "their songs of joy," the mood changes to curiosity and joy. The drama may conclude here or the scene may move with the shepherds to the manger. Original, childlike quality characterizes dramatizations when children are guided to create and interpret their ideas rather than to imitate traditional, adult concepts.

Winds through the olive trees
Softly did blow,
Round little Bethlehem
Long, long ago.

Sheep on the hillside lay
Whiter than snow;
Shepherds were watching them,
Long, long ago.

Then from the happy sky,
Angels bent low,
Singing their songs of joy,
Long, long ago.

For in a manger bed,
Cradled we know,
Christ came to Bethlehem,
Long, long ago.

LINES FROM "THE NEW COLOSSUS"

by Emma Lazarus

On Bedloe's Island in New York harbor stands the majestic Statue of Liberty, 152 feet in height. She holds a torch as a symbol of individual freedom. The quotation engraved on the base of the statue is given below. After learning about the statue and hearing the verse, children are often motivated to do something about it. Older children have dramatized "these lines" with noticeable originality.[7] One group had a representative mass of five weary immigrants huddle together on the shore. Each dreamed silently of a frontier which interested him—science, space, homemaking, entertainment, education. As each, in turn, saw Lady Liberty's torch beckon, each with renewed inspiration went forth in pursuit of his dream. The children planned that

[7] Particularly fine was the interpretation by Lillian Nochim's class, North Miami School, Miami Beach, Florida.

the Statue would reach out to spotlight each individual ten years later to show what had happened to him and his dream. The group organized the pantomimes with a narrator. Lady Liberty's freedom theme was chanted and sung by several children in a choir to set the mood at the start and to heighten the ending.

> Give me your tired, your poor,
> Your huddled masses yearning to breathe free,
> The wretched refuse of your teeming shore,
> Send these, the homeless, tempest-tossed, to me:
> I lift my lamp beside the golden door.

THE COUNTRY MOUSE AND THE TOWN MOUSE

by Horace (B.C. 65–08)[8]

This is recognized as the most famous literary version of this fable. The poet is considered the most truthful painter of the society of his time. His deft strokes with words offer an opportunity for the development of exciting drama. The two characterizations are distinctive in personalities and attitudes. Their conflict reveals the theme in two contrasting scenes set in the country and the city. As a child said, the play asks a question: "Do you prefer to live dangerously with luxury or peacefully with simple things?"

> One day a country mouse in his poor home
> Received an ancient friend, a mouse from Rome.
> The host, though close and careful, to a guest
> Could open still; so now he did his best.
> He spares not oats or vetches; in his chaps
> Raisins he brings, and nibbled bacon-scraps,
> Hoping by varied dainties to entice
> His town-bred guest, so delicate and nice.
> Who condescended graciously to touch

[8] From Horace, *Satires*, Book II, Satire 6, translated by Conington.

Thing after thing, but never would take much,
While he, the owner of the mansion, sat
On threshed-out straw, and spelt and darnels ate.

At length the town mouse cried, "I wonder how
You can live here, friend, on this hill's rough brow!
Take my advice, and leave these ups and downs,
This hill and dale, for humankind and towns.
Come, now, go home with me; remember, all
Who live on earth are mortal, great and small.
Then take, good sir, your pleasure while you may;
With life so short, 'twere wrong to lose a day."

This reasoning made the rustic's head turn round;
Forth from his hole he issues with a bound,
And they two make together for their mark
In hopes to reach the city during dark.
The midnight sky was bending over all,
When they set foot within a stately hall,
Where couches of wrought ivory had been spread
With gorgeous coverlets of Tyrian red,
And viands piled up high in baskets lay,
The relics of a feast of yesterday.

The town mouse does the honors, lays his guest
At ease upon a couch with crimson dressed,
Then nimbly moved in character of host,
And offers in succession boiled and roast;
Nay, like a well-trained slave, each wish prevents,
And tastes before the titbits he presents.
The guest, rejoicing in his altered fare,
Assumes in turn a genial diner's air,
When, hark, a sudden banging of the door!
Each from his couch is tumbled on the floor.
Half dead, they scurry round the room, poor things,
While the whole house with barking mastiffs rings.
Then says the rustic, "It may do for you,
This life, but I don't like it; so, adieu,
Give me my hole, secure from all alarms;
I'll prove that tares and vetches still have charms."

THE GRASSHOPPER AND THE ANT
by La Fontaine[9]

This modern translation of La Fontaine's fable appeals to most older children for dramatization because of the distinctive characterization in a simple, direct conflict. Children who are aware of the unique natures of grasshoppers and ants enjoy the development of these humanized insect characterizations. It is significant to see how children analyze the contrasting personality traits of frivolity and industry in the two contrasting characters as they prepare the two dramatic scenes of summer and winter.

> Grasshopper, who'd gaily sung
> Summer-long,
> Felt herself with hunger wrung
> When cold winter set in strong.
> She'd hoarded never a thing—
> No flies, no gnats, not a wing.
> Full of trust, she went to see
> Her neighbor, Ant, and make plea
> For the loan of some small crumb,
> Just enough till spring should come.
> "Gracious Insect, I take oath
> Before August shows green growth,
> I'll pay you, with interest. Please!"
> Asked Grasshopper, on her knees.
> But no ant wants to stand accused
> Of generosity; Ant said,
> "What was in your giddy head
> All summer? You seemed so amused!"
> "I sang, and sang. You don't by chance,
> Neighbor Ant, object to song?"
> "Object? No, there too you're wrong.
> You sang, then? Now, I say—go dance."

[9] Reprinted from *The Fables of La Fontaine*. Translated from the French by Marie Ponsot, by permission of Grosset & Dunlap, Inc., Publishers. Copyright 1957 by Grosset & Dunlap, Inc., Publishers.

THE TURTLE AND THE RABBIT
by La Fontaine[10]

A drama of boastful pride is presented with artistic honesty in this modern translation of La Fontaine's fable. Children who enjoy humanized animals respond with originality in dramatic interpretations of this fable, for almost every child is annoyed by a boaster. The two chief characterizations hold appeal by their very different natures and traits which stimulate the conflict. Questions such as the following challenge individual thought: "Why did Turtle offer such a bet to Rabbit? Why did she care? What do you believe the 'bet' might have been? Of all the animals, who would probably be chosen as referee? What three friends might encourage Rabbit as he rests upon the grass? How might Rabbit's dream or 'cloud-shapes' be included to heighten suspense? Who might encourage Turtle during her plodding?"

> No matter how you run, you can't make up lost time.
> The rabbit and the turtle prove it in this rhyme.
> "I'll bet," said Turtle, "you can't get from here to there
>   As fast as I can." Rabbit laughed. "You, race? You'd dare?
>   Do you need a doctor?"
>   The ribald rabbit sat and mocked her:
> "Poor thing, I think you've lost your wits!"
> "Well," said Turtle, "I won't call quits,
>   At least until we've raced."
>   And so their bets were made and placed.
>   (What they bet, and who refereed,
>   Are more details than we shall need.)
>   Long-legged Rabbit could have reached the goal-line tree
>   In nothing flat, but, stretching on the summer grass,
>   He thought, "I'll rest awhile, and watch the cloud-shapes pass.
>   Let Turtle plod. I'm invincible.
>   Just see her solemn, pompous tread—

[10] Ibid.

She's like our old school principal!"
While steady Turtle forged ahead,
Rabbit dreamed he saw himself, daring and glorious,
Handicapped, but victorious,
Too proud to stoop to compete.
He beamed and lay at ease. His dreams were as heady
As if he'd conquered already.
Then, when Rabbit saw Turtle had the goal in sight,
He sprang, he leaped, he bounded, dashed as fleet as
     fleet,
In vain. Despite his long, strong legs and all their might,
Turtle won. "See" she cried, "what good are speedy feet?
A prompt start and a prompt heart, mean more than feet do."
She added, with a little sniff,
"What would have happened, Rabbit, if
You'd had your house to carry, too?"

THE NEW DUCKLING

by Alfred Noyes[11]

Suggested by Dorothy Schwartz.[12] Mrs. Schwartz says: "This verse never fails to bring laughter from children. The appeal is to older boys and girls who are ready to individualize characterizations. They respond to the theme and suspense which is built through Duckling's pride as he refuses the advice given by distinct and well-meaning friends. The verse opens imaginations to original ideas for creating a fitting ending to tie in with the humor and style of the verse."

"I want to be new," said the duckling.
   "O, ho!" said the wise old owl,
While the guinea-hen cluttered off chuckling
   To tell all the rest of the fowl.

[11] From *Collected Poems in One Volume*, by Alfred Noyes. Copyright 1920, 1948 by Alfred Noyes. Published by J. B. Lippincott Company.
[12] Mrs. Schwartz is a drama consultant in the elementary schools, colleges, and universities of Alabama, courtesy of Lovemans' (Department Store) of Alabama.

"I should like a more elegant figure,"
  That child of a duck went on.
"I should like to grow bigger and bigger,
  Until I could swallow a swan.

"I won't be the bond slave of habit,
  I won't have these webs on my toes.
I want to run round like a rabbit,
  A rabbit as red as a rose.

"I don't want to waddle like mother,
  Or quack like my silly old dad.
I want to be utterly other,
  And frightfully modern and mad."

"Do you know," said the turkey, "You're quacking!
  There's a fox creeping up thro' the rye;
And, if you're not utterly lacking,
  You'll make for that duck-pond. Goodbye."

But the duckling was perky as perky.
  "Take care of your stuffing!" he called.
(This was horribly rude to a turkey!)
  "But you aren't a real turkey," he bawled.

"You're an Early-Victorian Sparrow,
  A ball of conventional fluff!
Do you think I believe in that narrow,
  Banal, hypocritical stuff?

I shall break all your fetters and tethers,
  And rock my dear Reynard to sleep.
I shall pillow his head on my feathers
  And give him the best ones to keep.

Now the curious end of this fable,
  So far as the rest ascertained,
Though they searched from the barn to the stable,
  Was that only his feathers remained.

So he wasn't the bond slave of habit,
And he didn't have webs on his toes;
And perhaps he runs round like a rabbit,
A rabbit as red as a rose.

LINES FROM "HIAWATHA'S CHILDHOOD"

by Henry Wadsworth Longfellow

This is a classic every child should experience. It is a dramatic presentation in verse form of an old Finnish epic, a romantic idealization of Indian life in early America. Children are impressed by the beauty, rhythm, imagery, and particularly by the characterization of Hiawatha. Groups have created a scene of "wonder in nature" as Nokomis shows Hiawatha characterizations of stars, comets, trees and "shining Big-Sea Waters." Others have created a scene in which Hiawatha makes friends with forest animals. Experienced groups of older children select most often the dramatic scene wherein Hiawatha becomes a hunter in the forest he has loved. Wagner's "Forest Murmurs" from *The Ring of the Niebelung* provides effective mood and rhythmic background.

> *By the shores of Gitche Gumee*
> *By the shining Big-Sea-Water,*
> *Stood the wigwam of Nokomis,*
> *Daughter of the Moon, Nokomis;*
> *Dark behind it rose the forest,*
> *Rose the black and gloomy pine-trees,*
> *Rose the firs with cones upon them;*
> *Bright before it beat the water,*
> *Beat the shining Big-Sea-Water.*
> *There the wrinkled, old Nokomis*
> *Nursed the little Hiawatha,*
> *. . . Many things Nokomis taught him*
> *Of the stars that shine in heaven;*
> *Showed him Ishkoodah, the comet,*
> *Ishkoodah, with fiery tresses;*

Showed the Death-Dance of the spirits,
Warriors with their plumes and war-clubs,
Flaring far away to northward
In the frosty nights of Winter;
... At the door on summer evenings
Sat the little Hiawatha;
Heard the whispering of the pine-trees,
Heard the lapping of the water,
Sounds of music, words of wonder;
"Minnewawa!" said the pine-trees,
"Mudway-aushka!" said the water.
    Saw the firefly, Wah-wah-taysee,
Flitting through the dusk of evening,
With the twinkle of its candle
Lighting up the brakes and bushes.
... When he heard the owls at midnight,
Hooting, laughing in the forest,
"What is that?" he cried in terror;
"What is that?" he said, "Nokomis?"
And the good Nokomis answered:
"That is but the owl and owlet,
Talking in their native language,
Talking, scolding at each other."
    Then the little Hiawatha
Learned of every bird its language,
Learned their names and all their secrets,
How they built their nests in Summer,
Where they hid themselves in Winter,
Talked with them whene'er he met them,
Called them "Hiawatha's Chickens."
    Of all beasts he learned the language,
Learned their names and all their secrets,
How the beavers built their lodges,
Where the squirrels hid their acorns,
How the reindeer ran so swiftly,
Why the rabbit was so timid,
Talked with them whene'er he met them,

Called them "Hiawatha's Brothers."
　　Then Iagoo, the great boaster,
He the marvelous story-teller,
He the traveler and the talker,
He the friend of old Nokomis,
Made a bow for Hiawatha;
From a branch of ash he made it,
From an oak-bough made the arrows,
Tipped with flint, and winged with feathers,
And the cord he made of deer-skin.
　　Then he said to Hiawatha:
"Go, my son, into the forest,
Where the red deer herd together,
Kill for us a famous roebuck,
Kill for us a deer with antlers!"
　　Forth into the forest straightway
All alone walked Hiawatha
Proudly, with his bow and arrows;
And the birds sang round him, o'er him:
"Do not shoot us, Hiawatha!"
Sang the robin, the Opechee,
Sang the bluebird, the Owaissa,
"Do not shoot us, Hiawatha!"
　　Up the oak-tree, close beside him,
Sprang the squirrel, Adjikaumo,
In and out among the branches,
Coughed and chattered from the oak-tree,
Laughed, and said between his laughing,
"Do not shoot me, Hiawatha!"
　　And the rabbit from his pathway
Leaped aside, and at a distance
Sat erect upon his haunches,
Half in fear and half in frolic,
Saying to the little hunter,
"Do not shoot me, Hiawatha!"
　　But he heeded not, nor heard them,
For his thoughts were with the red deer;

On their tracks his eyes were fastened,
Leading downward to the river,
To the ford across the river,
And as one in slumber walked he.

Hidden in the alder-bushes,
There he waited till the deer came,
Till he saw two antlers lifted,
Saw two eyes look from the thicket,
Saw two nostrils point to windward,
And a deer came down the pathway,
Flecked with leafy light and shadow.
And his heart within him fluttered
Trembled like the leaves above him,
Like the birch-leaf palpitated,
As the deer came down the pathway.

Then upon one knee uprising,
Hiawatha aimed an arrow;
Scarce a twig moved with his motion,
Scarce a leaf was stirred or rustled,
But the wary roebuck started,
Stamped with all his hoofs together,
Listened with one foot uplifted,
Leaped as if to meet the arrow;
Ah! the singing, fatal arrow,
Like a wasp it buzzed and stung him.

Dead he lay there in the forest.
By the ford across the river;
Beat his timid heart no longer,
But the heart of Hiawatha
Throbbed and shouted and exulted,
As he bore the red deer homeward,
And Iagoo and Nokomis
Hailed his coming with applauses.

From the red deer's coat Nokomis
Made a cloak for Hiawatha,
From the red deer's flesh Nokomis
Made a banquet in his honor.
All the village came and feasted,

All the guests praised Hiawatha,
Called him Strong-Heart, Soan-ge-taha!
Called him Loon-Heart, Mahn-go-taysee!

THE CHARGE OF THE LIGHT BRIGADE

by Alfred Tennyson

Children are impressed to learn that this great poem of heroism is based on an event in history. The battle occurred during the Crimean War when the British army was camped at the village of Balaklava. The cavalry of 600 troopers rode forth against a vastly superior enemy inside a strongly fortified redoubt. The drama centers in a battle inspired by courage and loyalty to country and obedience to a command. Older children have dramatized this with artistic force. Groups have created in pantomime to musical recordings of Von Suppe's *Light Cavalry Overture* and to Rossini's *William Tell Overture*.

Half a league, half a league,
Half a league onward,
All in the valley of Death
    Rode the six hundred.

"Forward the Light Brigade!
Charge for the guns!" he said.
Into the valley of Death
    Rode the six hundred.

"Forward, the Light Brigade!"
Was there a man dismay'd?
Not tho' the soldier knew
    Some one had blunder'd.
Their's not to make reply,
Their's not to reason why,
Their's but to do and die.
Into the valley of Death
    Rode the six hundred.

Cannon to right of them,
Cannon to left of them,
Cannon in front of them
    Volley'd and thunder'd;
Storm'd at with shot and shell
Boldly they rode and well,
Into the jaws of Death,
Into the mouth of hell
    Rode the six hundred.

Flash'd all their sabres bare,
Flash'd as they turned in air
Sabring the gunners there,
Charging an army, while
    All the world wonder'd.
Plunged in the battery-smoke
Right thro' the line they broke.
Cossack and Russian
Reel'd from the sabre-stroke
    Shatter'd and sunder'd.
Then they rode back, but not,
    Not the six hundred.

Cannon to right of them,
Cannon to left of them,
Cannon behind them
    Volley'd and thunder'd;
Storm'd at with shot and shell,
While horse and hero fell,
They that had fought so well,
Came through the jaws of Death,
Back from the mouth of hell,
All that was left of them,
    Left of six hundred.

When can their glory fade?
O the wild charge they made!
    All the world wonder'd.

Honour the charge they made!
Honour the Light Brigade!
Noble six hundred.

BARBARA FRIETCHIE

by John Greenleaf Whittier

Older children who have studied United States history generally appreciate Whittier's dramatic poem. It offers a strong scene of conflict centering chiefly on the gallant action of "old Barbara Frietchie" and the reaction of fiery Stonewall Jackson, aroused by his "nobler nature."

Up from the meadows rich with corn,
Clear in the cool September morn,

The clustered spires of Frederick stand
Green-walled by the hills of Maryland.

Round about them orchards sweep,
Apple and peach tree fruited deep,

Fair as the garden of the Lord
To the eyes of the famished rebel horde,

On that pleasant morn of the early fall
When Lee marched over the mountain wall—

Over the mountains winding down,
Horse and foot, into Frederick town.

Forty flags with their silver stars,
Forty flags with their crimson bars,

Flapped in the morning wind: the sun
Of noon looked down, and saw not one.

Up rose old Barbara Frietchie then,
Bowed with her fourscore years and ten:

Bravest of all in Frederick town,
She took up the flag the men hauled down;

In her attic window the staff she set,
To show that one heart was loyal yet.

Up the street came the rebel tread,
Stonewall Jackson riding ahead.

Under his slouched hat left and right
He glanced: the old flag met his sight.

"Halt!"—the dust-brown ranks stood fast.
"Fire!"—out blazed the rifle-blast.

It shivered the window, pane and sash;
It rent the banner with seam and gash.

Quick, as it fell, from the broken staff
Dame Barbara snatched the silken scarf.

She leaned far out on the window-sill,
And shook it forth with a royal will.

"Shoot, if you must, this old gray head,
But spare your country's flag," she said.

A shade of sadness, a blush of shame,
Over the face of the leader came;

The nobler nature within him stirred
To life at that woman's deed and word:

"Who touches a hair of yon gray head
Dies like a dog! March on!" he said.

All day long through Frederick street
Sounded the tread of marching feet.

All day long that free flag tost
Over the heads of the rebel host.

Ever its torn folds rose and fell
On the loyal winds that loved it well;

And through the hill-gaps sunset light
Shone over it with a warm good-night.

Barbara Frietchie's work is o'er,
And the Rebel rides on his raids no more.

Honor to her! and let a tear
Fall, for her sake, on Stonewall's bier.

Over Barbara Frietchie's grave,
Flag of Freedom and Union, wave!

Peace and order and beauty draw
Round thy symbol of light and law;

And ever the stars above look down
On the stars below in Frederick town!

I SAW THREE WITCHES

by Walter de la Mare[13]

Experienced groups of older children respond to the mood presented through de la Mare's sensitive poems. Imagery leads to distinct characterization of witches "bowed down like barley." The following questions will sharpen thinking: "What reason did the witches have for mounting the storm cloud this night? Why do you believe the hawk swooped down to end their secret plan? What do you believe the three did when they sailed in a shallop? Why do you believe the rising moon could cast a spell upon such evil ones? Why did the evil ones become 'bright scarlet' bushes? How? Who do you believe the moon to be?" Saint-Saens' *Dance Macabre* and *Night on Bald Mountain* by Moussorgsky have been effective for pantomime.

I saw three witches
That bowed down like barley,

[13] From *Poems For Children* by Walter de la Mare, by permission of The Literary Trustees of Walter de la Mare and The Society of Authors. Copyright 1930 by Walter de la Mare.

And straddled their brooms 'neath a louring sky,
And, mounting a storm-cloud
Aloft on its margin,
Stood black in the silver as up they did fly.

I saw three witches
That mocked the poor sparrows
They carried in cages of wicker along,
Till a hawk from his eyrie
Swooped down like an arrow,
Smote on the cages, and ended their song.

I saw three witches
That sailed in a shallop,
All turning their heads with a snickering smile,
Till a bank of green osiers
Concealed their wild faces,
Though I heard them lamenting for many a mile.

I saw three witches
Asleep in a valley,
Their heads in a row, like stones in a flood,
Till the moon, creeping upward,
Looked white through the valley,
And turned them to bushes in bright scarlet bud.

THE PIRATE DON DURK OF DOWDEE

by Mildred Plew Merryman[14]

When children become fascinated with the colorful plunderers of the sea this verse is a favorite. It offers a rare experience in vigorous characterization. After pirate characters are developed children work in groups to become Don Durk and his crew. Exciting conflicts have been created in pantomime with Don Durk's crew versus "mermaids," "puffs" in a sea storm, and sailors on a passing ship. The overture to

[14] From *Child Life* Magazine, Copyright 1923 by Rand McNally & Company.

Richard Wagner's *The Flying Dutchman* provides an effective musical background.

> Ho, for the Pirate Don Durk of Dowdee!
> He was as wicked as wicked could be,
> But oh, he was perfectly gorgeous to see!
>   The Pirate Don Durk of Dowdee.
>
> His conscience, of course, was a black as a bat,
> But he had a floppety plume on his hat
> And when he went walking it jiggled—like that!
>   The plume of the Pirate Dowdee.
>
> His coat it was crimson and cut with a slash,
> And often as ever he twirled his mustache
> Deep down in the ocean the mermaids went splash,
>   Because of Don Durk of Dowdee.
>
> Moreover, Dowdee had a purple tattoo,
> And stuck in his belt where he buckled it through
> Were a dagger, a dirk and a squizzamaroo,
>   For fierce was the Pirate Dowdee.
>
> So fearful he was he would shoot at a puff,
> And always at sea when the weather grew rough
> He drank from a bottle and wrote on his cuff,
>   Did Pirate Don Durk of Dowdee.
>
> Oh, he had a cutlass that swung at his thigh
> And he had a parrot called Pepperkin Pye,
> And a zigzaggy scar at the end of his eye
>   Had Pirate Don Durk of Dowdee
>
> He kept in a cavern, this buccaneer bold,
> A curious chest that was covered with mould,
> And all of his pockets were jingly with gold!
>   Oh jing! went the gold of Dowdee.
>
> His conscience, of course, it was crook'd like a squash
> But both of his boots made a slickery slosh,
> And he went through the world with a wonderful swash,
>   Did Pirate Don Durk of Dowdee.

It's true he was wicked as wicked could be,
His sins they outnumbered a hundred and three,
But oh, he was perfectly gorgeous to see,
  The Pirate Don Durk of Dowdee.

A VISIT FROM ST. NICHOLAS

by Clement C. Moore

Because this has become a traditional Christmas poem for children, it has become, also, a favorite for many groups to pantomime. Characterizations fall readily into two areas: Santa, Reindeer and Toys, and the family. Younger children have improvised to recordings of merry Christmas music. Older children have interpreted in mime while the verse is narrated, sung or chanted by a children's choir.

'Twas the night before Christmas, when all through the house
Not a creature was stirring, not even a mouse;
The stockings were hung by the chimney with care,
In hopes that St. Nicholas soon would be there;
The children were nestled all snug in their beds,
While visions of sugar-plums danced in their heads;
And mamma in her 'kerchief, and I in my cap,
Had just settled our brains for a long winter's nap,
When out on the lawn there arose such a clatter,
I sprang from my bed to see what was the matter.

Away to the window I flew like a flash,
Tore open the shutters and threw up the sash.
The moon on the breast of the new-fallen snow
Gave the lustre of mid-day to objects below,
When, what to my wondering eyes should appear,
But a miniature sleigh, and eight tiny reindeer,
With a little old driver, so lively and quick,
I knew in a moment it must be St. Nick.
More rapid than eagles his coursers they came,

And he whistled, and shouted, and called them by name:
"Now, Dasher! now, Dancer! now, Prancer and Vixen!
On, Comet! on, Cupid! on, Donder and Blitzen!
To the top of the porch! to the top of the wall!
Now dash away! dash away! dash away all!"
As dry leaves that before the wild hurricane fly,
When they meet with an obstacle, mount to the sky,
So up to the house-top the coursers they flew,
With a sleigh full of toys, and St. Nicholas too.
And then, in a twinkling, I heard on the roof
The prancing and pawing of each little hoof.
As I drew in my head, and was turning around,
Down the chimney St. Nicholas came with a bound.
He was dressed all in fur, from his head to his foot,
And his clothes were all tarnished with ashes and soot;
A bundle of toys he had flung on his back,
And he looked like a peddler just opening his pack.
His eyes—how they twinkled! his dimples how merry!
His cheeks were like roses, his nose like a cherry!
His droll little mouth was drawn up like a bow,
And the beard of his chin was as white as the snow;
The stump of a pipe he held tight in his teeth,
And the smoke it encircled his head like a wreath;
He had a broad face and a little round belly,
That shook, when he laughed, like a bowlful of jelly.
He was chubby and plump, a right jolly old elf,
And I laughed when I saw him, in spite of myself;
A wink of his eye and a twist of his head
Soon gave me to know I had nothing to dread;
He spoke not a word, but went straight to his work,
And filled all the stockings; then turned with a jerk,
And laying his finger aside of his nose
And giving a nod, up the chimney he rose;
He sprang to his sleigh, to his team gave a whistle,
And away they all flew like the down of a thistle.
But I heard him exclaim, ere he drove out of sight,
"Happy Christmas to all, and to all a good-night."

CASEY AT THE BAT

by Ernest Lawrence Thayer[15]

When baseballs zoom through outdoor skies baseball rhythms stir within baseball-minded boys and girls. This is the time to share and dramatize this popular American verse. Children respond to discussions where they may contribute baseball knowledge and give improvisations. The content of the poem divides participants into two distinct areas of characterization: baseball players on opposing teams, and grandstand patrons. Each character within an area offers a challenge in individual interpretation to fit within the whole. After building characterizations within scenes groups have dramatized the content in pantomime while a child narrated the poem. Other groups have built the drama in pantomime. They have then added dialogue, songs, and a pantomimed band tribute to Casey with a spirited Sousa recording. To include dialogue requires synchronization and teamwork which often challenges older children.

It looked extremely rocky for the Mudville nine that day;
The score stood two to four, with but an inning left to play.
So, when Cooney died at second, and Burrows did the same,
A pallor wreathed the features of the patrons of the game.

A straggling few got up to go, leaving there the rest,
With that hope which springs eternal within the human breast.
For they thought: "If only Casey could get a whack at that,"
They'd put even money now, with Casey at the bat.

But Flynn preceded Casey, and likewise so did Blake,
And the former was a pudd'n, and the latter was a fake.
So on that stricken multitude a deathlike silence sat;
For there seemed but little chance of Casey's getting to the bat.

[15] From *The Boy's Book of Verse*, by Helen Dean Fish. J. B. Lippincott Company, 1923.

But Flynn let drive a "single," to the wonderment of all.
And the much-despised Blakey "tore the cover off the ball."
And when the dust had lifted, and they saw what had occurred,
There was Blakey safe at second, and Flynn a-huggin' third.

Then from the gladdened multitude went up a joyous yell—
It rumbled in the mountaintops, it rattled in the dell;
It struck upon the hillside and rebounded on the flat;
For Casey, mighty Casey, was advancing to the bat.

There was ease in Casey's manner as he stepped into his place,
There was pride in Casey's bearing and a smile on Casey's face;
And when responding to the cheers he lightly doffed his hat,
No stranger in the crowd could doubt 'twas Casey at the bat.

Ten thousand eyes were on him as he rubbed his hands with dirt,
Five thousand tongues applauded when he wiped them on his shirt;
Then when the writhing pitcher ground the ball into his hip,
Defiance glanced in Casey's eye, a sneer curled Casey's lip.

And now the leather-covered sphere came hurtling through the air,
And Casey stood a-watching it in haughty grandeur there.
Close by the sturdy batsman the ball unheeded sped;
"That ain't my style," said Casey. "Strike one," the umpire said.

From the benches, black with people, there went up a muffled roar,
Like the beating of the storm waves on the stern and distant shore.
"Kill him! Kill the umpire!" shouted someone on the stand;
And it's likely they'd have killed him had not Casey raised his hand.

With a smile of Christian charity great Casey's visage shone;
He stilled the rising tumult, he made the game go on;
He signaled to the pitcher, and once more the spheroid flew;
But Casey still ignored it, and the umpire said, "Strike two."

"Fraud!" cried the maddened thousands, and the echo answered
        "Fraud!"
But one scornful look from Casey and the audience was awed;
They saw his face grow stern and cold, they saw his muscles strain,
And they knew that Casey wouldn't let the ball go by again.

The sneer is gone from Casey's lips, his teeth are clenched in hate,
He pounds with cruel vengeance his bat upon the plate;
And now the pitcher holds the ball, and now he lets it go,
And now the air is shattered by the force of Casey's blow.

Oh, somewhere in this favored land the sun is shining bright,
The band is playing somewhere, and somewhere hearts are light;
And somewhere men are laughing, and somewhere children shout,
But there is no joy in Mudville: Mighty Casey has struck out.

THE CREATION

by James Weldon Johnson[16]

The creation theme, particularly when stimulated by loneliness, is one that never fails to bring response from adolescents. This beautiful poem allows for a variety of original concepts in dramatic interpretation. Some groups have preferred to work only on the characterization of God, with each person pantomiming his interpretation simultaneously in groups of four or five. Large groups of more than thirty have also dramatized from this poem, with each person pantomiming a different characterization. Interpretations have been done to narrations of the poem, to verse-speaking choirs and to appropriate musical backgrounds. Other groups have found enjoyment in working in small groups of seven or eight persons with one characterization of God and each of the others interpreting a single representative character with sufficient space and feeling to portray the beauty and magnificence of God's first creations. Recordings of excerpts from Stravinsky's *The Rite of Spring* and excerpts from Wagner's *Ring of the Nibelung* have been effective for providing rhythm and mood.

> *And God stepped out on space,*
> *And he looked around and said:*
> *I'm lonely—*
> *I'll make me a world.*

[16] From *God's Trombones* by James Weldon Johnson. Copyright 1927 by The Viking Press, 1954 by Grace Nail Johnson. Reprinted by permission of The Viking Press, Inc.

And as far as the eye of God could see
Darkness covered everything,
Blacker than a hundred midnights
Down in a cypress swamp.

Then God smiled,
And the light broke,
And the darkness rolled up on one side,
And the light stood shining on the other,
And God said: That's good!

Then God reached out and took the light in his hands,
And God rolled the light in his hands
Until he made the sun;
And he set that sun a-blazing in the heavens.
And the light that was left from making the sun
God gathered it up in a shining ball
And flung it against the darkness,
Spangling the night with the moon and stars.
Then down between
The darkness and the light
He hurled the world;
And God said: That's good!

Then God himself stepped down—
And the sun was on his right hand,
And the moon was on his left;
The stars were clustered about his head,
And the earth was under his feet.
And God walked, and where he trod
His footsteps hollowed the valleys out
And bulged the mountains up.

Then he stopped and saw
That the earth was hot and barren.
So God stepped over to the edge of the world
And he spat out the seven seas—
He batted his eyes, and the lightnings flashed—
He clapped his hands, and the thunders rolled—

And the waters above the earth came down,
The cooling waters came down.

Then the green grass sprouted,
And the little red flowers blossomed,
The pine tree pointed his finger to the sky,
And the oak spread out his arms,
The lakes cuddled down in the hollows of the ground,
And the rivers ran down to the sea;
And God smiled again,
And the rainbow appeared,
And curled itself around his shoulder.

Then God raised his arm and waved his hand,
Over the sea and over the land,
And he said: Bring forth! Bring forth!
And quicker than God could drop his hand,
Fishes and fowls
And beasts and birds
Swam the rivers and the seas,
Roamed the forests and the woods,
And split the air with their wings.
And God said: That's good!

Then God walked around,
And God looked around
On all that he had made.
He looked at his sun,
And he looked at his moon,
And he looked at his little stars;
He looked on his world
With all its living things,
And God said: I'm lonely still.

Then God sat down—
On the side of a hill where he could think;
By a deep, wide river he sat down;
With his head in his hands,
God thought and thought,
Till he thought: I'll make me a man!

Up from the bed of the river
God scooped the clay;
And by the bank of the river
He kneeled him down;
And there the great God Almighty
Who lit the sun and fixed it in the sky,
Who flung the stars to the most far corner of the night,
Who rounded the earth in the middle of his hand;
This great God,
Like a mammy bending over her baby,
Kneeled down in the dust
Toiling over a lump of clay
Till he shaped it in his own image;

Then into it he blew the breath of life,
And man became a living soul.
Amen. Amen.

Stories for young children

"Goodbye," said the fox. "And now here is my secret, a very simple secret: It is only with the heart that one can see rightly; what is essential is invisible to the eye."

ANTOINE DE SAINT-EXUPERY, *The Little Prince*

To hear a good story is always an occasion. To be invited to play it with others is a particular delight for almost every child. Young hearts beat fast over such concerns as having to wait; wanting a pet and not getting one; wondering why snakes and foxes are snaky and foxy; getting in and trying to get out of trouble; wishing and then not wanting what one has wished for.

All of these stories have been "played" by young children in a variety of ways within the dramatic media. An entire story or single episode has been interpreted through "dramatic play." In this experience a teacher guides volunteers to dramatize freely. She encourages each child to express in his own spontaneous way, with or without dialogue, according to his readiness. A teacher purposely does not lead young children to explore characters and plot through discussion, but rather allows discussion to develop naturally after children become involved by playing and watching.

On occasion "dramatic play" has been recorded, unknown to the children, and shared later for enjoyment and stimulation. Stories have been interpreted through original finger play, shadow play, flannel boards, improvised puppets, and entirely in pantomime or interpretive dance. A single property or costume chosen by a child from a "dress-up trunk" has heightened enjoyment for beginning groups.

82

THE LITTLE FLOWER WHO NEVER GOT A BLOOM
by Brian R. Hubbard[1]

Children speak clearly to children. This story by a child provides within a nature concept a situation which arouses empathy in young children. Children are impatient. A child needs experiences to help develop an attitude of patience. The story plot builds quickly through clear and distinctively rhythmic characterizations—flowers, sun, rain. The sudden climax appeals. It offers a challenge for original endings.

One day there was a little flower who had no bloom. He lived in a garden with many other big flowers who had pretty blooms.

One morning the little flower asked a big flower, "How can I ever get a bloom?"

The big flower said: "Just drink in the sunshine."

The little flower said, "I do but I still do not bloom."

So the big flower said, "Well, just stay like you are then. Just wait and wait and drink in warm sunshine. Someday something will happen to make you have a bloom and pretty green leaves."

The little flower waited. It drank sunshine like the big flowers did.

That night way up in the sky it started to rain. The raindrops reached down to the little flower. The rain asked the little flower, "Why are you so unhappy?"

"Because I do not have a bloom."

The rain just rained and rained and rained on the little flower. The big flowers watched and drank rain too. Slowly the little flower grew to be a tall flower. The rain went away.

The sunshine came back. The flower reached out and drank in the warm sunshine again. Then something happened. He bloomed a big yellow bloom!

[1] By permission of Brian R. Hubbard and his parents, Mr. and Mrs. Harry F. Hubbard, Allentown, Pennsylvania. Brian, who was in a creative dramatics class sponsored by the School of Drama, University of Washington, told this story to his mother when he was six years old.

He was happy then because he was big and he was yellow and he was a flower with a bloom.

CATS FOR FREE

by Peter Hirschman[2]

Suggested by Mrs. Harry W. Gillies.[3] Mrs. Gillies says: "Since almost every child wishes for a pet, every child in the group entered into and invested in the dramatization whole-heartedly. In the class where the story originated the children: (a) first discussed their observations of cats—their distinctive rhythms and individual personalities; (b) pantomimed the 'kind of things cats do'—how they move, eat, wash themselves, sleep, etc.; (c) decided to dramatize a series of episodes in which two boys and six cats went to four different houses along one street. Children discussed and planned the different kinds of home-dwellers, their attitudes toward a cat and toward accepting one to live with them. Children 'paired-up,' enjoying planning, replanning, and playing with second and third partners, sometimes adding unexpected reactions of various families toward a cat. Because of the concise nature of the story, told in a child's own language, it is urged that the leader ask questions which will cause the children to understand the basic point of the story, which is the acceptance of disappointment. This is a theme all too often by-passed and left unresolved for boys and girls. Children will catch and develop spontaneously the humor of the story. The teacher will help the group gain more if he guides them to explore characterizations of the cats, the boys and the father, and guides children's discussions of attitudes toward responsibility and toward the ability to accept a father's answer of 'No.' "

Well, there was this boy who was not selling but giving away cats.

[2] By permission of Peter Hirschman and his parents, Mr. and Mrs. Stephen D. Hirschman, Eastchester, New York. Peter told this story to his classmates in school when he was eight years old, introducing his story with the remark: "But this is true, you know. That's what makes it dramatic."

[3] Mrs. Harry W. Gillies, consultant in creative dramatics, Pelham, New York, recorded Peter's story.

He was going from house to house to give them away because he had to, for his family couldn't support all the cats. I think they had at least six cats.

I met the boy and we went around from house to house to try to give the cats away, but nobody wanted them. We went down my street and when we got to my house, my father said, "No."

I left the boy after that. My father explained to me why he didn't want the cats, and I kept on telling him they were for free. Well, I was a little disappointed because I love cats. That's all.

HOME FOR A BUNNY

by Margaret Wise Brown[4]

Children everywhere play house. Home represents the center of their family security. The thought of looking for a home of his own arouses both delight and fear within a young child. Children react with humor and anxiety to the idea of living in a tree or a bog. Original ideas come from each different home as Robin, Frog, and the Bunny each shows why his home is "just right." Little children are curious about Groundhog's attitude.

> "Spring, Spring, Spring!"
> Sang the robin.
>
> "Spring, Spring, Spring!"
> Sang the frog.
>
> "Spring!"
> Said the groundhog.
>
> It was Spring.
> The leaves burst out.
> The flowers burst out.
> And robins burst out of their eggs.
> It was Spring.

[4] Reprinted from *Home for a Bunny*, by Margaret Wise Brown, illustrated by Garth Williams. Copyright 1956 by Golden Press, Inc.

In the Spring a bunny
came down the road.
He was going to find
a home of his own.

A home for a bunny,
A home of his own,
Under a rock,
Under a stone,
Under a log,
Or under the ground.
Where would a bunny find a home?

"Where is your home?"
he asked the robin.

"Here, here, here,"
sang the robin.
"Here in this nest is my home."
"Here, here, here,"
sang the little robins
who were about to fall out of the nest.
"Here is our home."
"Not for me," said the bunny.
"I would fall out of a nest.
I would fall on the ground."

So he went on
looking for a home.
"Where is your home?"
he asked the frog.

"Wog, wog, wog,"
Sang the frog.
"Wog, wog, wog,
Under the water,
Down in the bog."

"Not for me,"
said the bunny.

"*Under the water,*
I would drown in the bog."

So he went on
looking for a home.

"Where do you live?"
he asked the groundhog.

"In a log,"
said the groundhog.

"Can I come in?"
said the bunny.

"No, you can't come in my log,"
said the groundhog.

So the bunny went down the road.
Down the road
and down the road he went.
He was going to find
a home of his own.
A home for a bunny,
A home of his own,
Under a rock,
Or a log
Or a stone.
Where would a bunny find a home?

Down the road
and down the road
and down the road
he went, until—
He met a bunny.
"Where is your home?"
he asked the bunny.
"Here," said the bunny.
"Here is my home.
Under this rock,
Under this stone,

Down under the ground,
Here is my home."

"Can I come in?"
said the bunny.
"Yes," *said the bunny.*
And so he did.
And that was his home.

HOME ON SUNDAY

by Geraldine Brain Siks[5]

Empathy here is strong because almost every child longs for a puppy. Children enjoy playing the characterizations of Mrs. Tussy and Gray Dog, yet their sympathy is with Puppy and his persistence in seeking a home. Contrast in moods between the first two episodes and the last as well as sensory awareness appeals to almost all young children. Enjoyment and spontaneous ideas come when children work in groups of four to originate a family dinner scene with songs, blessings, and reactions to the surprise of the puppy.

It was Sunday. It was warm inside the homes in the little town at the crossroads, for all the chimneys were smoking. Outside it was cold. A sharp wind wailed a lonely song. In a clump of grass along the street a hungry puppy shivered. He had wandered down the long road all night long. He had stopped at every farmhouse looking for a home. No one, it seemed, wanted a puppy. He was tired and he cried:

Nnnnnngh, nnnngh, nnnngh
I'm cold, cold, cold
And lonesome too.
I have no home.
What shall I do?
Nnnnnngh, nnnngh, nnnngh.

[5] Told from a true tale when three young boys befriended a lonely puppy by giving him a home and naming him Nixie.

Puppy sniffed. He stopped crying. The wind blew a smell of Sunday dinner to his cold nose. He stood up and looked around. Down the street he saw a white house with the front door open. He knew that must be where the smell of Sunday came from. He looked toward the house and cried again:

> Nnnnnngh, nnnngh, nnnngh,
> I'm cold, cold, cold
> And hungry too.
> I'll find a warm home,
> That's what I'll do.

Puppy trotted down the street and walked up the steps of the house where the door was open. He walked softly as he walked over the doorstep. He liked the warm feeling. He liked the smell of dinner cooking. He cuddled down inside the door on a warm rug. He felt cozy and he curled up to go to sleep. Suddenly he heard the swish-swash of a sweeping broom. He heard a foot stamp and a sharp voice yell:

> Get out, get out
> I'll give you a clout
> You stray little dog
> Get out, get out.

It was Mrs. Tussy. She was thin and fussy. She was sweeping the hallway, getting her house ready for some of her particular friends. They were coming for Sunday dinner and Mrs. Tussy wanted her house to be particularly clean. While she swept away the puppy's tracks, she called out sharply:

> Stay out, stay out
> I'll give you a clout
> You stray little dog,
> Stay out, stay out.

Puppy hid in a ditch. He shivered while he listened. Finally he heard Mrs. Tussy slam the front door. He heard the wind wail its lonely song. He sniffed again. He smelled a different smell of Sunday. He stood up and looked around and saw a green house with a big back porch. He cocked his ears and whined:

> Nnnnnngh, nnnngh, nnnngh,
> I'm hungry and cold
> And lonesome too.
> I must find a home,
> I'll just have to.
> Nnnngh, nnnngh, nnnngh.

Puppy ran down the street and walked bravely up the steps to the back porch of the green house. He walked in on the porch where it was warm. The kitchen door was closed but he cuddled down next to it in a big basket. Puppy sniffed and found that a dog already lived here. Puppy hoped the dog would like him. Just as he began to get comfortable he heard a low growl. A big Gray Dog sprang up the steps and lunged toward Puppy. Puppy had learned to be quick. He jumped out of the way just as Gray Dog snapped at him. Puppy leaped down the steps and ran with all his might while Gray Dog raced after him. They both ran fast but Puppy could feel that Gray Dog was getting closer. Puppy saw a small hole under a wire fence ahead of him and he ran for it. He squeezed under just as Gray Dog sprang at him. Puppy was safe. He hid inside the fence in a corner of the yard while Gray Dog barked and tried to jump the fence. At last the Gray Dog stopped barking and ran back down the street. Puppy crouched in the corner and wondered if he would ever find a home. He was discouraged. He cried softly:

> Nnnnngh, nnnngh, nnnngh,
> I'm cold, cold, cold
> And lonesome too,
> I can't find a home.
> What shall I do?
> Nnnnngh, nnnngh, nnnngh.

All at once Puppy stopped crying. He pricked up his ears to listen. He heard a song coming from inside the little house. The kitchen door was open and the song sounded friendly as Puppy listened from the yard. Puppy was curious. He walked up the steps and into the kitchen and on through a doorway to a dining room. Then he stopped for he saw a happy family gathered around a table singing. When they finished singing Puppy heard someone speaking softly. Puppy felt good as he listened. Puppy barked. Everyone was surprised.

"Look!" squealed Jenny.

"What's this in our house?" Joe shouted as he jumped and ran to see. "I've wanted and wanted a puppy and here one is." Joe rubbed Puppy's back and held him close. "Poor little thing. He's shivering."

"Maybe he's hungry and wants a Sunday dinner too," said mother as she hurried to the kitchen to get a little pan. While everyone shared something from the table for Puppy's dinner father said: "It isn't everyday a puppy comes to our house, let alone on Sunday. We'll give this little fellow a good home until someone comes to claim him."

Jenny and Joe shouted with joy. Puppy barked two sharp barks. "Listen," said Jenny. "He likes us too."

Puppy wagged his tail to thank them for his dinner and for a home that was as sunny as Sunday.

THE HANUKKAH DREIDLE[6]

Author unknown

This story was suggested by Esther Wykell.[7] Mrs. Wykell says: "Before sharing the story a teacher should become aware of the presence of two strong themes: 'People are more important to happiness

---

[6] Adapted from *Moade Yisroel* published in Hebrew by the Board of Jewish Education, Chicago and the Midwest Hebrew Teachers' Federation. Copyright 1943 by the Board of Jewish Education. Reprinted from *Creative Dramatics in the Jewish School* by Esther Wykell, Board of Jewish Education, 1962.

[7] Esther Wykell is a creative dramatics teacher and author for the Board of Jewish Education, Chicago, Illinois.

than things'; and 'Hanukkah brings joy in friendship and creativity.' Hanukkah festival songs and customs may be woven into the playing and an experienced group may be guided to create original verses of their own as they sing and dance."

Once upon a time there was a family who had four children. The two sons were Uri and Kuri and the two daughters were Suri and Turi. The children had no fine clothes nor did they have toys with which to play. They liked each other so everyday they played together in their yard without any need for toys. On the other side of the fence from the small house of the four children stood a large mansion. In it lived a lad whose name was Saki. Saki had many beautiful clothes. He had unusual toys with which to play, but he had no friends. So everyday Saki played alone in his big yard with his toys.

When Hanukkah came Saki brought out to his yard his huge new Hanukkah top. On one side of the beautiful dreidle in beautiful, bright letters the word B I G was written. On the second side the word M I R A C L E was written, on the third side the word H A P P E N E D and on the fourth side the word HERE. Through the pickets of the high, iron fence which surrounded the mansion Uri, Kuri, Suri, and Turi could watch Saki as he played with his wonderful new dreidle. "Come on," said the children. "Let's ask Saki if we may come over and all play together with his Hanukkah top." They called through the fence, "Oh, Saki, oh, Saki." But Saki would not answer them. The four children were disappointed as they walked away from the fence by the mansion. Suddenly Uri shouted, "I have it," he cried. "Let's make a live dreidle! I know how to make a real live dreidle! Wait here and you'll see."

He ran quickly into the house and was out of doors again in no time carrying large sheets of paper, crayons and pins. He explained his plan to his brother and sisters. He then wrote the word B I G on one sheet and pinned it on himself. Then Kuri wrote the word M I R A C L E on another sheet and pinned it on himself, while Suri took some paper and wrote the word H A P P E N E D and pinned it on herself. Turi also took a sheet of paper and wrote the word H E R E on it in large letters and pinned it on herself. Then the children took a long pole and they each held one hand upon it. They danced merrily about the pole, twirling round and round singing happily. "Hurrah," they cried as they twirled. "A BIG MIRACLE HAPPENED HERE! We have a made a real live dreidle, a living dreidle . . . . A BIG MIRACLE HAPPENED HERE!" Round and round they danced again and again laughing and singing Hanukkah songs.

When Saki heard the laughing and singing he ran to the big fence and looked through it. "Oh," cried Saki, "They are having so much fun. If they would only let me play with them, how happy I would be."

He ran out of the big yard through the huge gate to the little yard of the four children. "Uri, Kuri, Suri, Turi," he called in a pleading voice, "Please let me play with you. I want to be part of a living dreidle, too."

"We have no place for you," replied Uri. "The dreidle has only four words," said another.

"Please," begged Saki, "I could stand in the center in place of the pole."

"Well," said Uri, "I never thought of that. What do you say Kuri, Suri and Turi?"

"Let's let him try," answered Kuri.

"But I don't think it will work," said one of the sisters.

Saki hurried on and stood in the center in place of the pole and then they all twirled about him, singing and dancing. Everyone enjoyed it more with Saki. They played and played. When it started to grow dark, a tired and happy Saki said good-bye to his friends. As he turned to go, he said, "Uri, Kuri, Turi, and Suri, will you be my friends for always and let me play with you? You can play with me and with my toys and with anything I have."

The children felt kind. They saw that Saki felt kind too. They invited him to join them in lighting and blessing the Hanukkah candles. Saki was delighted. From that day on, Uri, Kuri, Suri, Turi, and Saki became the best of friends, playing and sharing with one another.

THE PEDDLER AND THE MONKEYS

Adapted by Geraldine Brain Siks from an old tale

This tale is told from the viewpoint of the Peddler. It is *his* dramatic experience. His strength and weakness lie within his unique personality. His "dreaming" leads him to become an unusual Peddler but it also leads him into conflicts with his wife and the monkeys. This is a favorite story for children of all ages, for they like monkeys and their mimicking. They respond to the theme because it is difficult for almost every alert child to "keep his mind always on his work," and to "think his way out of his troubles." When children understand the Peddler's problem they enjoy creating the "home scene." They respond to the challenge to "look for an idea for a hat which has never been made before." But the jungle scene with its spirited conflict is the scene which children ask to play again and again. "How might we make it seem as if the jungle is thick with palm trees?" generally brings a desire from many children to become trees. A child, as a tree, enjoys the responsibility of hiding a monkey from the worried peddler.

A friendly old man and his wife once lived in a quaint hut on the edge of a jungle. The man was a dreamer and a maker of dreams. He made his dreams in the shape of caps, beautiful and unusual caps, and his wife helped him make caps too. When the caps were finished the man sold them in the villages. He was known throughout the land as the Peddler who made caps as rare as those one dreams about.

Now the Peddler and his wife were happy except for a little trouble which was always between them. He was such a dreamer that he often got lost in his dreams. He would dream while he was awake and quite often he forgot where he was going or what he was doing. This worried his wife who was always wide awake when she was awake. Everytime the Peddler went to the village she reminded him that he must try to keep his mind on his work. The Peddler always promised in order to quiet her constant reminders, but he kept right on dreaming in his own wonderful and forgetful way.

One morning the Peddler and his wife were in front of their hut preparing to make caps for the day. The man was walking about looking for an idea when all at once a bird flew through the trees. The bird's feathers were as bright as rainbows.

"Look wife! There's an idea flying around us. I shall make a morning cap with seven rainbow feathers."

And he did. While the Peddler snipped and stitched the wife looked for an idea. "Look, my good man," she said. "A daytime moon still shines above the tree tops. It has shone now for three days waiting for one of us to see it."

"Indeed," said the Peddler as he kept on stitching. "I am certain that is exactly why the moon has shone in the morning sky as well as at night."

"What?" said the wife sharply as she watched him stitching. "Well, nonetheless, I shall make a sky blue cap and trim it with a white moon slice."

And she did. When the Peddler finished his cap he reached to put it inside the big, brown pack. "Well, see here wife. The pack is full. I will go to the village this day and sell our beautiful caps."

"What?" asked the wife in sharp surprise. "You go to the village at this time of day? Look, the sun is now where the moon was when you started stitching. It will soon be midday. No! It is too late for you to start now."

"What is wrong with going to the village at midday?"

"What, indeed? You know your failing," said the wife firmly. "You get to dreaming when you get there. You sit down and talk with anyone who will listen. You visit on and on and forget what you've gone for. If you go at this hour of the day you'll have to walk home after the jungle has grown dark. You know there are always unexpecteds in the jungle."

"Forget what I've gone for! Unexpecteds in the jungle? Humph!" repeated the ruffled Peddler. "I'll go to the nearest village, sell the caps and be back before sunset. I will show you that I can remember what I'm about."

"Well you sound wide awake. See that you do then," said the wife believing that her words had reached him.

The Peddler lifted the pack up and over his back. He pulled his bright red cap trimmed with yellow sunshine down on his head and set out at once. He was determined to show his wife that he could remember what he was doing. As the Peddler walked along he decided to make up songs about his caps to sing to the villagers. His songs would help to sell his caps in a hurry. He thought of the beautiful caps inside the pack. He started singing aloud to himself, "Caps for sale, Caps for sale, Red and pink and white and green; Finest caps you've ever seen; Caps for sale; Caps for sale."

The Peddler liked his song but he believed he could think of a better one. He remembered a particular cap he had made and he sang out: "Buy a cap with a bell and feather; Buy a cap for every weather. Try a cap; Buy a cap today."

When the Peddler finished this song he made up another; and another and another. In all his making-up of songs he forgot to watch where he was going. He stopped all at once. He looked around for he had wandered deep into the jungle. "Where am I? Where is the village?" he said in alarm.

He was puzzled. He looked in every direction where there were jungle paths through the palm trees. It was warm and he was worried. He stretched and yawned. As he looked through the palm trees he became more mixed-up about which way led to the nearest village. "Well," he said with a sigh, "I think I'll have a short nap at the foot of this tree. After I've slept for a little while I'm certain I can think more clearly to decide which path I should take."

The Peddler put his pack beside a big palm tree. He untied the string and loosened the pack so the caps would not be crushed. He sat down, leaned against the tree, and pulled his red cap over his eyes. After two deep sighs he was fast asleep.

The Peddler did not know that he had wandered into a grove of palms where a family of monkeys lived. There was a father monkey, a mother monkey, and sister and brother monkeys. There was a grandfather monkey, too, who was the boss of the family. Whenever there was danger Grandfather would warn the monkeys to hide. When the Peddler came into the grove singing his songs, Grandfather heard. He gave a shrill cry. The monkeys knew his warning. Away they scurried up the tree trunks. They hid in the branches. They were as quiet as the sky so the Peddler would not know they were near.

As soon as the Peddler was asleep Grandfather came down the tree. He was curious about the Peddler's red cap. He saw a red cap inside the pack too. Now a monkey likes to do whatever he sees another do, so Grandfather reached into the pack, picked up a red cap and put it on his head. He liked it. He felt merry. He called to the other monkeys to see him. "Chee! Chee—chee, chee—chee, chee—chee!" he sang as he danced around the tree.

The monkeys watched. Down the trees they came. They wanted caps too. Each monkey reached into the pack and got himself a beautiful cap. Around the tree they danced. Each monkey felt so merry with his beautiful cap that he chattered and sang, "Chee! chee—chee, chee—chee, chee—chee!" With all the monkeys chattering it became noisy. The Peddler began to stretch and turn over.

"Cheeeeeee!" warned Grandfather.

Away the monkeys scurried up to the tree tops. They hid quietly again in the branches. The Peddler woke up slowly as he yawned and stretched. Suddenly he remembered his wife. He reached for his pack. Then he became wide awake. He turned the pack inside out. "Where are my caps? Where are my beautiful caps?" he called.

The Peddler looked around the trees. He looked up into the trees but the quiet monkeys were hiding, and he didn't see them. The Peddler ran around, frantically looked behind each tree, and called for his caps. He looked so funny that Grandfather laughed right out loud. "Chee—chee—chee—chee—chee!" he laughed.

All of the monkeys laughed, "Chee—chee—chee—chee—chee!"

The Peddler looked up into the trees. There he saw his caps—red, pink, green, lavender, blue, yellow, orange, rainbows, moon-slice, bells and feathers. "Give me my caps!" he called as he shook his fist at the monkeys.

The monkeys shook their paws at him, and chattered just as he had done, "Chee—chee—chee—chee."

This made the Peddler cross. He stamped his foot and called, "Monkeys!"

The monkeys stamped their feet on tree branches and chattered just as he had done, "Chee—chee."

The Peddler looked at the monkeys. He calmed down a little, held out his hands in a friendly way and said in a quiet voice, "Please." Up in the trees the monkeys held their paws out in a friendly way, and said very quietly, "Chee."

"Give me my caps," said the Peddler loudly and firmly as he realized his caps were lost to the monkeys.

"Chee—chee, chee—chee," chattered the monkeys in the same firm way.

The Peddler didn't know what to do. He shook his head and sat down on the ground to think. He folded his arms and thought of his wife. He thought about how she had tried to help him learn to remember. He shook his head and sighed. He stroked his chin as he tried to think how he might get his caps back again. As he thought he looked up and watched closely. He saw that each monkey was sitting on a branch and stroking his chin just as he was doing. The Peddler thought this a little strange. "The monkeys do just as I do," he whispered to himself. He thought about this. Suddenly he had an idea.

The Peddler stood up. He watched, and saw that the monkeys stood up too. The Peddler reached for his red cap. He took it off slowly and held it out in front of himself. With a friendly bow he dropped the cap to the ground and called, "Thank you, monkeys."

The monkeys took off their caps, bowed, and dropped their caps to the ground as they chattered just as he had done, "Chee—chee, chee—chee."

Caps came falling down—red, pink, green, lavender, blue, yellow, orange, rainbows, moon-slice, bells and feathers. The Peddler picked them up as fast as he could and put them back into his pack. When he had all of his caps he put the pack over his back and shook his finger as he called, "You litt—le mon—keys!"

The monkeys shook their paws and called, "Chee—chee—chee—chee—chee!" They watched as the Peddler hurried down a jungle path, and they laughed and chattered about the trick they had played on him.

As for the Peddler, he found his way, hurried to the village, sold his caps, and arrived home just as the sun was setting. He greeted his wife cheerfully. He knew at last that she had tried to help him all these years with her reminders. He felt hopeful for he was going to try to be wide awake, even when he was dreaming his wonderful daytime dreams.

PUA AND THE MENEHUNES

Adapted by Vera Bachman Frazier from an old Hawaiian legend[8]

Every country has its legendary little people who surprise deserving human beings. Menehunes are the elf-like people of Hawaii. They are said to be friendly, obedient, industrious folk, about three feet in height. They are merry and strong, with bandy legs, short arms, and sturdy bodies. They do their secret deeds only at night so no one will see them. Any task they set out to do must be finished before dawn. If this cannot be done they never return to that work, for it is part of their ritual which they always honor. This fantasy reveals the golden rule theme in a fresh version through the appealing characters of Pua, Tutu, the Menehunes, and children playing on the beach. Original thinking has been encouraged by Pua's songs, dances, beach play, and by the singing stream.

Pua was happy. She lived with Tutu, her kind, old grandmother on the slopes of Haleakala on a beautiful island in a blue ocean. Pua

[8] By permission of Vera Bachman Frazier. Mrs. Frazier is a classroom teacher, Shoreline Public Schools, Seattle, Washington.

had been named for a flower. She was cheerful and graceful like a bright Hawaiian flower when it dances gently with a breeze.

Every summer morning after Pua finished with the morning work she made Tutu comfortable under the shade of a big banyan tree. Then down the hillside Pua would run to the beach to play with her friends. The children were always happy when Pua joined them for Pua thought of new water games and new dances on the sands. Often she showed her friends how to make presents from flowers and stones and surprises they found on the beach. Every day Pua took a surprise from the beach to Tutu.

One afternoon when Pua came up from playing she saw that her grandmother was deeply troubled. "Tutu, why have your smiles gone away? The sun shines yet you are quiet like a dark cloud. What is it that troubles you?"

"Oh, my little Pua. I see I cannot keep my thoughts from you. It is the taro patch. Look, the sun burns down upon it. The water boy comes no more. I am too old to carry water. I fear my taro fields will soon wilt and die."

"So that is it," said Pua cheerfully, for she was somewhat relieved. "Never fear, Tutu. I can carry water. I will go now and give the taro a fresh drink of water."

"Oh, my little one, the patch is so big. You are so small." Tutu shook her head for she knew it was too great a task for little Pua.

"Watch and you will see what I do," Pua said as she found wooden pails behind the hut and hurried to the mountain stream which ran down behind the house away from the taro patch.

Pua sang as she worked. Her friends called to her from the beach, but Pua told them she would be carrying water all the rest of the day. Tutu sat patiently and watched. She worried about the taro and she worried even more about Pua, for her frail little body bent almost double under the weight of the wooden pails. Pua was happy while she worked. She was so busy carrying water that she did not know that anyone was near. Neither did Tutu.

But the Menehunes watched closely. They hid in their secret hiding places in holes under rocks and under big, brown roots. Each Mene-

vates sudden action"; and in the words of a child, "You have to watch out all the time." A problem-solving situation comes when children are asked: "Who can make believe Wolf swallows and eats six little kids so that it seems as if they are hiding safely inside of Wolf's tummy?"

Once upon a time there lived a Mother Goat who had seven little kids whom she loved as every good mother loves her children. They lived together in a little hut in the woods, and in that woods there lived a wicked old Wolf. One day Mother Goat said, "Dear children, I am going to fetch some food while you do the housekeeping. Be on your guard against the wolf, for if he comes in, he will eat you all up —skin, hair, and hoofs. He is sly, but you may know him by his rough voice and his black paws."

The eldest little kid said, "Dear mother, we will mind what you have said. Have no fear."

With that the Mother Goat opened the door and said, "Very well, I shall be back soon."

The little kids started to clean the house but as soon as Mother Goat was out of sight the wicked wolf went straight to the hut. He had been listening from behind a bush, so he knocked at the door and called out, "Open, my dear children. Your mother is back soon. She forgot something."

The little kids were surprised. They asked questions and listened to the voice and then said, "We will not open the door. You are not our mother. She has a gentle voice, but yours is gruff. You are the wolf. We will not let you in."

"Grrr," snarled the wolf. The little kids danced for joy when they heard his growl and then went back to their work. The wolf ran off to the woods and ate a big mouthful of honey to make his voice sweet.

In no time at all the wolf was back at the door. He knocked and called in his honey voice, "Open, my dear children. Your mother is here and has brought something for each of you."

The little kids listened but the eldest little kid looked on the window sill of the door. She saw the wolf's black paws. "No, we will not open the door," she said. "Our mother has white feet. Your feet are black. You are a wolf."

"Grrr," snarled the wolf and he ran off to the village to make his feet white. Again the little kids danced for joy when they heard the wolf's growl. When they grew tired from dancing they went back to finish the housework.

Now for the third time the wicked wolf ran to the hut and knocked at the door. "Open, my dear children," he called sweetly. "Your mother is home and has brought something for each of you from the forest."

The little kids listened to the sweet voice. The eldest little kid said, "Show us your feet so we may see whether you are our mother."

So the wicked Wolf, who had had the miller throw flour on his feet, put his white paws on the window sill. The eldest little kid thought it was her mother so they threw open the hut door.

Who should come in but the wolf! The little kids were scared and ran to hide. One ran under the table, the second one got into bed, the third hid in a cupboard, the fourth hid in the kitchen closet, the fifth hid in the oven, the sixth hid in the washtub, and the seventh, who was the littlest, hid in the clock. The sly, hungry wolf found them. He swallowed one, two, three, four, five, six, all except the littlest kid. The wicked Wolf then went outside and he settled down on the green, meadow grass and was soon fast asleep.

Mother Goat hurried home from the forest. What a sight she saw! The hut door stood wide open. The table, the stools and the benches were overturned. The washtub was broken. She called her children. She looked for them anxiously, but she could not find them. Mother Goat was frightened. "Little kids, little kids, where are you?" she called.

The littlest kid answered softly, "Here I am, dear mother. I'm inside the clock."

Mother Goat opened the clock door. Out leaped littlest kid who told Mother what had happened. You cannot think how sadly she wept for her poor little kids. "Come, we shall search until we find the wolf," Mother Goat said. She hurried out into the meadow with littlest kid following after her. They found the wolf snoring under the tree. Mother Goat looked him over from all sides and saw that something was stirring inside. Mother Goat took the scissors very quietly from her apron pocket. Snip-snap, snip-snap! She cut a long slit in the wicked wolf's tummy. Out leaped one, two, three, four, five, six little kids! They were as good as new. They danced about and hugged their mother with joy. She quieted them down and bid each one get a large stone from the river bank.

The little kids brought big stones. Mother Goat put the stones carefully in the wolf's empty tummy. Then stitchety-stitchety-stitch! She sewed up the slit. Mother Goat and her little kids trotted home. They locked the door and watched from the window.

They saw wicked Wolf wake up and lick his chops. He looked thirsty and he waddled down to the river. The stones inside of him were so heavy that when he leaned over to drink, he fell kersplash! He tumbled deep down into the river bed and went to sleep. The little kids danced for joy around their dear mother. They sang as they had never sung before, "The wicked wolf is gone for good! The wicked wolf is gone for good! The wicked wolf is gone for good and we'll be happy forever!"

TEENY-TINY

An English folktale as told by James Orchard Halliwell

Every child has done something a teeny-tiny bit wrong which haunts his conscience. This fantasy seldom "fails to rivet the attention of children, especially if well told. The last two words should be said loudly with a start." A discussion of why it is wrong to take anything from a graveyard (universal reverence for the dead) strengthens mood for interpretive playing. Characterization of the woman builds always with the presence of tangible antagonists in the cupboard. Questions like the following stir imaginations and bring a desire for such characters as ghosts, skeletons, or spirits: "Whose teeny-tiny bone would make good soup for the woman? Why might the rest of this creature's bones want to get the teeny-tiny bone back before it is boiled for soup? How could 'they' possibly get inside the house and cupboard? How will they move and speak to haunt the woman's conscience so she returns the bone?"

Once upon a time there was a teeny-tiny woman who lived in a teeny-tiny house in a teeny-tiny village. Now, one day this teeny-tiny woman put on her teeny-tiny bonnet, and went out of her teeny-tiny house to take a teeny-tiny walk. And when this teeny-tiny woman had gone a teeny-tiny way, she came to a teeny-tiny gate; so the teeny-tiny woman opened the teeny-tiny gate, and went into a teeny-tiny churchyard. And when this teeny-tiny woman had got into the teeny-tiny churchyard, she saw a teeny-tiny bone on a teeny-tiny grave, and the teeny-tiny woman said to her teeny-tiny self, "This teeny-tiny bone will make me some teeny-tiny soup for my teeny-tiny supper." So the teeny-tiny woman put the teeny-tiny bone into her teeny-tiny pocket and went home to her teeny-tiny house.

Now when the teeny-tiny woman got home to her teeny-tiny house, she was a teeny-tiny bit tired; so she went up her teeny-tiny stairs to her teeny-tiny bed, and put her teeny-tiny bone into a teeny-tiny cupboard. And when this teeny-tiny woman had been to sleep a teeny-tiny time, she was awakened by a teeny-tiny voice from the teeny-tiny cupboard, which said:

GIVE ME MY BONE!

And this teeny-tiny woman was a teeny-tiny frightened, so she hid her teeny-tiny head under the teeny-tiny clothes and went to sleep again. And when she had been to sleep again a teeny-tiny time, the teeny-tiny voice again cried out from the teeny-tiny cupboard a teeny-tiny louder,

GIVE ME MY BONE!

This made the teeny-tiny woman a teeny-tiny more frightened, so she hid her teeny-tiny head a teeny-tiny farther under the teeny-tiny clothes. And when the teeny-tiny woman had been to sleep again a teeny-tiny time, the teeny-tiny voice from the teeny-tiny cupboard said again a teeny-tiny louder,

GIVE ME MY BONE!

And this teeny-tiny woman was a teeny-tiny bit more frightened, but she put her teeny-tiny head out of the teeny-tiny clothes, and said in her loudest teeny-tiny voice,

TAKE IT!

LITTLE MOUSE AND MR. SCARE CROW
by Ann Kimball[9]

Miss Kimball says: "For the past several Octobers my kindergarten children have enjoyed this story. They enjoy the free rhythmic movement as they play the mouse, the crows and particularly the scarecrows. They like to become scarecrows to frighten crows away with sudden movement only. One incident children are delighted with is when the mouse approaches the old scarecrow to inquire about him. Each group has laughed aloud and reacted to this spontaneous dialogue in a similar surprised way. After playing scarecrows children become aware of wind and its different ways of blowing. Often they play wind and scarecrows in free dramatic play. My children respond, also, to painting and drawing original scarecrows, jack-o-lanterns, and 'pictures' of the story. Some groups have made original jack-o-lanterns from pumpkins and saved pumpkin seeds for planting in the spring."

Little Mouse lived in Farmer John's pumpkin patch. Little Mouse had a soft grey coat, a very long tail, curious eyes and very curious ears. He had a cozy house under a large pumpkin and all around him pumpkins grew bigger and riper each day. They were beginning to turn yellow, for Halloween was coming soon. Little Mouse had heard

[9] By permission of the author. Miss Kimball is a kindergarten teacher in the Shoreline Public Schools, Seattle, Washington.

Farmer John say that the pumpkins were for girls and boys so they could make jack-o-lanterns.

One morning Little Mouse was curious. He listened from inside his house. He heard a strange cawing sound. He scurried out, poked his head around the pumpkin and saw three black crows perched on a branch in a tall, maple tree. "Caw, caw, caw," called the biggest crow to the others.

Suddenly the crows swooped down toward Little Mouse. He scurried into his house. He waited and then crept out quietly, thinking the crows had gone away. There they were! Each one was pecking on a fat round pumpkin and eating it. "Oh, dear," Little Mouse squeaked. "Farmer John has worked hard to get the pumpkins to grow. Now the crows are spoiling them!"

As Little Mouse spoke he heard a different noise. "Shoo! Shoo! Shoo! Get out of my garden!" called Farmer John to the crows as he hurried into the patch. Little Mouse watched closely. He saw a curious sight. Farmer John was carrying something strange. It looked a little like a wooden man. He carried a wooden post with a board and some hay nailed across it near the top. "Wonder what it's for?" said Little Mouse curiously.

"Caw, caw, caw," called the crows from the maple tree. They wanted to eat the juicy pumpkins again, but they were afraid of Farmer John. "I'll show you, Blacky, you big crow," called Farmer John as he shook his fist at the crows. "I didn't raise these pumpkins for you and your brothers. They are for jack-o-lanterns."

As Little Mouse watched he was more curious than ever. Farmer John dug a hole in the ground right in the middle of a pumpkin patch. He put the big post in the hole and packed dirt around the post so it would stand straight and tall. Then Farmer John took a big pumpkin, cut a hole in the bottom and fastened it on top of the post. He took off his worn, straw hat and fastened it on top of the pumpkin. He took off his old, red jacket, put it on the board and buttoned it to the post. He took bright scarves and ribbons from his pocket and fastened them around the post. When he was finished Farmer John waved, and laughed and hurried away.

The crows were curious. "Caw, caw, caw," called Blacky. "Caw, caw, caw," answered his brothers. They wondered who was standing in the pumpkin patch. They watched closely.

Little Mouse was curious too. Ever so quietly he crept over to the stranger. "H . . . h . . . hello. What's your name? What are you doing in my field?"

"Ho, ho, ho, don't you know? I'm Mr. Scare Crow," he said laughing. "Farmer John made me and put me here to scare those pesky crows, especially Blacky."

"How will you scare them?" asked Little Mouse curiously.

"Well, see my torn hat with a hole in the top and my torn coat all stuffed with loose hay, and take a close look at my scarf and pretty necktie. Now go behind your house and watch closely. You'll see how I scare Blacky when the time comes."

Little Mouse scurried behind his pumpkin house. He peeked out to watch. For a long time Blacky and his brothers circled and flew around the pumpkin patch so they could take a close look at the stranger. At last Blacky spread out his great wings and got ready to swoop down into the pumpkin patch. Little Mouse scurried inside his house, for he was afraid of the bright-eyed crows with their sharp beaks. Blacky and his brothers swooped down and walked around and looked closely at Mr. Scare Crow. When they saw that he meant no harm the hungry crows started eating pumpkins again. Blacky found the biggest pumpkin and started breaking into it. It was Little Mouse's house. Little Mouse was afraid that Blacky would eat up his house and then eat him too. He shivered inside but he was afraid to move.

Peck, peck, peck went Blacky's sharp bill on top of Little Mouse's house. While Blacky pecked he kept one eye on Mr. Scare Crow. "Caw-caw-caw, haw-haw-haw," Blacky called to his brothers. "I'm not afraid of that funny, old wooden man." Blacky went on eating Little Mouse's pumpkin house.

"Caw-caw-caw, haw-haw-haw, he doesn't scare us either," called the crow brothers. Little Mouse shivered again as he listened to the peck, peck, pecking.

All at once a quick breeze blew through the pumpkin patch. Mr. Scare Crow began to sway from side to side, back and forth, back and forth. His arms flopped this way and that way. His necktie and ribbons fluttered up and down. The breeze grew stronger. "Twwwwrrrr," twirled his tie. "Twwwrrr, TWWWrrr, TWWWWRRRRRRRrrr!"

Blacky jumped. He gave a loud caw as he flew out of the field as fast as a wink. His brothers flew after him, cawing loudly. Little Mouse scurried out of his house and poked his head out carefully. He saw Blacky and his brothers flying high in the sky. They never came back again. Little Mouse knew he was safe with Mr. Scare Crow. He knew that Farmer John's pumpkins were safe too. Now he knew they would make pretty jack-o-lanterns for the children on Halloween.

A FIRST THANKSGIVING

Adapted by Geraldine Brain Siks from a true American tale

This story has been played by children's groups ranging in age from five through twelve years. Children are curious about American Indians and are generally eager to express brief knowledge and interest through convincing characters. The Indians' unexpected reaction to the jack-o-lantern is a favorite dramatic episode. Groups respond to the mood of the Thanksgiving feast when guided to sense the depth of feeling. A teacher who participates in the role of a neighbor or one of the Indians is in a position to guide and, indirectly, to inspire spontaneous expressions of thanksgiving from characterizations of pilgrims and Indians.

Faith and Hope were two little sisters. They were pilgrims who lived with their mother and father in a cabin in the deep woods. One cold November day Faith and Hope were alone in the cabin for their mother and father had gone to the far-off hill to help their only neighbors, who were ill with fever. Father had warned the little sisters to stay inside the cabin and keep the door locked because there were many dangers in the woods.

All afternoon Faith and Hope sang songs and played with their dolls, which were made from corn husks. When they grew tired of this they played Indian. With their father they had often watched as the Indians stole through the forest on moccasined feet and aimed their bows and arrows at deer and bear and wild turkeys. The sisters had always watched from the cellar when the Indians had come to the cabin door to speak with father.

While the sisters played Indian, Hope, the younger one, looked up at the one cabin window. "Look, Faith. It is growing dark already and father and mother have not come. What if the Indians did come to see father? What would we do?"

Faith answered calmly. "We would just keep brave. Have no fear, little sister. Father and mother will be home soon." Faith wanted to keep Hope from thinking about the Indians. "I know what we'll do. We'll make a jack-o-lantern to put our candle in. He will make such a friendly light we will not think of Indians."

They ran to the end of the cabin and took a pumpkin from the cellar, which was in a dark corner behind a curtain. They were happy while they cut and scooped seeds and carved a pumpkin face. They laughed aloud when Faith lit the candle from the fireplace and Jack-o-lantern smiled with his big eyes and crooked mouth and three broken teeth.

While they laughed, a hooting call sounded through the woods. "Listen," said Hope in a loud whisper as she ran to the cellar to hide. "It is the Indians."

Faith listened closely to see if Hope had heard the Indians or an owl. "Hoooo—hooooo—hoooo," came the sound again.

"Hoooo—hooooo—hooooo," the sound was answered in true Indian fashion.

The Indians were sending signals to one another as they came near the cabin. They wanted to let each other know where they were and that they were safe. They hooted like owls so the white men would not know they were coming. The Indians were afraid of all the white men because they never knew whether a white man would be friendly or cruel.

"Hoooo—hoooo—hooooo," the sound came nearer to the cabin.

"Hoooo—hoooo—hooooo," the sound was answered.

Faith knew she must think of what to do. She knew she had to be brave. She had never talked to the Indians and she wanted them to know she was as friendly as her father was. She would open the door if the Indians knocked.

"Hoooo—hoooo—hoooo," the sound was at the cabin door.

Suddenly Faith thought of a plan. She saw Jack-o-lantern's friendly smile. She carried him to the door and put him on the floor. Hope peeked from the cellar and told Faith to hide. Just then a heavy knock came on the door. The Indians stood outside. Two of them held wild turkeys while three braves had their bows and arrows aimed for any trouble that might come from the white man's door.

The knock came again. Faith's heart beat fast. She unfastened the door and opened it. Faith saw the Indians. The Indians saw her. Then they saw Jack-o-lantern with his fiery smile.

"Ugh, ugh," they spoke to one another as they stared at the lighted lantern face and drew their bows tighter.

"Evil spirits," said the chief.

"Ugh, evil spirits," said the others as they stared at the lighted eyes and teeth. The chief shouted suddenly and ran like the wind into the woods. The other Indians shouted and ran after him. Faith closed the door. Hope peaked out from the cellar curtain and was ready to speak when sounds came outside the door again. Hope hid. Faith listened and smiled and called Hope. They both went to the door and opened it. There stood father and mother. On the ground were two big, wild turkeys.

When father and mother heard about the Indians, mother said friendly Indians were a blessing in the wilderness. Father agreed but he laughed heartily as he looked at the funny, lighted jack-o-lantern.

The next day father found the Indians and invited them to the cabin for a feast of their wild turkeys. The Indians and the pilgrim family sat together on the cabin floor for their first thanksgiving. Father and the Indians gave thanks for peace and friendship. Mother gave thanks for brave little pilgrims and Faith gave thanks for kind Indians. Hope spoke up and said what she was feeling deep inside her heart. She was thankful for pumpkins and jack-o-lanterns.

WHERE IS CHRISTMAS?

by Geraldine Brain Siks

Little children like to wonder where Christmas is. Answers from different groups reveal such individual concepts as these from five-year-olds: "On the calendar"; "In a Christmas tree"; "In the snow"; "At Grandma's"; "At Frederick and Nelson's"; "In Church"; "Inside of me." Little children enjoy particularly the characterizations of Frisky, Bird, Santa, and his Reindeer. Most children, eager to put their knowledge into action, insist that there be eight reindeer who "fly in twos and are hooked together with bells." (Red yarn or cord and a few bells have been used by kindergarten teachers to help ten five-year-olds organize themselves for greater enjoyment.) Most teachers find it helpful to be a member of the family to guide the dramatic play which emerges as Mary and her family discover the feeling of Christmas when they find Frisky on Christmas morning.

It was Christmas eve. Big, soft snowflakes fluttered down from the sky. The pine tree forest was beautiful. Everything seemed ready for Christmas except Frisky, a little gray squirrel. He was lost.

"I must find Christmas," Frisky chattered. He looked around the foot of the trees near him. He hopped to the bushes and looked about, for he thought maybe he could find Christmas in a rabbit's home. He looked up to the tree tops, but Frisky couldn't find Christmas anywhere. He had started out bravely from his home and he had looked for many days. Now he couldn't find Christmas and he couldn't find his way back home, for the snow had grown deep.

Frisky decided he must find Christmas before it grew dark. He leaped to the tallest pine tree and chattered:

> Chee, chee, chee
> If you hear me
> Could you tell me a way
> To find Christmas today—please?

Frisky listened. Soon from up in the sky, Frisky heard a friendly sound. A bird swooped down through the snowflakes. Frisky was happy to see her and he called, "Little Bird, do you know a way to find Christmas today?"

Little Bird cocked her head, shook the snow from her feathers and chirped:

> Twee, twee, twee
> Fly with me to a cherry tree
> That's the way
> To find Christmas today.

Frisky chattered, "Is Christmas in a cherry tree?"

"It is for me," sang Little Bird. "High over the tall mountain peaks is a valley of trees. Some have flowers and some have fruit. We'll work hard and build a nest, then we'll eat and sing and rest. That's where we'll find Christmas."

Frisky wanted to go with Little Bird but he knew he couldn't fly. "Little Bird, you had better go on without me before it gets dark. I could never fly through the sky even if I try and try."

Little Bird knew she must be on her way. She was sorry to leave Frisky. "Keep on looking, Frisky. Never give up hoping and you'll find Christmas. Maybe I can find a way to help you, too." Away Little Bird flew.

Frisky scampered up the tree to watch her fly off through the thick snowflakes. Frisky felt more lost than before. He chattered loudly:

> Chee, chee, chee
> If you hear me
> Could you tell me a way
> To find Christmas today—please.

Red Fox heard. He sniffed slyly over in his dark cave and thought of the Christmas dinner he would have with young squirrel's company. Red Fox ran through the deep snow to the pine tree. He spoke in a voice as sweet as Christmas candy, "Good day, I am Red Fox.

I heard you call, little squirrel. Come to my cozy den to play and I will help you find Christmas today."

While Red Fox talked sweetly, Frisky wondered. He remembered that Mother Squirrel had told him that foxes and wolves and bears did not honestly want to be friends with squirrels. They only pretended. But as Frisky listened Red Fox sounded as if he really knew about Christmas.

"Come squirrel. My cave is warm," Red Fox said slyly. Frisky leaped down to a branch below which was nearer to Red Fox. "My, you are big, brave and handsome," Red Fox said foxily as Frisky came nearer. Red Fox opened his mouth and smiled, for he was pleased with Frisky's size. Frisky leaped down on a lower branch so he could see the fox better. He saw Red Fox's sharp teeth which shone in the snowlight and he remembered again what Mother Squirrel had said. Red Fox lifted his sharp paw up toward Frisky and said sweetly, "Come now. I will help you down."

Frisky leaped back up to a higher branch. "No," he said suddenly. "I don't think I'd better find Christmas with you."

Red Fox barked. He was wild with anger. He leaped straight up toward the branch and reached for Frisky's tail just as Frisky scurried up the tree trunk. Red Fox was mad. "WOW-wow-wow; WOW-wow-wow," he barked. "I'll outfox you yet. I'll trick you with my whirl-whirl-whirl." Around the tree Red Fox ran swiftly, around and around in circles. Frisky was surprised. He watched until he started to get dizzy. Then he closed his eyes and was so still that he could listen. At first he heard only the angry barks of Red Fox. All at once he heard a new far-away sound, coming it seemed, from the mountains: "Jingle-jangle; jingle-jangle; jingle-jangle jee; jingle-jangle; jingle-jangle; jingle-jangle-jee."

Frisky called loudly above the barking of Red Fox:

> Chee, chee, chee
> If you hear me
> Please show me the way
> To find Christmas today.

The jingle-jangle grew louder. A friendly voice called: "Ho-ho-ho; Ho-ho-ho, Call again Frisky, so we'll know where to go." Frisky called again. The jingle-jangles came nearer. Red Fox heard, too, and away he flew back to his cave. Frisky looked through the branches. He saw a most wonderful thing. A little old man dressed all in red was flying through the sky in a sleigh with beautiful reindeer leading the way. They circled gracefully through the sky and swooped down to the ground by the tall pine tree.

"Frisky, I'm Santa Claus," said the jolly old man. "Come, climb into my sleigh. I've been looking for you all the day."

"How did you know about me?" asked Frisky. "Did you see Little Bird?"

Santa laughed. "It's a Christmas secret. Come, jump right up here and sit on the seat beside me."

Frisky leaped up. "Are you Christmas?" he asked as he looked closely at Santa.

"Well, not exactly," laughed Santa. "But we'll find Christmas." Santa called to his reindeer and loosened the reins. The jingle-jangle bells rang out and Frisky felt happy as he started to fly through the sky with Santa and his reindeer. Frisky snuggled close to Santa while the reindeer mounted high in the sky and danced as they pulled the sleigh over the treetops, and swooped down to a smooth stop on the roof of a little cabin up in the woods.

"Come along, Frisky," Santa said as he carried his pack of toys on his back and went down the chimney. Frisky was excited as he went zooming down the chimney with Santa. There they were in a big room where a Christmas tree was bright with shiny balls, and a great big star and strings of popcorn. Frisky started to eat the popcorn, but Santa showed him a bowl of peanuts. "Look," he said. "Here's your supper and a letter for you and me from a little girl named Mary." Frisky was so hungry that he ate his supper while Santa read the letter and put toys and presents around the tree and in the stockings.

"Merry Christmas, Frisky," Santa whispered softly as he backed into the fireplace. Up the chimney he flew. Frisky felt so warm and happy that he curled up by the fireplace and went sound asleep.

The next thing he heard was voices: "Merry Christmas! Merry, Merry Christmas!" It was morning. Mary and her family were gathering around the Christmas tree. Mary saw Frisky waking up by the fireplace. She ran to him and held him gently while everyone gathered around and offered him nuts and candy and a bowl of water. "Oh, daddy," Mary called. "I never thought we'd get a live squirrel when I wrote to Santa. This is the merriest Christmas ever."

"It certainly is!" said father. "It's a merry, merry Christmas! A merry, merry Christmas, glad and gay!" Father started singing and everyone joined in. Frisky chattered and sang with them in his own happy way, for now he knew that he had found Christmas too.

THE STORY OF CHRISTMAS

Adapted by Geraldine Brain Siks from The Holy Bible, *King James version*

This version was told to children for many years but was first put in writing for the Lake Forest Park Pre-School Christmas meeting for parents and children in 1949.[10] Since that time it has been dramatized by young children and older children in schools and Sunday schools with various media of dramatic interpretation. A frequent way is for groups to pantomime the episodes while the story is read by an older child. This version sets forth the sequence of scenes most familiar in the traditional *Nativity*. However each episode needs development in characterization and conflict if children desire to interpret the story with greater dramatic force and dialogue.

Long, long ago, so long that only the stars and moon remember, there lived a kind and beautiful woman. She was good and always happy in her heart, and her name was Mary. One day when Mary was feeding crusts of bread to hungry birds she heard triumphant music in the sky. Mary looked upward. Coming down out of the clouds was an angel dressed in robes of flowing white, sounding a golden trumpet.

[10] Lake Forest Park School, Shoreline Public Schools, Seattle, Washington.

"Hail Mary," the angel said as he spoke to her. "I am Gabriel, sent by God to bring you good tidings."

Mary was fearful when Gabriel spoke to her, for she had never before seen or heard an angel. The angel saw and he spoke again.

"Fear not, Mary. God is with thee. Blessed art thou among women. Behold thou shall have a child. He will be sent from God and born to you to dwell upon the earth. Thou shall call his name *Jesus*. He shall grow strong in truth and grace. He shall be called W*onderful, Counsellor, Son of the Highest,* the *Prince of Peace.*"

Mary listened and pondered. She did not understand all that she had heard from the angel. She knelt down to pray, for her heart and mind were filled with great wonderings. While Mary prayed the angel went silently away; high into the heavens he went.

It came to pass in those long-ago days that all the world should be taxed and counted. All went to be taxed according to the law, each one unto his own city. Joseph, the kind husband of Mary, made ready a donkey for Mary to ride, for it was a long journey to the little town of Bethlehem where they were to go. Mary and Joseph and the donkey traveled along the rough roads for many days. When they came to Bethlehem the stars were out and all the city slept in darkness. Mary and Joseph and the donkey found shelter in a manger because the town was crowded with people, and there was no room for them at the inn.

It was on this night that Mary brought forth her baby son. She held him in her arms and looked upon him with love. Then she wrapped him in swaddling clothes and laid him in soft hay in the manger. The cattle and sheep and the donkey and even the littlest lambs made gentle sounds while the baby slumbered.

Now there were in the same country shepherds on the hillsides, keeping watch over their sheep by night. An angel from the Lord came down to the shepherds and a great light shone around about them, and they, too, were afraid. The angel spoke to them and said, "Fear not, for behold I bring you good tidings of great joy which are for all people. Unto you is born this day in Bethlehem a child which is *Christ the Lord.* And this shall be a sign unto you: ye shall find the babe wrapped in swaddling clothes, lying in a manger."

Suddenly there were with the angel hundreds of angels with voices like music calling from the sky and singing: "Glory to God in the highest, and on earth peace, good will toward men." Then the angels went away like fleecy white clouds in a night sky and the shepherds were filled with great wonder. They said, one to another, "Let us now go to Bethlehem and see this thing which is come to pass which the Lord hath made known unto us."

The shepherds came in great haste and found the babe sleeping in the manger. The littlest shepherd brought a mountain flower which he had found. He gave it to Mary for the baby Jesus.

Great kings traveled swiftly on camels from the East for they, too, had heard the tidings. They brought costly treasures to honor the newborn son.

Wise Men were sent from Jerusalem by King Herod. They followed the brightest star in the sky which went before them like the light of a thousand candles until it came and shone over the manger where the little child lay. The Wise Men came into the manger and when they saw the babe with Mary, his mother, they knelt down to worship him. They gave the babe rich gifts of gold and frankincense and myrrh. People from near and far came to worship and to bring gifts and there was great rejoicing in Bethlehem.

Every season since that long-ago night people throughout the earth give gifts of love as they remember the birthday of the Christ child. They remember, too, the voices of heaven calling to all the world and saying, "Glory to God in the highest, and on earth, *peace*, good will toward men."

CLAIRE AND THE NUTCRACKER

Adapted by Geraldine Brain Siks from an old French tale and from Peter Tchaikovsky's "Nutcracker Suite"

This version has been told to children for many years. It was first written down for David Dunnington[11] who was fascinated by the

[11] Son of Mrs. Hazel Dunnington, Assistant Professor of Speech and Drama, Central Washington State College, Ellensburg, Washington.

music when he learned to play it on the piano when he was ten. Children should first enjoy Tchaikovsky's enchanting music. Seven- and eight-year-olds prefer to select two or three episodes from the tale to play in free dramatic pantomime to the music. Older children generally prefer to develop the characterizations of Claire, the Nutcracker and the Mice, after which they like to play the story in sequence, entirely in pantomime to the music. Groups respond to opportunities to originate surprise characterizations of soldiers, dolls, fairies, flutes, trumpets, and flowers. The strong appeal lies in the dream. Almost every child has dreamed fancifully about something that has been of particular concern to him. This is Claire's never-to-be-forgotten dream of Nutcracker, whom she loves in a delightful way. Children respond to the dream-style.

It was Christmas night. Everyone in the big house was asleep except Claire. She was thinking about her presents, and she was so worried about her new wooden nutcracker that she couldn't sleep. Her grandfather had given it to her, and it was the present she liked best of all. Nutcracker looked like a merry brown dwarf. He had a big mouth that smiled and showed his sharp teeth which he used for cracking nuts. In the excitement of Christmas, Nutcracker had been broken and Claire wanted to mend him. She tiptoed down the stairs in the darkness. As she stood in the doorway of the big room where the Christmas tree stood, the moonlight shone in through the window. Claire thought it was the most beautiful tree she had ever seen, with its branches decorated with shining toy flutes, and clarinets and piccolos.

Claire crept close to the low branches. She knelt down and reached under the tree to find Nutcracker. She knew he was somewhere in the midst of all her bright tin soldiers and new Christmas dolls. She found him in his box and took him out and talked softly while she tried to fix him. When she saw that she could not help, she promised that grandfather would do it the next day.

Just as Claire put Nutcracker back in his box, the big clock started to strike the hours of midnight. Claire tiptoed to the door but stopped to listen, for she heard a strange clattering under the Christmas tree. As the clock struck twelve, Nutcracker sprang from his box. He leaped out into the room. His hands and feet danced as he bowed to Claire. She was breathless. She saw Nutcracker go crickety-crack and the candles on the Christmas tree lit up. She heard him go crickety-crack and the soldiers stood up and stretched and reached to the branches for flutes, and piccolos and clarinets. As they tuned the ornament instruments, Nutcracker snapped for attention. At once the soldiers made music and followed Nutcracker as he led a merry march around the Christmas tree. The new dolls from China, Arabia, and Russia paraded behind in fancy costumes and each one entertained Claire with some special delight. Claire clapped her hands and told Nutcracker that it was the most enchanting music and parade she had ever known.

Suddenly, Claire noticed something flashing in the darkness of the corner. It was a sword being brandished by a king. It was a mouse king, an angry mouse king. He waved the sword in the air as he headed straight for Nutcracker. Behind Mouse King came an army of mice, each flourishing a sword. Mouse King challenged Nutcracker and the soldiers to a battle. Nutcracker answered his challenge. Immediately the battle was raging. Each of the toy soldiers fought bravely against a mouse. The soldiers tried to keep the mice and Mouse King from cornering Nutcracker, but in the valiant battle Claire saw that Nutcracker was being backed into the corner, and she was frightened. Mouse King waved his sword wildly as he came closer to Nutcracker. When Claire saw that Mouse King was closing in on Nutcracker she pulled off her slipper, threw it at Mouse King and it killed him.

It was a moment of magic. Nutcracker changed into a handsome prince. In a puff the mice disappeared. Claire was astonished. Prince Nutcracker bowed before her. He was overcome with appreciation. He explained that a wicked witch had enchanted him long ago while he gathered hazel nuts and cracked them with his teeth. His spell could only be broken by kindness. He invited Claire to fly at once with him to the Land of the Sugar Plum Fairies. Away they flew through the window into the starry night of Christmas and came almost at once to the open doors of the exquisite ballroom in Sugar Plum Palace.

The dainty Queen of Sugar Plums welcomed them and invited them to sit on plump, plum cushions to enjoy a victory celebration planned in their honor. Claire was surprised to see the queen open the program. She danced a story dance with her Sugar Plum Fairies to tell of the Prince's enchantment. It was beautifully fearful.

Claire was amazed with the next happenings on the program. She saw her Christmas dolls whisper to the Prince and then to the Fairy Queen. She heard the Queen announce that the dolls would show Claire different places that Nutcracker had seen as a nutcracker that he could never have visited as a prince. First there was a spirited visit to Russia and a dance of friendship by the Russian dolls. Next, a mysterious journey to Arabia brought Arabian dolls to dance an ancient secret of beauty, and last of all the Chinese dolls lilted Claire and the Prince to a Chinese celebration showing a riddle of happiness. Claire and the Prince clapped with joy at the splendiferous celebration.

When the clapping stopped the lights in the ballroom twinkled and darkened. Out on the floor in a beam of moonlight danced the dazzling flutes. They whistled tuneful tunes for themselves until the trumpets joined in and trumpeted for the dancing.

When the flutes fluted back to their places, the Queen announced that the celebration would continue in the palace garden. The doors swung out into a mass of dancing flowers. Everyone danced to the joyous rhythm. At the height of the grand dance Claire screamed in sudden fright. She saw two black shadows. "Look!" she called to the Prince. "There's Mouse King's shadow and who is that old bent shadow with him?"

As Claire spoke the others screamed and hurried away, frightening themselves as well as the shadows out of sight. Claire was bewildered. She looked around for the Prince. She rubbed her eyes to see better. Imagine her surprise. It was morning. She was under her Christmas tree with her dolls and soldiers all around her. Nutcracker was beside her, out of his box and smiling.

Claire rubbed her sleepy eyes again. She stared closely at Nutcracker. "Why, you are as good as new. However could this be?" She shook her head in wonder as she stood up and looked slowly all around the room and back at her Christmas tree. Claire smiled as she knelt down beside Nutcracker. "I don't quite understand it, Nutcracker," she said. "It must be the way of Christmas."

FRAIDY-CAT AND THE WISE ONE

Adapted by Lillian M. Bushnell from an old tale[12]

Mrs. Bushnell says: "This story has been told as a narrative or dramatized as it is told with kitten and owl hand puppets or flannel board characters. The point of the story 'as a man thinketh in his heart, so he is' becomes understood generally by children once they begin to interpret the story. They are frequently motivated to express personal experiences similar to those of Fraidy-Cat."

Fraidy-Cat was a tiny, black kitten whose mama loved him very much. She named him Licorish because he was sweet but his brothers and sisters called him Fraidy-Cat. Soon all of their friends in the neighborhood were calling him Fraidy-Cat too. He began to think he really *was* a Fraidy-Cat.

He was afraid of the dark and anyone knows there's nothing in the dark that isn't in the light. Whenever the little kittens ran out to play the friendly dog who lived nearby began to bark. As soon as Fraidy-Cat heard a bark he would hide and all of the neighborhood friends as well as his brothers and sisters would tease and sing:

> Fraidy-Cat, Fraidy-Cat—
> 'Fraid of this and 'fraid of that!

Fraidy-Cat would put his paws over his ears so he couldn't hear

---

[12] By permission of the author, Lillian M. Bushnell. Mrs. Bushnell has taught creative dramatics in the King County Parent-Teacher Association Creative Dramatics Program in the Seattle Public Libraries, Seattle, Washington, for fourteen years.

their singing but they kept on teasing and teasing. Mama Kitty watched. "This will never do," she said.

Mama Kitty walked out where Fraidy-Cat was hiding. She touched him gently and said, "Come, we will go to see the Wise One."

"Who *is* the Wise One?" asked Fraidy.

"Old Mr. Owl. He lives in the hollow tree at the other edge of the forest," said Mama Kitty. So while all the other kittens curled up like little round, furry balls to rest from their running and playing and teasing, Mama Kitty hurried off through the woods with Fraidy-Cat's soft paw in hers. The first neighbor to greet them was the friendly dog. "Arf-arf!" he said. "It's a beautiful morning! Arf-arf!"

"F-f-f-ft! F-f-f—t!" went scared little Fraidy-Cat. He climbed a tree as fast as he could scamper and he wouldn't come down until friendly dog had gone away.

The next neighbor they met was a brown cub bear. He was sitting on a hollow log, licking a stick covered with honey. His red tongue darted back and forth, as he said: "M-m-m! Lickin's good! Come on— I'll give you some." Fraidy-Cat only said, "F-f-f-t! F-f-f-t!" and hid behind his mother. Just then Fraidy-Cat stepped on something that *moved!* It was a baby fawn all curled up in the tall grass. The mama deer had been watching and she ran back quickly to protect her baby. But Fraidy-Cat ran faster than mama deer. He ran *away*. He kept on running until finally he bumped right into a tall, hollow tree at the other edge of the wood.

"Whoooo—whoooo—whoooo are you?" asked a voice that seemed to come right out of the sky.

Fraidy-Cat was so scared he couldn't speak or run. He looked around, but he *couldn't* see where the voice was coming from. He couldn't even see his *mother* but she was watching him from the shadows at the edge of the wood.

"Whoooo—whoooo—whoooo are you?" called the voice again.

Fraidy-Cat was so scared that he climbed straight up the hollow tree, digging in with his sharp little claws until he stood on a branch at the very top of the tree. And there on the branch right beside him he saw a great, big, sleepy-looking owl!

The owl opened its great yellow eyes and blinked twice at little Fraidy-Cat. "Whoooo—whoooo—whooo are you?" asked the owl once again.

Fraidy-Cat was so scared he wanted to climb higher. He looked all around but there wasn't any place higher to go. So he backed right out to the end of the branch, and arched his little back, and twitched his tail. "F-f-f-t! F-f-f-t!" said Fraidy-Cat.

"Don't be afraid," said the owl. "Come here."

Fraidy-Cat was shaking like a leaf and his fur was standing right on end; but he couldn't go backward any further, so he crept forward just a tiny step.

"That's better," said the owl, opening his big yellow eyes very wide. "That's much better. Now—whoooo—whoooo—whoooo are *you?*"

Fraidy-Cat nearly fell off the branch; but he managed to hang on with his sharp little claws. He said: "Me-ou! I'm Fraidy-Cat. I'm looking for the Wise One."

"I'm called the Wise One," said the owl, blinking his big yellow eyes three times. "People come from miles around to ask my advice. But they don't climb right up into my tree to talk to me, as you have done . . . Why do you want to see me?"

"Me-ou. My mama sent me to look for you, so I wouldn't be a Fraidy-Cat any more."

"Whoooo—whoooo—whooo says you are a Fraidy-Cat?"

"Me-ou! Everyone says I'm a Fraidy-Cat!"

The owl closed his eyes and said nothing for several minutes. Fraidy-Cat began to think the owl had gone to sleep! Then, suddenly, the owl opened his big yellow eyes and looked straight at Fraidy-Cat.

"You know," said the owl, "I don't believe you're a Fraidy-Cat at all!"

"You don't? Why?" asked Fraidy-Cat in surprise.

"Because you climbed up here to the top of my hollow tree to talk to me," said the owl. "No one else has ever done that before!"

"But—but I did it because I was scared!" said Fraidy-Cat, who was an honest kitten.

"Doesn't matter," said the owl. "You came—that's the point."

"But if I'm not Fraidy-Cat—who am I?" asked the kitten.

The owl closed his eyes again. After awhile he opened them and said: "You're little Brave-Heart. I know you're little Brave-Heart."

The owl reached under his wing and pulled out a tiny, candy heart. He stuck it in the kitten's fur, right on his little soft chest.

"You'll never be afraid again," said the Wise One.

"Never again?"

"Never again. You are little Brave-Heart from now on."

"Oh, thank you, Mr. Wise One," said little Brave-Heart. "I must go and tell my mother right away." He knew his mother would be glad to know what the Wise One had told him. Little Brave-Heart was so excited that he scrambled right down the tree head first and went racing off through the woods to find his mother.

Suddenly he stepped on something that moved! It was little fawn. But this time Brave-Heart wasn't afraid, not even when mama deer came bounding up to protect her baby. "Let's have a race!" said little Brave-Heart; and they went running through the forest until they came to the hollow log where the brown cub bear sat licking his stick dipped in honey. Little Brave-Heart went right up to the cub bear. "Hi! Meow! Meow! I'm sorry I was afraid of you before."

"G-r-r-r!" said cub bear. "M-m-m-m! Have a lick!"

"Thank you," said Brave-Heart as he licked the honey stick. Just then friendly dog came bouncing through the woods. "Arf-arf! Arf-arf!" he said. He couldn't believe his eyes when he saw little Brave-Heart licking on the same stick of honey with the brown cub bear. The friendly dog went bouncing back through the woods to tell the neighbors what was going on. Brave-Heart's brothers and sisters came running out to meet him. Brave-Heart told them his story and pointed one paw at his furry little chest.

"See?" he said. "See the heart the Wise One gave me? He says I'll never be afraid again."

But when the other animals looked at Brave-Heart's furry little chest, there wasn't any candy heart there at all! It had melted off while little Brave-Heart was racing through the woods.

"It's all right," said Brave-Heart. "I don't need a candy heart." He ran to find his mother. She had been watching from the shadows but she took good care to be home before Brave-Heart. When she saw him come bounding home she came out to meet him. She gave him a gentle lick on the ear with her tongue.

Brave-Heart looked right into his mother's eyes and said: "I'll never be a Fraidy-Cat again. Me-ow! Me-ow! Me-ow!"

And he never was.

THE GINGERBREAD BOY

Adapted by Geraldine Brain Siks from an old tale

Suggested by Miss Ann Kimball[13] who says: "The theme: 'Use your head as well as your feet' appeals to young children. After playing this story they have told me how they 'used their heads' by crossing the streets carefully on their ways home or following safety rules on the playground, etc. Children enjoy the gingerbread boy's chant. They chant it over and over again. Sometimes in the middle of an art period a whole table will start it, and then another and another. Children like to paint and make large, gingerbread boys on their own from cardboard or packing boxes. Often their creations are delightful with rhythm and originality. Children frequently urge their mothers to make cookie gingerbread boys at home. We always have a gingerbread boy party at the end of a week of playing the story. Altogether it is one of our favorite creative and dramatic experiences."

Once upon a time there was a little old woman and a little old man who lived in a cozy little house in the woods. Everyday the little old man worked hard while he chopped trees and cleared the land. And every day the little old woman worked hard while she cleaned and scrubbed and baked. They were very happy except that they were lonely. They had no little child and they wanted one very much.

One morning when the little old woman was baking gingerbread she laughed to herself and said, "I'll make my little old man a ginger-

13 See note 9.

bread boy." So she rolled the spicy dough until it was very smooth. Then she cut it in the shape of a good-sized little boy. She gave him raisin eyes, a raisin nose, a smiling raisin mouth, and a row of raisin buttons down his jacket.

She could hardly wait until he was done. When she thought he was ready, she opened the oven door to peek in. Out jumped the gingerbread boy! He skipped around the kitchen, and sang to the little old woman:

> *I'm a gingerbread man, I am, I am*
> *I can run away from you, I can, I can.*

"Well," said the little old woman in surprise. "Listen to me. Why run away? If you stay here we will all be happy."

But the gingerbread boy did not listen. He ran out the door with the little old woman following. "Come back, gingerbread boy, come back." But the gingerbread boy kept on running. The little woman hurried after him so fast that she was soon out of breath. She sat on a log to rest. She saw that he kept on running until he came to the little old man. He looked at the little old man who was very surprised to see him. The gingerbread boy laughed and cried out:

> *Run, run as fast as you can,*
> *You can't catch me, I'm the gingerbread man.*
> *I've run away from a little old woman*
> *And I can run away from you too, I can, I can*

The gingerbread boy started running through the woods with the little old man following. "Listen, listen little man," he called as he hurried after him. The old man ran so fast that he was soon out of breath, and he sat down on a log, huffing and puffing. He watched the gingerbread boy who went on running until he met Cottontail Rabbit. The rabbit was surprised but the gingerbread boy laughed and cried out:

Run, run as fast as you can
You can't catch me, I'm the gingerbread man.
I've run away from a little old woman and a little
old man
And I can run away from you too, I can, I can.

The gingerbread boy started running with the rabbit hopping after him. "Listen, listen, little man," called Cottontail as he hopped as fast as he could to try to get the gingerbread boy to listen. Cottontail couldn't catch the gingerbread boy, so he stopped to rest and to watch. The gingerbread boy went on running and running and would not listen to anyone.

Soon the gingerbread boy met a big brown bear. Gingerbread boy stopped and cried out:

Run, run as fast as you can,
You can't catch me, I'm the gingerbread man.
I've run away from a little old woman and a
little old man, and a rabbit,
And I can run away from you too, I can, I can!

The gingerbread boy started running with the big brown bear running after him. "Listen, listen, little man," called the brown bear as he ran as fast as he could to try to get the gingerbread boy to listen. Brown Bear couldn't catch the gingerbread boy so he stopped to rest and to watch. Soon the gingerbread boy met Sly Fox. He stopped and laughed and cried out:

Run, run as fast you can,
You can't catch me, I'm the gingerbread man.
I've run away from a little old woman and a
little old man
And a rabbit and a bear,
And I can run away from you, I can, I can!

"Well," said Sly Fox sitting back and smiling sweetly. "I don't want to run after you, but there's a river ahead of you. I will be pleased to give you a ride across so the others won't be able to catch you."

The gingerbread boy looked at the river and he looked at the woods. He saw the little old man and the little old woman and the rabbit and the bear walking after him. He looked at the fox and said, "You look kind. I will accept your ride to go across the river."

"Very well," said Sly Fox. "Get on my back or you will get wet." The gingerbread boy hopped on the fox's back, and the fox swam out into the river. As the water got deeper, Sly Fox said very kindly, "Hop up closer to my head, little boy, or you will get wet."

So the gingerbread boy hopped on the fox's head. The fox lifted his head with a quick start, opened his mouth, and—SNAP! The gingerbread boy hopped into the fox's mouth. Mmmmmmmmm! Mmmmmmmmmm! Mmmmmmmmmmmm! Sly Fox licked his chops.

All that was left of the gingerbread boy was one of his little raisin buttons that kept on running away with the river.

RAGGYLUG

Adapted by Geraldine Brain Siks
from Ernest Thompson Seton's "Raggylug"[14]

This is a dramatic favorite for children of all ages. It may be played in pantomime, or with dialogue if the children are ready. Mr. Seton says: "Those who do not know the animals well may think I have humanized them, but those who have lived so near them as to know somewhat of their ways and their minds will not think so. . . . I made the acquaintance (of these cottontails) and gathered, in a hundred different ways, the little bits of proof and scraps of truth that at length enabled me to write this history."

Over in Olifant's Swamp lived Molly and Rag. Molly was a wise Mother Cottontail and Rag was her only little rabbit. Rag was unusually quick and bright and strong. Whenever Rag was awake he

[14] Adapted with the permission of Charles Scribner's Sons, from *Wild Animals I Have Known* (1898) by Ernest Thompson Seton.

was wide awake and wanted to go hopping out into the big, brambly swamp. Molly knew that it would take **Rag** a long time to learn the ways of the swamp, for rabbits must always be learning about safety.

One morning Rag woke up with a feeling that he was getting bigger. He was curious. He wanted to get out of his nest and go exploring. Sunlight was flooding the swamp. Everything seemed to be soaking in the warm radiance and Rag believed his mother was still sleeping. He wiggled easily out of the nest and rose up on his hind legs. He saw little brown swamp-sparrows teetering on long rushes. He heard them singing morning songs. He saw big Mr. Bullfrog out on a sunken log in deep water. Mr. Bullfrog was singing praises too. Rag started hopping toward the deep water. Molly's nose and ears went up. She thumped her hind legs on the ground with a slow *thump thump*. Rag hopped back. He knew that two thumps meant *come come*.

"Good for you, Rag," said Molly. "You know this signal."

"I know almost everything. I want to see the places Mr. Bullfrog and the sparrows sing about."

"You are still a little rabbit, but it's good to see you are brave and ready to go out. I'll scout through the trails and if it's safe I will take you for your first run today."

Molly thumped her hind legs in one sharp *thump*. Rag froze in the nest like a little brown stone. He never moved nor winked. Molly was pleased. "Good bunny," she said. "I think you know this law of the forest too."

"I know it, mammy," said Rag sitting up. "When I hear one thump I lie low and freeze. I don't wiggle my ears. I don't wiggle my nose. I don't move. I just stay 'froze.' "

"That's right," said Molly. "It's one thing to know it **and quite** another thing to show it. We shall see. Now lie low and say nothing. No matter what you hear, no matter what you see, lie low and lie still."

Molly leaped off to scout the trails. The brown swamp-sparrows flew in and perched on reeds above Raggy's nest. Old Mr. Bullfrog and some of his friends swam and splashed close by. Rag wanted to talk to them but he stayed "froze."

Suddenly Rag heard a strange rustling of leaves in the near thicket. It was a strange new sound. It seemed to be coming and going. Rag listened and heard: ZZZzzz, SSSsss, ZZZzzz, SSSsss, ZZZsss, SSSsss. Rag was curious. He had never heard anything like this. It sounded gentle. "I must find out who it is so I can tell mammy," Rag said to himself. "Hmph, I'm not a baby any more." So he peeped over the grass to see who was singing. As soon as Rag moved the sound stopped. Rag saw nothing. He took one leap forward to get a clear view. He stood up on his hind legs and stared straight into the ugly face of a Black Snake.

"Mammy," screamed Rag. He could not take his eyes off the ugly snake. Black Snake stuck out his bright red tongue and swung swiftly toward Rag. Rag turned and tried to run but in a flash Black Snake grabbed Rag's ear. Black Snake whipped around Rag, curling himself tighter and tighter. "Mammy, mamm . . ," Rag could say no more. He could hardly breathe, for Black Snake had a good hold on him. The sparrows and frogs saw what was happening and they gave cries of alarm.

Far across the swamp Molly heard. She was no longer a timid cottontail. She was a brave mother whose baby was in danger. Through the swamp she leaped faster than the wind. She hopped straight to the nest. She took one look and saw the trouble.

Whack! She struck at Black Snake, sending her sharp, hind claws into his back. "ZZZZZZZssssssss," Black Snake hissed in anger. He squirmed in pain but held fast to Rag's ear. "Mamm . . . yyy," came feebly from little Rag.

Whack! Molly leaped again and struck harder and fiercer. Black Snake was hurt. He twisted and turned and curled a little tighter. Rag gave a faint little cry.

Whack! Molly struck with all her might. Black Snake cried in pain. He let go Rag's ear but kept a tight hold around him. Black Snake tried to bite Molly as she leaped over him. Back and forth Molly leaped, each time giving the snake a fierce blow. Her blows began to tell, for she tore long rips in Black Snake's scaly armor. Bracing himself for the next blow from Molly, Black Snake lost his tight hold on Rag.

Rag felt this. With all his strength he wriggled away from the snake. He crawled into the underbrush and kept crawling. Molly saw him. She had gained all she wanted. She had no notion of fighting to get even. All she wanted was the safety of her little bunny. Molly hopped after Rag. He was watching. He followed her shining white tail while Molly led him to safety in the rose brier bushes. When they stopped Molly looked closely at Rag.

"You're all right," she said, quite relieved. "Except for one ear."

"Will it hurt forever, mammy?"

"No, it won't hurt forever, but it will be ragged forever," Molly said. "But that's all right, Raggylug. Now I believe you know how to lie low."

"Oh, mammy, I do. No matter what happens I will lie low and stay still."

And you'd better believe that Raggylug always did. One *thump* by Molly and he "froze," didn't wiggle at all, not even his nose.

THE LITTLE RABBIT WHO WANTED RED WINGS

by Carolyn S. Bailey[15]

Suggested by Winifred Ward.[16] Miss Ward says: "Have you ever wished that you could fly? Wouldn't it be fun to have a pair of little red wings so that you could fly to school? Perhaps we all try learning to fly before we tell this story about a little rabbit and how he got red wings. It would be a sad experience to find that our own mother did not know us. Every child would want to get rid of his wings as soon as ever he could!"

[15] From *The Little Rabbit Who Wanted Red Wings*, by Carolyn Sherwin Bailey, published and copyrighted by The Platt & Munk Co., Inc. Reprinted by special permission of The Platt & Munk Co.

[16] Winifred Ward is Professor Emeritus of Children's Drama, Northwestern University, Evanston, Illinois, and author of *Playmaking with Children* and *Stories to Dramatize*.

Once upon a time there was a little White Rabbit with two beautiful long pink ears and two bright red eyes and four soft little feet— *such* a pretty little White Rabbit, but he wasn't happy.

Just think, this little White Rabbit wanted to be somebody else instead of the nice little rabbit that he was.

When Mr. Bushy Tail, the gray squirrel, went by, the little White Rabbit would say to his Mammy:

"Oh, Mammy, I *wish* I had a long gray tail like Mr. Bushy Tail's."

And when Mr. Porcupine went by, the little White Rabbit would say to his Mammy:

"Oh, Mammy, I *wish* I had a back full of bristles like Mr. Porcupine's."

And when Miss Puddle-Duck went by in her two little red rubbers, the little White Rabbit would say:

"Oh, Mammy, I *wish* I had a pair of red rubbers like Miss Puddle-Duck's."

So he went on and on wishing until his Mammy was clean tired out with his wishing and Old Mr. Ground Hog heard him one day.

Old Mr. Ground Hog is very wise indeed, so he said to the little White Rabbit:

"Why don't you go down to the Wishing Pond, and if you look in the water at yourself and turn around three times in a circle, you will get your wish."

So the little White Rabbit trotted off, all alone by himself through the woods until he came to a little pool of green water lying in a low tree stump, and that was the Wishing Pond. There was a little, *little* bird, all red, sitting on the edge of the Wishing Pond to get a drink, and as soon as the little White Rabbit saw him he began to wish again:

"Oh, I wish I had a pair of little red wings!" he said. Just then he looked in the Wishing Pond and he saw his little white face. Then he turned around three times and something happened.

He began to have a queer feeling in his shoulders, like he felt in his mouth when he was cutting his teeth. It was his wings coming through.

So he sat all day in the woods by the Wishing Pond waiting for them to grow, and, by and by, when it was almost sundown, he started home to see his Mammy and show her, because he had a beautiful pair of long, trailing red wings.

But by the time he reached home it was getting dark, and when he went into the hole at the foot of a big tree where he lived, his Mammy didn't know him.

No; she really and truly did not know him, because, you see, she had never seen a rabbit with red wings in all her life.

And so the little White Rabbit had to go out again, because his Mammy wouldn't let him get into his own bed. He had to go out and look for some place to sleep all night.

He went and went until he came to Mr. Bushy Tail's house, and he rapped on the door and said:

"Please, kind Mr. Bushy Tail, may I sleep in your house all night?"

But Mr. Bushy Tail opened his door a crack and then he slammed it tight shut again. You see he had never seen a rabbit with red wings in all his life.

So the little White Rabbit went and went until he came to Miss Puddle-Duck's nest down by the marsh and he said:

"Please, kind Miss Puddle-Duck, may I sleep in your nest all night?"

But Miss Puddle-Duck poked her head up out of her nest just a little way and then she shut her eyes and stretched her wings out so far that she covered her whole nest.

You see she had never seen a rabbit with red wings in all her life.

So the little White Rabbit went and went until he came to Old Mr. Ground Hog's hole and Old Mr. Ground Hog let him sleep with him all night, but the hole had beech nuts spread all over it. Old Mr. Ground Hog liked to sleep on them, but they hurt the little White Rabbit's feet and made him very uncomfortable before morning.

When it came morning, the little White Rabbit decided to try his wings and fly a little, so he climbed up on a hill and spread his wings and sailed off, but he landed in a low bush all full of prickles, and his four feet got mixed up with the twigs so he couldn't get down.

"Mammy, Mammy, Mammy, come and help me!" he called.

His Mammy didn't hear him, but Old Mr. Ground Hog did, and he came and helped the little White Rabbit out of the prickly bush.

"Don't you want your red wings?" Mr. Ground Hog asked.

"No, *no!*" said the little White Rabbit.

"Well," said the Old Ground Hog, "why don't you go down to the Wishing Pond and wish them *off* again?"

So the little White Rabbit went down to the Wishing Pond and he saw his face in it. Then he turned around three times, and, sure enough, his red wings were gone.

Then he went home to his Mammy, who knew him right away and was so glad to see him that he never, *never* wished to be something different from what he really was again.

THE BIG SPIDER

*Adapted by Geraldine Brain Siks from the legend on which
Felix Mendelssohn based his "Tarantelle"*

Suggested by Linda Shay. When Linda was five years old, she played Mendelssohn's *Tarantelle* for the other children in her creative dramatics class, and then she told them the story of the music. The children played her story with strong response. Since then other groups have found similar appeal. Children recognize the themes: "There's power in the rhythm of music and dancing"; and "Necessity is the mother of invention." Children particularly enjoy the characterizations of the Witch Doctor, Tony, and the Spider, and also an opportunity to dance to such lilting music "not just a little while but almost forever." Children are always curious about the Witch Doctor's unusual treatment.

Long ago in a little village in Italy there lived a young boy named Tony. He liked to dance and sing and make music with a piano, a violin, and best of all, with his accordion. His mother and father enjoyed making music too, and everyone in the village knew that

Tony and his family were musicians. Often they played for dancing and singing in the village square.

One evening when Tony's father was away, Tony and his mother were enjoying music together. Tony played his accordion and danced gaily about the room while his mother played their favorite melodies on the piano. In the midst of their merriment Tony screamed. "Mother," he shouted. "Something bit me—on my leg—at the top of my shoe."

Tony put his accordion down on the floor, pulled off his shoe and stocking. His mother hurried to look at his leg where he felt the sharp stinging. When she saw the bite she looked quickly about the floor. She gave a sudden start for she saw a big spider. It was a Tarantula— a poisonous spider. It was crawling toward the piano.

Tony's mother was afraid that the spider had poisoned Tony but she did not want to frighten him. "It's a spider bite, Tony. I will call the wise Witch Doctor to look at it. She will know what to do. Stay away from the spider. I shall be back as fast as I can," the mother said as she ran from the door.

Tony danced around the room in pain, for the bite stung and smarted. "I've never before had a bite that hurt like this," Tony said as he writhed with pain. As he stopped to rub his leg, he saw the spider crawling up the piano, but Tony could not stop for long. The pain caused him to move about and rub his leg to try to keep it from hurting.

Tony's mother hurried in, out of breath from running. She was followed by the old, bent Witch Doctor who was dressed in her long, black cloak and carried a big, black bag with her. The Cobbler and his wife followed after the Witch Doctor and while the Cobbler looked for the spider to trap it in a box the Witch Doctor looked first at Tony's leg and then at the spider.

Everyone watched her. She nodded her head wisely and spoke, "Yes, the Tarantula has sent its poison into your leg, Tony. It is up to us to get it out in a hurry."

"But how?" asked Tony fearfully, for he had always been afraid of the strange old Witch Doctor whenever he saw her wandering in the village. She stroked her sharp chin as she thought aloud. "There are many ways to get the poison out. We could cut it out. We could soak it out. Or, we could ask a wise lad like you to get it out for himself. That is what we shall do," she said mysteriously.

"But how?" asked Tony curiously as he watched the old woman hobble to the piano and make herself comfortable on the piano bench. He saw her run her sharp, long fingers up and down the keys.

"Listen, my lad," she said as she turned and looked closely at Tony. "I have heard you sing and play in the village streets. You like music because you listen and *hear* it." She struck a loud chord on the piano. "There's power in music for everyone who listens and hears it. Let my music speak to you. You will then know what to do."

With that the old Witch Doctor started playing. Her tune was lively and quick. Tony listened. The music started him dancing. He danced and danced and danced. As he listened to the music he forgot about the pain. He skipped and leaped and whirled. Tony's mother listened too. The music was so spirited that she took up her violin and played the merry tune along with the old woman. The cobbler and his wife enjoyed the music too. They started clapping and soon they were dancing around the room with Tony, each in his own merry way. They stamped and clapped and twirled, and Tony turned and leaped and whirled.

Some of the villagers heard the music and hurried to the doorway. They looked and listened and soon joined in with clapping while they watched Tony and the others dancing. As the Witch Doctor played she watched Tony closely with her piercing, black eyes. At last she saw little drops of water on his face and forehead. She nodded and smiled as she played the piano with even greater spirit and enjoyment.

When the Witch Doctor saw that Tony was getting tired she stopped playing. Tony threw himself down on the couch. He was out of breath and his clothes were wet with perspiration. The Witch Doctor went over to him. She spoke wisely, "You will be all right, my lad. You have cured yourself."

As the old woman picked up her bag and hobbled to the door, Tony's mother called to her. "Thank you, wise woman," she said as she covered Tony with a heavy quilt. "What music was it that you played with such spirit?"

"I made it up as I went along," said the Witch Doctor. "It was Tony dancing from the spider bite. I shall write it down this night and I shall call it the *Tarantelle*."

The Witch Doctor did. In a few days Tony himself played the music. Villagers heard it and some of them played it and danced with their children. And so the music has traveled all around the world. Perhaps when you grow up you may play the *Tarantelle* for your children. If they listen as Tony did, they, too, will dance and dance and dance.

THE BIG TURNIP

Adapted by Geraldine Brain Siks from an old Russian tale

When children are ready to individualize characters they enjoy playing this. They find unusual delight and humor in Katrinka's ability to solve the problem in her childlike way. The themes of "thinking," "cooperation," and "individual worth" come through in children's reactions and discussions. Original thinking results when groups figure out how to create a turnip character who won't budge and who will be bigger than grandfather. (Some groups decide on two children, others three, etc., each with arms outstretched for turnip leaves, etc.) After the scene of concentration in which the characters solve the problem cooperatively, a spontaneous picnic scene is generally welcome. Independent thinking is encouraged when each character reaches into Katrinka's imaginary basket to choose his surprise. "A cheese cookie," was the reply of one five-year-old Mishka followed by "an aspirin" from a six-year-old grandfather. A teacher may find that his role of a passer-by who joins the picnic serves to heighten, organize and pace the thinking in the spontaneous picnic scene.

Once upon a time there was a little girl named Katrinka. One spring she went to stay with her Grandpa and Grandma who lived in the country. Every day she helped Grandma with the housework and then she went out to help Grandpa with his garden. Katrinka loved her grandparents very much and she could see that they had grown quite old. Katrinka cheered them with her happy surprises.

One morning Grandpa said, "Today I am going to plant turnips in the garden. Come along, Katrinka, as soon as you have finished helping Grandma."

"Yes, Grandpa. I shall hurry and I shall bring a surprise for you!" Katrinka said as she thought of what she would do. Grandpa took the turnip seeds and went out to the garden. He found his tools in the shed and he spaded the ground and found that it was soft and ready for planting. He took his hoe and made a long straight row for the turnip seeds. Grandpa knelt down on the ground and dropped a seed carefully into the earth. He pushed the soft dirt over it, patted the ground and said kindly, "Grow, little turnip seed. Grow sweet, grow strong." Grandpa planted another, and another, and another, each in the same way until, at last, the long row was planted. When he stood up to rest he was surprised to see a few raindrops coming down from the sky.

He hurried into the shed, for the rain was coming down in a sudden shower. Raindrops seemed to dance right along the row of turnip seeds, and Grandpa was afraid the rain might wash the seeds out of their places. While he watched he saw that the rain went away as suddenly as it had come, and Grandpa hurried out to look at his row of turnip seeds. "What's this? What's this?" he called aloud as he looked at the ground. He couldn't believe what he saw.

A turnip was growing right up out of the ground. It grew and grew. It pushed its leaves higher and higher and higher. Soon the turnip was taller than Grandpa. Grandpa was afraid that it would never stop growing.

"Grandma, Grandma!" he called.

Grandma heard from inside the house. She opened the door quickly. "What is it, Grandpa?"

"Come here! Come now," Grandpa called. Grandma hurried straight to the garden for she was worried by the way Grandpa called. When she saw the turnip she was as anxious as Grandpa.

"What will we do?" asked Grandpa. "The turnip will grow as big as our whole garden. We must pull it out at once."

Grandpa started to pull on the turnip.

"Indeed, we must pull it up," said Grandma, and she started to pull on the turnip too. Grandpa pulled and Grandma pulled and they both pulled from different sides, but they couldn't budge the big turnip.

"Katrinka! Katrinka! Come here," called Grandma as loudly as she could call. Katrinka heard. She opened the door and called, "What is it?"

"Come here! Hurry, Katrinka!" Grandpa called.

Katrinka ran out to the garden carrying her big surprise picnic basket but when she saw the big turnip she was more surprised than ever. "Where did you get such a big turnip?" she asked.

"It just grew!" said Grandpa. "We must pull it out." So Grandpa started to pull, and Grandma started to pull, and Katrinka started to pull, each one on a different side of the big turnip. With all of their pulling they couldn't budget the turnip. "What shall we do?" asked Grandpa, who was worried.

Katrinka thought as she looked at the turnip. "I know," she said all at once, "We must all pull together."

"I don't see what you mean," said Grandpa.

"We have all pulled together," said Grandma.

"That is not what I mean. This is what I mean," said Katrinka. She showed them what she meant. "Here, Grandpa, you pull on the turnip. Grandma will pull on you, and I will pull on Grandma." So they got ready to pull. "Ready now!" called Katrinka. They pulled, and pulled, and pulled. Even when they all pulled together, they couldn't budget the big turnip. They stopped and puffed. They had pulled hard and were out of breath from pulling.

"What will we do?" said poor old Grandpa.

"I just don't know," said poor, old, worried Grandma.

"I know," said Katrinka, who had been thinking. "We'll have Dishka help us." So Katrinka called Dishka, the dog. He came running to the garden and Katrinka told him they needed his help.

"I'm afraid he does not know what we mean," said Grandpa.

"I think he does," said Katrinka. "Let's try again."

So Grandpa took hold of the turnip. Grandma took hold of Grandpa's belt. Katrinka took hold of Grandma's apron, and Dishka put his front paws on Katrinka's apron strings. Katrinka called, "Ready, Now!" They pulled and pulled and pulled, but they couldn't budge the big turnip.

"What'll we do? What'll we do?" asked Grandpa and Grandma and they huffed and puffed, and Dishka barked and barked as he looked at the big turnip.

"I know," said Katrinka. "We need just a little more help because I think the turnip wiggled a little when we pulled. Who else might help us?" asked Katrinka.

But Grandpa and Grandma shook their heads. "No one lives near us for miles and miles out here in the country. There's no one to help us."

Katrinka kept thinking. "I know," she said eagerly. "Kiska the cat will help us." So Katrinka called Kiska, who came running to the garden. Grandpa and Grandma and Dishka all looked at the little Kiska and shook their heads, but Katrinka told Kiska that they needed her help.

"I'm afraid Kiska doesn't know what you mean," said Grandpa.

"I think she does," said Katrinka. "Let's try again."

So they all lined up and watched Kiska. Kiska watched Grandpa take hold of the turnip; Grandma take hold of Grandpa; Katrinka take hold of Grandma; Dishka take hold of Katrinka, and then Kiska very slowly took hold of Diska's tail. "Ready now," called Katrinka. Then they all pulled, and pulled, and pulled together and they got the turnip to budge a little.

"Now," said Katrinka, "If we only had a little more help we could pull the turnip out before it grows over the garden."

"Well, there's no one else to help," said Grandpa.

"No, there's no one around for miles and miles," said Grandma.

Dishka barked. Kiska mewed, and Katrinka thought.

"I know," Katrinka said. "I will call Mishka, the mouse. He will help us."

So Katrinka called Mishka, the little field mouse. Everyone listened. Soon they heard a little squeak. It was Mishka. She ran in from the field and poked her head around the great big turnip. Grandpa and Grandma and Dishka and Kiska all looked at little Mishka and shook their heads while Katrinka told Mishka that they needed her help.

"I'm afraid Mishka is afraid of Kiska," said Grandma.

"I'm afraid Mishka doesn't know how to help," said Grandpa.

So Katrinka explained everything to Mishka and to Kiska. Then they all lined up and watched little Mishka. Grandpa took hold of the turnip; Grandma took hold of Grandpa; Katrinka took hold of Grandma; Dishka took hold of Katrinka; Kiska took hold of Dishka's tail; and Mishka took hold of Kiska's tail. Katrinka said, "Ready, now!"

They pulled and pulled and pulled and pulled. Zoom! Up came the big turnip! Down went Grandpa, Grandma, Katrinka, Dishka, Kiska, and little Mishka. Each one laughed as he brushed off the dirt and stood up to see the big turnip. Katrinka ran to the shed to get her basket. "Everyone gets a surprise from my picnic basket while we rest from such hard pulling," she called.

And so they had a picnic in the shade of the big turnip. Each one reached into the basket to find his surprise—a surprise that was just right for Grandpa, Grandma, Katrinka, Dishka, Kiska, and little Mishka.

HENNY-PENNY

An old English folktale as told by Joseph Jacobs

This story was suggested by Ann La Brose.[17] It always brings laughter. Joseph Jacobs believes "the fun consists in the avoidance of all pronouns which results in jawbreaking sentences." Modern, sky-minded children seem, also, to find downright humor in Henny-Penny's reaction to the "sky-a-falling." Children enjoy playing this

[17] Ann La Brose is a classroom teacher at Cossitt Avenue School, La Grange Public Schools, La Grange, Illinois.

when they are free to interpret with spontaneous dialogue. They respond to the variety of rhythmic, animal characterizations and find frightening, yet pleasant delight in the dramatic ending provided by sly Foxy-woxy. They enjoy solving the problem of deciding how it may seem as if Foxy-woxy snaps off the heads of Turkey-lurkey, Goosey-poosey, and Ducky-daddles.

One day Henny-Penny was picking up corn in the cornyard when —whack!—something hit her upon the head. "Goodness gracious me!" said Henny-Penny. "The sky's a-going to fall; I must go and tell the king."

So she went along, and she went along, and she went along till she met Cocky-locky. "Where are you going, Henny-penny?" says Cocky-locky. "Oh! I'm going to tell the king the sky's a-falling," says Henny-penny. "May I come with you?" says Cocky-locky. "Certainly," says Henny-penny. So Henny-penny and Cocky-locky went to tell the king that the sky was a-falling.

They went along, and they went along, and they went along, till they met Ducky-daddles. "Where are you going to, Henny-penny and Cocky-locky?" says Ducky-daddles. "Oh! we're going to tell the king the sky's a-falling," said Henny-penny and Cocky-locky. "May I come with you?" says Ducky-daddles. "Certainly," said Henny-penny and Cocky-locky. So Henny-penny, Cocky-locky, and Ducky-daddles went to tell the king the sky was a-falling.

So they went along, and they went along, and they went along, till they met Goosey-poosey. "Where are you going, Henny-penny, Cocky-locky, and Ducky-daddles?" said Goosey-poosey. "Oh! we're going to tell the king the sky's a-falling," said Henny-penny and Cocky-locky and Ducky-daddles. "May I come with you?" said Goosey-poosey. "Certainly," said Henny-penny, Cocky-locky, and Ducky-daddles. So Henny-penny, Cocky-locky, Ducky-daddles, and Goosey-poosey went to tell the king the sky was a-falling.

So they went along, and they went along, and they went along, till they met Turkey-lurkey. "Where are you going, Henny-penny, Cocky-locky, Ducky-daddles, and Goosey-poosey?" said Turkey-lurkey. "Oh!

we're going to tell the king the sky's a-falling," said Henny-penny, Cocky-locky, Ducky-daddles, and Goosey-poosey. "May I come with you, Henny-penny, Cocky-locky, Ducky-daddles, and Goosey-poosey?" said Turkey-lurkey. "Oh, certainly, Turkey-lurkey," said Henny-penny, Cocky-locky, Ducky-daddles, and Goosey-poosey. So Henny-penny, Cocky-locky, Ducky-daddles, Goosey-poosey, and Turkey-lurkey all went to tell the king the sky was a-falling.

So they went along, and they went along, and they went along, till they met Foxy-woxy, and Foxy-woxy said to Henny-penny, Cocky-locky, Ducky-daddles, Goosey-poosey, and Turkey-lurkey: "Where are you going, Henny-penny, Cocky-locky, Ducky-daddles, Goosey-poosey, and Turkey-lurkey?" And Henny-penny, Cocky-locky, Ducky-daddles, Goosey-poosey, and Turkey-lurkey said to Foxy-woxy: "We're going to tell the king the sky's a-falling." "Oh, but this is not the way to the king, Henny-penny, Cocky-locky, Ducky-daddles, Goosey-poosey, and Turkey-lurkey," said Foxy-woxy. "I know the proper way; shall I show it to you?" "Oh, certainly, Foxy-woxy," said Henny-penny, Cocky-locky, Ducky-daddles, Goosey-poosey, and Turkey-lurkey. So Henny-penny, Cocky-locky, Ducky-daddles, Goosey-poosey, Turkey-lurkey, and Foxy-woxy all went to tell the king the sky was a-falling.

So they went along, and they went along, and they went along, till they came to a narrow and dark hole. Now this was the door of Foxy-woxy's cave. But Foxy-woxy said to Henny-penny, Cocky-locky, Ducky-daddles, Goosey-poosey, and Turkey-lurkey: "This is the short way to the king's palace; you'll soon get there if you follow me. I will go first and you come after, Henny-penny, Cocky-locky, Ducky-daddles, Goosey-poosey, and Turkey-lurkey." "Why, of course, certainly, without doubt, why not?" said Henny-penny, Cocky-locky, Ducky-daddles, Goosey-poosey, and Turkey-lurkey.

So Foxy-woxy went into his cave, and he didn't go very far, but turned round to wait for Henny-penny, Cocky-locky, Ducky-daddles, Goosey-poosey, and Turkey-lurkey. So Turkey-lurkey went first through the dark hole into the cave. He hadn't got far when "Hrumph," Foxy-woxy snapped off Turkey-lurkey's head and threw his body over his left shoulder. Then Goosey-poosey went in, and "Hrumph," off went her head and Goosey-poosey was thrown beside Turkey-lurkey. Then Ducky-daddles waddled down, and "Hrumph," snapped Foxy-woxy, and Ducky-daddles' head was off and Ducky-daddles was thrown alongside Turkey-lurkey and Goosey-poosey. Then Cocky-locky strutted down into the cave, and he had not gone far when "Snap, Hrumph!" went Foxy-woxy and Cocky-locky was thrown alongside of Turkey-lurkey, Goosey-poosey, and Ducky-daddles.

But Foxy-woxy had made two bites at Cocky-locky, and when the first snap only hurt Cocky-locky, but didn't kill him, he called out to Henny-penny. But she turned tail and off she ran home, so she never told the king the sky was a-falling.

Stories for older children

Out of your cage,
Come out of your cage
And take your soul on a pilgrimage!
Please in your shoes, an if you must!—
But out and away, before you're dust. . . .

JOSEPHINE PRESTON PEABODY, *The Piper*

These stories are representative of the vast inheritance of dramatic,
literature for children and youth. Included here are true tales, folk and
fairy tales, fables, myths, legends, stories from the Bible, and modern
fantasy and realistic happenings.

Each of these stories has been dramatized by children. Through the
myriad reflections of life in literature children have been led on vigorous pilgrimages through dramatization. They have quested for courage on a Bridge of One Hair; for peace in the midst of war in Norway;
for eternal youth in waters at the bottom of the sea; for faith in the
valley of Elah; for love in a peasant hut in a Russian village, and for
truth and its consequences in various imaginative times and places.

After these stories were first heard and enjoyed they were interpreted in a variety of dramatic ways: single characterizations; episodes; entire stories integrated with arts experiences; tape recorded;
original finger and shadow plays; improvised with puppets and marionettes; and pantomimed, on occasion, to musical and rhythmical accompaniment.

Many have been read or told to motivate children to express themselves in writing, painting, and other creative arts.

149

A PLACE OF PEACE:
AN IMPRESSION FROM MY CHILDHOOD IN NORWAY

by Ingrid Bowman[1]

Miss Bowman was a Fulbright student at the University of Washington in 1960. She first told her story to a university class in creative dramatics. When she recognized the students' interest in improvising from it she told it to many children's groups. Boys and girls were motivated into discussions of war, subterfuge, patriotism, and peace. They responded to an opportunity to dramatize "the most beautiful thing *you* would find in your place of peace." Characterizations included animals, insects, flowers, trees, waterfalls, etc. Each character pantomimed with freedom of movement and feeling to the accompaniment of "Morning," from Grieg's *Peer Gynt Suite*. The soldier scene was developed by boys who enjoyed dramatizing knowledge of warfare. The parade scene motivated strong involvement as soldiers marched to the music of Grieg's "Triumphal March" from *Sigurd Jorsalfar*, and listened to Tom Fiddler and the Norwegian songs and dances. Children planned to have a group of Norwegian wives and mothers lead the parade with a chant of peace. The chant was developed spontaneously when Miss Bowman asked: "What do you believe peace really is? What might the women chant that is simple and yet show that they know that peace has come to the hearts of everyone in the land?" The chant became: "Peace is wonderful; Peace is glorious; It is not fighting; It is not dying; It is living free; Peace is love."

When I was eight years old, the enemy occupied Norway. To me that meant that my school was taken, and that Mummy and Daddy very often wanted to go aside and talk alone without the four children listening. We were not supposed to understand anything, but each time some unexpected visitor rang our doorbell, we were scared. I noticed Mummy was too, even if she tried to hide her fear when she

---

[1] By permission of the author, Ingrid Bowman, who teaches creative dramatics in Oslo, Norway.

went to open the door. Could it be the enemy who wanted to take my dad? Everything was turned the wrong way. Kind men were put into prison while the killers marched around singing in our streets.

One day in May, 1941, I was sitting on a stone in the woods, ten minutes from my home. My friend Gretha and I used to imagine that this little open place was not discovered by the enemy and not one of them had ever disturbed its peace. It was a wonderful day. The birds were singing cheerfully and the sun was shining. Gretha had left me to go home, but I wanted to remain a little longer to enjoy the beauty and peace around me.

Suddenly I heard a strange sound as if a branch were broken and as I turned around I discovered a man hiding behind a bush a few yards from me. I could not see his face, just his brown trousers and a pair of very dirty black boots. I was frightened and disappointed. Did not he know that this was the *Place of Peace* where he was not allowed to do any harm? I remained sitting because I was too scared to move. I felt my heart beat so hard that I thought he must hear it. Nothing happened, and the minutes crept away.

Then, as if shot up from the earth, four enemy soldiers with guns and helmets came marching into my *Place of Peace*. They looked around carefully and it struck me that they were looking for the man behind the bush. In that moment I felt that I might save a man's life if I exercised sound judgment. I got up from my stone and went down toward the enemy. By this sound they pointed their guns against me, but seeing that it was a little girl, they lowered them quickly and became kind uncles. Out from a big pocket in a green uniform came a nice looking chocolate. I was now so aware of the situation that I was expecting the question they asked me in broken Norwegian, "Hello, little girl. By the way, have you seen a man around here lately?"

I do not think my voice sounded very natural, but suddenly I felt very strong. In this very moment I was an important person for my country. "Oh yes," I said. "You mean a man in brown trousers and black boots?" They nodded eagerly, and one of them, clasping both my hands, said, "Yes, little girl. This is a friend of ours, you see. Did you notice where he went?"

"Went?" I answered. "He was running as fast as a deer down there."

I pointed in the direction opposite to the bush where the man was hiding. Another chocolate was my reward for this information, and the soldiers left quickly to look for their "friend."

As soon as they were out of view I ran up to my stone and put my two chocolates on it. They were a present for the Norwegian if he were so hungry that he dared to take it. Without turning once, I ran away to Gretha's home and told her that our *Place of Peace* was destroyed. We never went there again during the war.

I have recalled this event many times in my mind dreaming of how wonderful and important this moment was. Actually I never found who the soldier was, and I do not know if my little lie was of any help at all.

Peace came in May, 1945. Our own "Underground" men were marching in the streets of Oslo. All people in the town gathered along the streets and shouted "hurrah" and threw flowers to them. I stood on the pavement and watched and thought. I stretched my neck to find the man in my dreams. And as one of them smiled to me as he passed by, I felt sure that this was the man whose life I had saved in my beautiful, little *Place of Peace*.

HOW THE POTATO FACE BLIND MAN ENJOYED HIMSELF ON A FINE SPRING MORNING

by Carl Sandburg[2]

This story never fails to arouse discussion. Children find it a rare privilege to hobnob with Sandburg in his *Rootabaga Stories*. This is a splendid story for the enjoyment of character study and development in dramatic interpretation. In most older groups a few children respond to the challenge of developing the characterizations of Potato Face Blind Man and Pick Ups. Once they recognize that the strength of Potato Face lies in his awareness and the strength of Pick Ups lies in his curiosity and questioning ability (who? what? when? why?)

[2] From *Rootabaga Stories* by Carl Sandburg, copyright, 1922, 1923, by Harcourt, Brace & World, Inc.; renewed, 1950, 1951, by Carl Sandburg. Reprinted by permission of the publisher.

they enjoy creating dialogue which evolves from the street scene near the postoffice. Children who are not quite ready for these two roles like to work in groups where each child develops a characterization (singly, in pairs, or in threes) with such singleness of purpose or attitude that he "misses the morning" and particularly the delight of Potato Face and Pick Ups. Some groups have enjoyed placing the street scene on a familiar landmark, locally or nationally. A child who plays an accordion has become "Potato Face's best friend to play real music for him while he gives all his time to deep discussions of space rockets and flummywisters."

On a Friday morning when the flummywisters were yodeling yisters high in the elm trees, the Potato Face Blind Man came down to his work sitting at the corner nearest the postoffice in the Village of Liver-and-Onions and playing his gold-that-used-to-be accordion for the pleasure of the ears of the people going into the postoffice to see if they got any letters for themselves or their families.

"It is a good day, a lucky day," said the Potato Face Blind Man, "because for a beginning I have heard high in the elm trees the flummywisters yodeling their yisters in the long branches of the lingering leaves. So—so—I am going to listen to myself playing on my accordion the same yisters, the same yodels, drawing them like long glad breathings out of my glad accordion, long breathings of the branches of the lingering leaves."

And he sat down in his chair. On the sleeve of his coat he tied a sign, "I Am Blind *Too*." On the top button of his coat he hung a little thimble. On the bottom button of his coat he hung a tin copper cup. On the middle button he hung a wooden mug. By the side of him on the left side on the sidewalk he put a galvanized iron washtub, and on the right side an aluminum dishpan.

"It is a good day, a lucky day, and I am sure many people will stop and remember the Potato Face Blind Man," he sang to himself like a little song as he began running his fingers up and down the keys of the accordion like the yisters of the lingering leaves in the elm trees.

Then came Pick Ups. Always it happened Pick Ups asked questions and wished to know. And so this is how the questions and answers ran when the Potato Face filled the ears of Pick Ups with explanations.

"What is the piece you are playing on the keys of your accordion so fast sometimes, so slow sometimes, so sad some of the moments, so glad some of the moments?"

"It is the song the mama flummywisters sing when they button loose the winter underwear of the baby flummywisters and sing:

> Fly, you little flummies,
> Sing, you little wisters.

"And why do you have a little thimble on the top button of your coat?"

"That is for the dimes to be put in. Some people see it and say, 'Oh, I must put in a whole thimbleful of dimes.'"

"And the tin copper cup?"

"That is for the baseball players to stand off ten feet and throw in nickels and pennies. The one who throws the most into the cup will be the most lucky."

"And the wooden mug?"

"There is a hole in the bottom of it. The hole is as big as the bottom. The nickel goes in and comes out again. It is for the very poor people who wish to give me a nickel and yet get the nickel back."

"The aluminum dishpan and the galvanized iron washtub—what are they doing by the side of you on both sides of the sidewalk?"

"Sometime maybe it will happen everybody who goes into the postoffice and comes out will stop and pour out all their money, because they might get afraid their money is no good any more. If such a happening ever happens then it will be nice for the people to have some place to pour their money. Such is the explanation why you see the aluminum dishpan and galvanized iron tub."

"Explain your sign—why is it, 'I Am Blind *Too*'?"

"Oh, I am sorry to explain to you, Pick Ups, why this is so which. Some of the people who pass by here going into the postoffice and coming out, they have eyes—but they see nothing with their eyes. They look where they are going and they get where they wish to get, but they forget why they came and they do not know how to come away, They are my blind brothers. It is for them I have the sign that reads, 'I Am Blind *Too.*'"

"I have my ears full of explanations and I thank you," said Pick Ups.

"Good-by," said the Potato Face Blind Man as he began drawing long breathings like lingering leaves out of the accordion—along with the song the mama flummywisters sing when they button loose the winter underwear of the baby flummywisters.

ADVENTURE IN THE ORCHARD

by Isabel B. Burger[3]

This story has universal appeal. It has been dramatized with children in Germany, Holland, England, and America. Mrs. Burger says: "The story plays well in pantomime with six or seven children. A larger group finds it confusing. It needs to be made clear in discussion that the child playing the character of Jean is to find the bird, the child playing Jimmy is to help the bird into its nest, and the other children are to chase the cat away. If children interpret with an imaginary cat and birds, their sound cues *must be* planned carefully and *given on cue.* After several playings in pantomime, ideas for conversation which will carry the story forward may be discussed and dialogue included to play the entire story."

One day when we were coming home from a picnic, we passed along an old stone wall. It was broken in several places and we were curious about it. On the other side was a deserted apple orchard, mostly overgrown with high grass. It must have belonged to that empty, dilapi-

[3] By permission of the author. Mrs. Burger is founder and Administrative Coordinator of the Children's Theatre Association, Inc. of Baltimore, Maryland, author of *Creative Play Acting,* and a Life-Fellow of the International Institute of Arts and Letters.

dated old house up on the hill, but strangely enough there were beautiful red apples on the trees and on the ground. It seemed a long time since our picnic so we decided to gather some apples.

When we were inside the orchard Amy said suddenly, "Listen! What is that strange whistling sound?"

None of us had heard anything. We thought that she must have imagined it, but Amy called again, "Really, there is something curious around here. It sounds sort of like a bird's chirp. Listen."

We listened. This time we did hear the sound, but when we looked we couldn't find where it came from. All at once Jean pointed to something. "There it is. Come here. Come," she said.

We followed and found her kneeling in the high grass pointing to a tiny baby robin. It was barely able to move. It looked very frightened in the big, green orchard where it had fallen. We didn't know what to do. We knew we shouldn't touch it, because they say the mother bird won't claim it again. We gathered around the poor little thing wondering how we might help.

A sudden sharp cry startled us. "MEOW—MEOW," snarled a huge black cat. We turned to look and saw its green eyes staring at the little bird. It was ready to pounce. Amy and Jean shouted and chased the cat away. Jimmy looked up in the tree while the rest of us threw apples after the cat so it wouldn't come back.

"Here's the nest," Jimmy called. We hurried back and watched as Jimmy picked up the frightened little bird ever so carefully and lowered it into the nest beside two other little heads that peeped over the edge. We were thankful that we had been there to save the baby bird when another sound caused as to look up suddenly. It was a sharp, frightened cry. It came from the mother bird as she swooped down frantically, almost to the nest and then as frantically she flew up again. She flew around the tree in big circles chirping in shrill, quick calls. She must have thought we were robbing her nest. How could she know that we were trying to keep one of her little birds from a dangerous enemy?

"Quick," Amy whispered. "Let's hide. It's the mother. We mustn't frighten her any more."

We hurried over the old wall and watched through the broken stones. Soon we saw the mother bird come closer and closer to the nest. At last she flew down and settled in the nest with her little ones. We could hear the baby birds' chirps of greeting and her soft answers as she comforted them. As quiet as mice we sneaked over the wall and into the orchard. We picked up our jackets and bags and a few apples from the ground. We crept away and started down the road. Jimmy spoke first. "It's a good thing we went after apples when we did," he said.

"Yes, and it's a good thing Amy's curiosity made her listen," Jean said.

Amy laughed. "My curiosity? Why I'd say it was everyone's," she said, "Ours and the birds' and the cat's!"

INJUN SUMMER

by John T. McCutcheon[4]

Suggested by Mrs. Harry Gillies.[5] Mrs. Gillies says: "Each fall when John T. McCutcheon's classic cartoon of 'Injun Summer' has been re-printed in the *Chicago Tribune,* countless Middle Western teachers and parents have displayed it in their schools and homes to herald the return of a brilliant season. The text of the cartoon is printed below. One of its special assets for dramatization lies in its use with groups involving a wide range of ages and abilities . . . everything from remedial or special education classes in schools, to recreational groups in the children's wards of hospitals. For here is a setting in which every child can participate, no matter how dynamic his energy or how limited his physical, mental or emotional capacity to enter in. He may choose to lead the entire group creating a role as commanding as an Indian chief; or he may feel more secure supporting the rest, helping improvise the rhythms which often grow as a natural accompaniment to the dramatization, and which can be beat

[4] Reprinted from *Chicago Tribune* by permission of Chicago Tribune. Copyright 1912 by Chicago Tribune.
[5] Mrs. Harry Gillies is a consultant in creative dramatics, Pelham, New York.

out on table-tops, school books, or the sides of wheel-chairs. Recordings of authentic American Indian songs and chants may be used to heighten mood and enjoyment. It is quite a different experience for a child to interpret first a 'reg'lar sure 'nough Injun' and then an 'Injun sperrit'!"

Yep, sonny, this is sure enough Injun summer. Don't know what that is, I reckon, do you?

Well, that's when all the homesick Injuns come back to play. You know, a long time ago, long afore yer granddaddy was born even, there used to be heaps of Injuns around here—thousands—millions, I reckon, far as that's concerned. Reg'lar sure 'nough Injuns—none o' yer cigar store Injuns, not much. They wuz all around here—right here where you're standin'. Don't be skeered—hain't none around here now, leastways no live ones. They been gone this many a year. They all went away and died, so they ain't no more left.

But every year, 'long about now, they all come back, leastways their sperrits do. They're here now. You can see 'em off across the fields. Look real hard. See that kind o' hazy, misty look out yonder? Well, them's Injuns—Injun sperrits marchin' along an' dancin' in the sunlight. That's what makes that kind o' haze that's everywhere—it's jest the sperrits of the Injuns all come back. They're all around us now. See off yonder; see them tepees? They kind o' look like corn shocks from here, but them's Injun tents, sure as you're a foot high. See 'em now? Sure, I knowed you could. Smell that smoky sort o' smell in the air? That's the campfires a-burnin' and their pipes a-goin'. Lots o' people say it's just leaves burnin', but it ain't. It's the campfires, an' the' Injuns are hoppin' 'round 'em t' beat the old Harry.

You jest come out here tonight when the moon is hangin' over the hill off yonder an' the harvest fields is all swimmin' in th' moonlight, an' you can see the Injuns and the tepees jest as plain as kin be. You can, eh? I knowed you would after a little while.

Jever notice how the leaves turn red 'bout this time o' year? That's jest another sign o' redskins. That's when on old Injun sperrit gits tired dancin' an' goes up an' squats on a leaf t' rest. Why, I kin hear 'em rustlin' an' whisperin' an' creepin' round among the leaves all the time; an' ever' once 'n a while a leaf gives way under some fat old Injun ghost and comes floatin' down to the ground. See—here's one now. See how red it is? That's the war paint rubbed off'n an Injun ghost, sure's you're born.

Purty soon all the Injuns 'll go marchin' away agin, back to the happy huntin' ground, but next year you'll see 'em troopin' back— th' sky jest hazy with 'em and their campfires smolderin' away jest like they are now.

WHY THE CHIMES RANG
by Raymond Macdonald Alden[6]

This is a Christmas miracle-type story which may be created simply in two acts (hillside and church) or it may be done more elaborately by experienced groups. It lends itself readily to dramatic interpretation, which has been done effectively entirely in pantomime with appropriate Christmas songs and music. Its theme emphasizes the divine beauty of love through sacrifice by a young boy. Children's discussions of the theme come as a result of attempting to answer the story's title. When children recognize the theme they find a greater challenge in the interpretation of individual characters in relationship to the central core. The depth of appeal in this story motivates children to ask to play it for two or three Christmas seasons, with a desire for establishing a memorable tradition.

There was once, in a far-away country where few people have ever traveled, a wonderful church. It stood on a high hill in the midst of a great city; and every Sunday, as well as on sacred days like Christmas, thousands of people climbed the hill to its great archways, looking like lines of ants all moving in the same direction.

[6] From *Why the Chimes Rang and Other Stories* by Raymond Macdonald Alden. Copyright (c) 1906, 1945, 1954 by the Bobbs-Merrill Company, Inc., 1934 by Barbara Hitt Alden. Reprinted by special permission of the publishers, the Bobbs-Merrill Company, Inc.

When you came to the building itself, you found stone columns and dark passages, and a grand entrance leading to the main room of the church. This room was so long that one standing at the doorway could scarcely see to the other end, where the choir stood by the marble altar. In the farthest corner was the organ; and this organ was so loud that sometimes when it played, the people for miles around would close their shutters and prepare for a great thunderstorm. Altogether, no such church as this was ever seen before, especially when it was lighted up for some festival, and crowded with people, young and old.

But the strangest thing about the whole building was the wonderful chime of bells. At one corner of the church was a great gray tower, with ivy growing over it as far up as one could see. I say as far as one could see because the tower was quite great enough to fit the great church, and it rose so far into the sky that it was only in very fair weather that anyone claimed to be able to see the top. Even then one could not be certain that it was in sight. Up and up and up climbed the stones and the ivy; and, as the men who built the church had been dead for hundreds of years, everyone had forgotten how high the tower was supposed to be.

Now, all the people knew that at the top of the tower was a chime of Christmas bells. They had hung there ever since the church had been built, and were the most beautiful bells in the world. Some thought it was because a great musician had cast them and arranged them in their place; others said it was because of the great height, which reached up where the air was clearest and purest. However that might be, no one who had ever heard the chimes denied that they were the sweetest in the world. Some described them as sounding like angels far up in the sky; others, as sounding like strange winds singing through the trees.

But the fact was that no one had heard them for years and years. There was an old man living not far from the church who said that his mother had spoken of hearing them when she was a little girl, and he was the only one who was sure of as much as that. They were Christmas chimes, you see, and were not meant to be played by men or on common days. It was the custom on Christmas Eve for all the people to bring to the church their offerings to the Christ child; and when the greatest and best offering was laid on the altar, there used to come sounding through the music of the choir the Christmas chimes far up in the tower. Some said that the wind rang them, and others that they were so high the angels could set them swinging. But for many long years they had never been heard.

It was said that people had been growing less careful of their gifts for the Christ child, and that no offering was brought great enough to deserve the music of the chimes. Every Christmas Eve the rich people still crowded to the altar, each one trying to bring some gift better than any other, without giving anything that he wanted for himself, and the church was crowded with those who thought that perhaps the wonderful bells might be heard again. But although the service was splendid and the offerings plenty, only the roar of the wind could be heard, far up in the stone tower.

Now, a number of miles from the city, in a little country village where nothing could be seen of the great church but glimpses of the tower when the weather was fine, lived a boy named Pedro and his little brother. They knew very little about the Christmas chimes, but they had heard of the service in the church on Christmas Eve, and had a secret plan, which they had often talked over when by themselves, to go see the beautiful celebration.

"Nobody can guess, Little Brother," Pedro would say, "all the fine things there are to see and hear; and I have even heard it said that the Christ child sometimes comes down to bless the service. What if we could see Him?"

The day before Christmas was bitterly cold, with a few lonely snowflakes flying in the air and a hard white crust on the ground. Sure enough, Pedro and Little Brother were able to slip quietly away early in the afternoon; and although the walking was hard in the frosty air, before nightfall they had trudged so far, hand in hand, that they saw the lights of the big city just ahead of them. Indeed, they were about to enter one of the great gates in the wall that surrounded it when they saw something dark on the snow near their path, and stepped aside to look at it.

It was a poor woman who had fallen just outside the city, too sick and tired to get in where she might have found shelter. The soft snow made of a drift a sort of pillow for her, and she would soon be so sound asleep in the wintry air that no one could ever waken her again. All this Pedro saw in a moment, and he knelt down beside her and tried to rouse her, even tugging at her arm a little as though he would have tried to carry her away. He turned her face toward him so that he could rub some of the snow on it, and when he had looked at her silently a moment, he stood up again and said:

"It's no use, Little Brother. You will have to go on alone."

"Alone?" cried Little Brother. "And you not see the Christmas festival?"

"No," said Pedro, and he could not keep back a bit of choking sound in his throat. "See this poor woman. Her face looks like the Madonna in the chapel window, and she will freeze to death if nobody cares for her. Everyone has gone to the church now, but when you come back you can bring someone to help her. I will rub her to keep her from freezing, and perhaps get her to eat the bun that is left in my pocket."

"But I cannot bear to leave you, and go on alone," said Little Brother.

"Both of us need not miss the service," said Pedro, "and it had better be I than you. You can easily find your way to the church; and you must see and hear everything twice, Little Brother—once for you and once for me. I am sure the Christ child must know how I should love to come with you and worship Him: and oh! if you get a chance, Little Brother, to slip up to the altar without getting in anyone's way, take this little silver piece of mine, and lay it down for my offering when no one is looking. Do not forget where you have left me, and forgive me for not going with you."

In this way he hurried Little Brother off to the city, and winked hard to keep back the tears as he heard the crunching footsteps sounding farther and farther away in the twilight. It was pretty hard to lose the music and splendor of the Christmas celebration that he had been planning for so long, and spend the time instead in that lonely place in the snow.

The great church was a wonderful place that night. Everyone said that it had never looked so bright and beautiful before. When the organ played and the thousands of people sang, the walls shook with the sound, and little Pedro, away outside the city wall, felt the earth tremble around him.

At the close of the service came the procession with the offerings to be laid on the altar. Rich men and great men marched proudly up to lay down their gifts to the Christ child. Some brought wonderful jewels, some baskets of gold so heavy that they could scarcely carry them down the aisle. A great writer laid down a book that he had been making for years and years. And last of all walked the king of the country, hoping with all the rest to win for himself the chime of the Christmas bells. There went a great murmur through the church, as the people saw the king take from his head the royal crown, all set with precious stones, and lay it gleaming on the altar, as his offering to the holy Child. "Surely," everyone said, "we shall hear the bells now, for nothing like this has ever happened before."

But still only the cold old wind was heard in the tower, and the people shook their heads; and some of them said, as they had before, that they never really believed the story of the chimes, and doubted if they ever rang at all.

The procession was over, and the choir began the closing hymn. Suddenly the organist stopped playing as though he had been shot, and everyone looked at the old minister, who was standing by the altar holding up his hand for silence. Not a sound could be heard from anyone in the church, but as all the people strained their ears to listen, there came softly, but distinctly, swinging through the air, the sound of the chimes in the tower. So far away and yet so clear the music seemed—so much sweeter were the notes than anything that had been heard before, rising and falling away up there in the sky, that the people in the church sat for a moment as still as though something held each of them by the shoulders. Then they all stood up together and stared straight at the altar, to see what great gift had awakened the long-silent bells.

But all that the nearest of them saw was the childish figure of Little

Brother, who had crept softly down the aisle when no one was looking, and had laid Pedro's little piece of silver on the altar.

WAHOO

by Joel Chandler Harris[7]

"I tell you what, honey," said Uncle Remus . . . "What you want
is a laughin'-place, whar you kin go an' tickle yo' se'f an' laugh whed-
der you wanter laugh er no." This is just such a laughin' story, as are
most of these folktales which are unique in children's literary heritage. Like "The Wonderful Tar Baby," this tale never fails to arouse
laughter and a desire to dramatize it by children who have had some
experience in creative dramatics. The story with its clear plot, three
distinct characterizations and a theme which characterizes the witty
Brer Rabbit, provides an excellent initial experience in impromptu
dialogue. Classes have worked in groups of three to plan and share
creative interpretations. Other classes have worked in groups of six
to interpret the three essential characters and to originate "de neighborhood whar de talk is 'bout der way Brer Rabbit 'ceives Brer Fox."

Brer Fox feel so bad, en he git so mad 'bout Brer Rabbit, dat he
dunner w'at ter do, en he look mighty down-hearted. Bimeby, one
day w'iles he wuz gwine 'long de road, old Brer Wolf came up wid
'im. W'en dey done howdyin' en axin' atter wunner nudder's fambly
connection, Brer Wolf, he 'low, he did, dat der wuz sumpin wrong
wid Brer Fox, en Brer Fox, he 'lowed der weren't, en he went on en
laff en make great terdo kaze Brer Wolf look like he 'spicion sumpin.
But Brer Wolf, he got mighty long head, en he sorter broach 'bout
Brer Rabbit's kyar'ns on, kaze de way dat Brer Rabbit 'ceive Brer
Fox done got ter be de talk er de neighborhood. Den Brer Fox en
Brer Wolf dey sorter palavered on, dey did, twel bimeby Brer Wolf
he up'n say dat he done got plan fix fer ter trap Brer Rabbit. Den

[7] From *Uncle Remus: His Songs and Sayings,* by Joel Chandler Harris. Permission by Lucien Harris, Jr., Treasurer, Estate of Joel Chandler Harris and Esther
LaRose Harris, Avondale Estates, Ga.

Brer Fox say how. Den Brer Wolf up'n tell 'im dat de way fer ter git de trap on Brer Rabbit wuz ter get 'im in Brer Fox house. Brer Fox done know Brer Rabbit of ole, en he know dat sorter game done wo' ter a frazzle, but Brer Wolf, he talk mighty 'swadin'.

"How you gwine git 'im dar?" sez Brer Fox, sezee.

"Fool 'im dar," sez Brer Wolf, sezee.

"Who gwine do de foolin'?" says Brer Fox, sezee.

"I'll do de foolin'," sez Brer Wolf, sezee, "ef you'll do de gamin'," sezee.

"How you gwine do it?" sez Brer Fox, sezee.

"You run 'long home, en git on de bed, en make like you dead, en don't you say nothin' twel Brer Rabbit come en put his han's onter you," sez Brer Wolf, sezee, "en ef we don't git 'im fer supper, Joe's dead en Sal's a widder," sezee.

Dis look like mighty nice game, en Brer Fox 'greed. So den he amble off home, en Brer Wolf, he march off ter Brer Rabbit house. W'en he got dar, hit look like nobody at home, but Brer Wolf he walk up en knock on de do'—blam! blam! Nobody come. Den he lam aloose en knock agin—blim! blim!

"Who dar?" sez Brer Rabbit, sezee.

"Fr'en'," sez Brer Wolf.

"Too many fr'en's spiles de dinner," sez Brer Rabbit, sezee; "w'ich un's dis?" sezee.

"I fetch bad news, Brer Rabbit," sez Brer Wolf, sezee.

"Bad news is soon tole," sez Brer Rabbit, sezee.

By dis time Brer Rabbit done come ter de do', wid his head tied up in a red hankcher.

"Brer Fox died dis mawnin'," sez Brer Wolf, sezee.

"Whar yo' moanin' gown, Brer Wolf?" sez Brer Rabbit, sezee.

"Gwine atter it now," sez Brer Wolf, sezee. "I des call by fer ter bring de news. I went down ter Brer Fox house little bit 'go, en dar I foun' 'im stiff," sezee.

Den Brer Wolf lope off. Brer Rabbit sot down en scratch his head, he did, en bimeby he say ter hisse'f dat he b'lieve he sorter drap roun' by Brer Fox house fer ter see how de lan' lay. No sooner said'n done. Up he jump, en out he went. W'en Brer Rabbit got close ter Brer Fox house, all look lonesome. Den he went up nigher. Nobody stirrin'. Den he look in, en dar lay Brer Fox stretch out on de bed des ez big ez life. Den Brer Rabbit make like he talkin' to hisse'f.

"Nobody roun' fer ter look atter Brer Fox—not even Brer Tukkey Buzzard aint come ter de funer'l," sezee. "I hope Brer Fox aint dead, but I speck he is," sezee. "Even down ter Brer Wolf done gon en lef' 'im. Hit's de busy season wid me, but I'll set up wid 'im. He seem like he dead, yit he mayn't be," sez Brer Rabbit, sezee. "W'en a man go ter see dead folks, dead folks allers raises up der behime leg en hollers, *Wahoo!*" sezee.

Brer Fox he stay still. Den Brer Rabbit he talk little louder:

"Mighty funny. Brer Fox look like he dead, yit he don't do like he dead. Dead folks hists de behime leg en hollers *Wahoo!* w'en a man come ter see um," sez Brer Rabbit, sezee.

Sho'nuff, Brer Fox lif' up his foot en holler *Wahoo!* en Brer Rabbit he tear out de house like de dogs wuz atter 'im.

SNOW MAIDEN

Adapted by Geraldine Brain Siks from a Russian fairy tale

This fairy tale appeals to children in winter when snow creates a mood of wonder and mystery. It is a miracle tale based on the theme of love. The drama belongs to the old couple. The plot shows their problem to be that of wanting a child; complication develops when the snow maiden comes to life in her mysterious but endearing way; and resolution is experienced when the couple realizes that they must be content with the maiden for only a short time each year. Characters fall into two areas: the couple (protagonist) supported by the children, and the snow maiden (antagonist) supported by Baboushka and the star flowers.

In a friendly hut on the edge of a faraway village lived a good peasant named Ivan with his wife Marfa. They worked hard and were kind to the village folk, to weary travelers, and especially to the children. They appeared to be very happy but in their hearts they felt a deep loneliness because they had no child of their own to make their home happy.

One winter morning Ivan looked from the window. Snow was falling steadily and the ground was white with deep snow. Several of the village children were already out to play. They laughed as they threw snowballs and shaped figures out of snow. Ivan called Marfa to come and enjoy the children's excitement. "See what a merry time they are having!" he said. "Come, we shall go and play with them in the beauty and mystery of snow."

Marfa needed no coaxing. She wrapped herself warmly and went out in the snow to talk with the children while Ivan got into his boots and hooded coat and hurried to join her. "Come," said Marfa as she walked to a clean patch of snow and made a soft snowball in her hands. "Look at the wonder in the snow. Let us make a Snyegurochka, a beautiful, little snow-white maiden to surprise the children."

"Well," smiled Ivan at the thought. "Why not! Let us make her like the little girl we have hoped for, the very one we have talked about."

So they set to rolling snowballs and to sculpture a little child of snow. The children became interested. They gathered near to watch the deft way Marfa and Ivan worked with the snow. The children were disappointed when they were called to their homes to help with the morning chores, but Ivan and Marfa kept on working, for they were excited with their plan.

While they worked an old Baboushka tramped through the snowy streets. She saw Ivan and Marfa and joined them to watch them at their work.

"Good morning to you," said Ivan as he looked up from the snow to find Baboushka peering at the snow maiden.

"Good morning to you," Baboushka nodded. "Indeed it is a morning of mystery with such whiteness."

"You must have come from afar?" Marfa inquired as she saw heavy snow upon Baboushka's hood. "Would you like to warm yourself by our oven and have tea and bread with us?" While Marfa spoke a single snowflake fell on her bright red hood. The old Baboushka gave a sudden start and smiled as she saw the snowflake lighting there.

"Look, a star from heaven shines upon you," said Baboushka in awe. She nodded, "It is a blessing from above."

"A blessing?" asked Marfa in surprise, for she was puzzled. "I am grateful for many blessings and I thank you, kind woman."

"Thank me not," said Baboushka. "I do not bring the blessings. I only see them. Let me thank you for your kind offer of food and warmth, but I must be on my way in the silent mystery of snow."

Ivan and Marfa bid her farewell and watched until she disappeared in the turn of the road. They spoke of Baboushka's strangeness as they worked again on their little Snyegurochka. Marfa worked carefully to shape the white boots while Ivan sculptured the eyes to make them twinkle. When they finished they stood back to see the little snow maiden. They smiled as they saw how beautiful she was. At this moment the sun shone through the clouds and sunshine covered the maiden. At once her twinkling eyes turned blue. Her lips and cheeks became rosy and her snowy hair became as golden as the sun.

"What's this?" Marfa and Ivan whispered to one another as they knelt in haste and made the sign of the cross. As they watched, the little maiden breathed and stretched and smiled. She came slowly to life as if she were awakening from a long sleep. She started to walk in the snow. "Heaven has heard our prayers," Ivan whispered to Marfa.

Marfa nodded. "It's true," she whispered. "The old Baboushka spoke of a blessing, but little did we know this was to be." Marfa stood up and went slowly to the maiden. "Little Snyegurochka, you are ours," she said kindly. "This is Ivan and I am Marfa. We have waited long for a little girl like you."

The snow maiden smiled. "Yes," said Ivan. "We have dreamed and prayed for you to come and live with us in our little hut yonder."

The snow maiden looked at both of them and smiled the sweetest smile they had ever seen. "You are kind. You have brought me here.

I shall stay as long as I may," she said with a voice which sounded like laughing, mountain streams. "I see that you understand the mysteries and will be patient when I stay close to the beauty that I know."

Ivan and Marfa did not understand the little maiden but they invited her to come into their hut. They did not insist when she asked if she might stay out to play with the children who had returned from their chores. The children were amazed to see the snow maiden and they marvelled at the way she danced and lilted through the snow and sculptured exquisite snow figures with her delicate fingers. She helped the children with their sculpturing and she danced with them and played their games. At last when it grew dark Snyegurochka entered Ivan's hut to sleep in a cool room which Marfa had made ready for her. Altogether, this winter with Snyegurochka was the happiest that Marfa and Ivan had ever known.

Spring came early the next year. On a warm morning Snyegurochka asked Ivan and Marfa and three of her village friends to go with her to the forest. As they walked along the path in the warm sunshine Snyegurochka ran ahead to hide in the shadows of the underbrush. At first Ivan and Marfa were puzzled, for the maiden seemed fearful like a frightened fawn, but Marfa soon realized that Synegurochka was extremely weary and sat often to rest. "What is the matter, my little one?" Marfa asked as she sat beside the maiden and gently touched her delicate white hands and face.

"Nothing is the matter which you can help, good mother," Snyegurochka said cheerfully. "I hoped I might find a patch of snow, but I fear it has melted away. If only I could find a cool drink of snow water I believe I could sing and dance again."

So Ivan and Marfa and the children left the maiden resting in the shade of a tall fir tree while each one hurried on a different pathway to look for a patch of hidden snow. Marfa returned soon, for she felt anxious. Imagine Marfa's surprise when she saw that Snyegurochka was no longer waiting there. Marfa called and listened and there was no answer. Soon Ivan and the other children hurried back. Everyone was curious as they called and searched for little Snyegurochka. When they saw that no trace of her was to be found Marfa sat again upon the log and in her sadness she looked downward to the ground. There she saw a white star blooming.

"Look," she said to the others. "The little maiden has left us her star flower."

"Indeed," said Ivan, a little puzzled. "Perhaps you are right. Perhaps it is her promise that we shall see her when snow stars fall again from heaven."

"It is! It is her promise!" cried the children. "Look! She has left star flowers all along the homeward path. They were not blooming when we came!"

The children hurried to pick the freshly bloomed star flowers as they walked homeward toward the village. Ivan and Marfa were happy with hope that the little maiden might come again with the first snow of winter. And, blessing of blessings, she did for seven winters after.

THE FROG PRINCE

Adapted by Geraldine Brain Siks
from Margaret Hunt's translation of the Grimms' fairy tale

"A promise is to be kept" is the theme of this enchantment which holds unusual appeal for children. The king's stern insistence, reinforced by the enchanted prince (frog) provides a real struggle for the princess which children understand and like to "get their teeth into." Characterizations fall into two areas: the princess (protagonist) supported by her ladies, and king (antagonist) supported by the frog, witches, and loon. Originality in dramatic interpretations comes when children understand characterizations and motives and are guided to express them with emotion which brings involvement and conviction.

In olden times when golden happenings happened as mysteriously as rainbows there lived a princess. Her eyes were deep blue like the sea at dawn and her hair shone like the sea at sunrise. News of her beauty spread like wind across the kingdoms, but as bad news spreads even faster than good, everyone knew that the beautiful princess could not keep a promise. The king, her father, was greatly troubled because he knew she would never be happy until she could be trusted. He sent messages throughout the lands announcing that he who could teach the princess to keep a promise should receive her hand in marriage as well as half of his fortune.

In a neighboring kingdom a young prince learned about the princess and he set out to see what he might do to help her. The prince was handsome and kind, yet firm as castle walls when it came to obeying the laws of life. After traveling for many days the prince found himself in a deep forest with a large clearing in its midst. In the center of the clearing he found a deep well in the shape of a heart. He stopped to get a drink when a large frog hopped to the bank and croaked in anxious greeting. "Well, old Hopper, what are you trying to tell me?" the prince inquired, as he listened to the frog and stretched out on the grass to watch him. The prince soon fell fast asleep, for unbeknown to him he was in an enchanted forest.

A sudden clap of thunder awakened the prince. He jumped up with a quick start just as a loon flew into the clearing and circled the well. The loon called in her weird lonely call and seemed to be crying to the prince as she flew off to the woods. The sky grew dark as night and out of the trees flew the ugly witch sisters with gleeful rage. They circled the well and the prince hid quickly behind a tree to watch them. The ugliest of the witches silenced the others with a shrill voice as she called: "Hark the cry of the loon! The sun goes down at noon! The time has come, our evil will be done!"

All of the others gathered near the Ugly One as she continued to speak, "Sisters, fetch an evil token to replenish the enchanted well. The loon's call and the darkened sun are signs for which we have waited long. While the sun stays set we have power to enchant one of royal blood. No doubt the princess will come as she does every day. Make haste, I wait by the enchanted water."

The sisters flew off in wild glee while the Ugly One studied the well sharply. While she peered into the water an old frog leaped out and onto the bank. The Ugly One cried wildly and hobbled after him.

"Hee! Hee! An evil potion ye shall be," she said as she poked him with a stick and tried to catch him. The helpless frog leaped high and out into the dusty path as the witch pursued him. The prince stepped from behind the tree and called to the witch as he hurried to help the frog, "Pray, why do you poke a poor helpless creature and drive him into the dust? He means no harm."

"Who are you?" asked the witch in surprise.

"I am a prince from yonder kingdom, but little does that matter. It is the poor frog who needs help. Dust will choke him." With this the prince took the poor frog back to the well. The old witch crept from behind and waved her stick over the prince's head as she chanted: "One, two, wiggitywog, Royal Blood is in the Bog; One, two wiggity-wog, Change the prince into a frog."

Immediately the prince was transformed into a frog. He hopped on the bank of the pool croaking helplessly while the witch sisters flew back to the well. The Ugly One told them what had happened and as she spoke the Frog Prince leaped into the well and swam out of sight. The weird sisters cackled in glee and the Ugly One bid each of the others toss her poison token into the well. This they did in turn and as they finished the sun began to appear behind a dark cloud. Away the sisters flew in great haste to celebrate their enchantment of a prince.

Old Hopper, the frog who had lived in the well all his life, was curious about the new Frog Prince. When the two of them swam to the top of the well Hopper taught the Frog Prince many of the true joys of leaping, jumping, swimming, and croaking. The frogs were startled when the beautiful princess and her two ladies-in-waiting ran into the clearing and the frogs swam to the bottom of the well. The princess and the ladies played with the ball of gold. They tossed it to one another to catch as they stood around the well.

"I can't understand why father bids me promise never to come to this beautiful forest," said the princess.

"Nor I," said one of the ladies. "What harm has ever come from an enchanted forest? It is beautiful here."

"We've been here every day this summer and nothing has happened," said the other. While they spoke they tossed the golden ball higher into the air as they moved farther back from the well's edge to play. All at once the princess missed the ball when it was thrown to her, and it fell to the ground, rolled over the bank and deep into the well. "Look my golden ball is at the bottom of the deep well," she cried. "What will I do?"

While the princess and her ladies looked to see how they might get the ball, the princess exclaimed in sudden fear, "Father will punish me for breaking my promise when he learns that I've been here in the forest. What shall I do?" The princess was afraid and her ladies tried to calm her even though they too were afraid.

"Never fear, never fear, king's daughter," said a strange old voioo. "You wail so even the trees shudder." The princess looked and saw that the leaves of the trees seemed indeed to be quivering. It was then that she saw the frog on the edge of the bank and realized he was the one who had spoken. "Ah, old Hopper, it is you," she said. "It is the first time I have ever heard you speak instead of croaking."

"True, probably true," said the Frog Prince. "But perhaps, princess, this is the first time you have ever listened. Tell me, why do you weep?"

"For my golden ball," she said remembering her plight.

"Weep not, weep not, princess, I can help you if you will promise to reward me, and to keep your promise."

"Whatever you ask for will be yours," said the princess lightly. "I shall give you my ring, my necklace, my bracelet, why even the golden crown I wear. What shall it be?"

"It is not jewels nor gold for which I care, princess," answered the Frog Prince. "It is for your happiness that I ask you to promise."

"I do not understand," said the princess.

"I shall explain," said the Frog Prince carefully. "I will bring up your golden ball if you promise to be kind and let me sit at your table, eat from your plate, and sleep on your bed. Do you promise?"

"Yes," laughed the princess a little surprised. "I promise all you have asked if only you bring back my golden ball." But as the princess spoke she thought the frog to be very silly. She knew in her heart that she would never be kind to an ugly frog, let alone keep her promise to him.

As soon as the Frog Prince heard the promise he swam to the bottom of the well and returned with the golden ball. The princess was greatly relieved when the ball was in her hands again. She thanked the frog and called to her ladies, for she feared they had been away from the castle too long.

"Wait! Wait for me," called the Frog Prince. "Remember your promise." The Frog Prince continued to call but it was of no use. As she had always done, the princess treated her promise lightly. She was soon out of sight and the Frog Prince waited by the well wondering just what he might do to help the princess and himself.

Three nights later the king and the princess with their attendants were having dinner in the royal dining room. All at once a strange clapping sound was heard on the outer door and a choking voice called, "Princess, remember your promise. I am choking for want of water."

The princess was frightened. The king was curious, as the princess left the table suddenly and hurried to the door. The princess intended to send the frog away without her father noticing, but as the door opened in hopped the Frog Prince, who called for water. Once his thirst was satisfied he demanded to have his supper and to sit on a chair beside the princess. The king and his attendants were astonished and the king inquired until he learned the entire story. "What you have promised, my daughter, you must perform," said the king. "I have tried to teach you the honor of your word. You must obey once you have given your promise."

So the frog sat on a chair next to the princess and ate his dinner with great enjoyment from the plate of the princess. While he enjoyed the meal with unusual relish, the princess was so disturbed that she could not eat a bite. When the Frog Prince had finished his dinner he said, "Princess, I am tired. Take me to your bedroom so I may sleep."

The princess began to cry. She did not want to think of the ugly, slimy frog sleeping in her beautiful gold and white bedroom. The king listened while the Frog Prince continued to demand a bed to sleep upon, but the princess in her selfishness only wept. The king was resolute and spoke firmly, "A promise is to keep. He who helped you when you were in trouble should not be despised. Take the frog to your bedroom so he may sleep upon your bed as you promised."

The princess realized, at last, that she had to obey so she took hold of the frog's front legs and helped him to her bedroom. Her ladies went ahead to make the room ready and the king and his attendants followed. The ladies spread the golden coverlet back and were ready to put the frog on the bed but the princess insisted that the frog sleep on the carpet by the window.

The frog spoke loudly so the king who was in the hallway might hear. "I must sleep on the bed. I am tired, even though I am a frog. You promised I could sleep on your bed," he said and as he spoke he hopped up to the middle of the bed and started croaking softly with his eyes closed. The ladies looked at one another helplessly and the princess sat down in a chair and wept tears, the first tears she had ever wept since she was a baby. "Why did I ever promise? I must listen to whatever I promise and never give my word unless I intend to keep it," she said aloud amidst her weeping. "I shall never sleep in my bed again after that ugly old frog has been there."

The king stepped in the doorway. "If you sleep every night in that chair, my daughter, you will certainly learn this hard lesson." This thought angered the princess all over again. She rose up, stamped to the bed, reached for the frog's front legs and threw him with all her might against the wall.

When he fell to the floor he changed at once into the prince. The princess was astonished. So, too, were the king and the attendants.

"Please forgive me," begged the princess as tears of shame filled her eyes.

"Your tears speak for you," spoke the prince. "Your father and I have caused you great anguish to bring you to this moment."

Great was the rejoicing in the castle and throughout the kingdom, for the castle bells sounded and the happy news traveled swifter than the winds of summer. In the midst of excitement and explanations a golden carriage drawn by eight white horses drove up to the castle. The carriage was driven by the prince's faithful servant who drove the prince and princess back to his kingdom where they were married and lived happily by making promises and keeping them.

BOOTS AND HIS BROTHERS

Adapted by Geraldine Brain Siks
from an old Norwegian folktale

"To wonder" is the key to Boots' happiness and success. This story always impresses children, for most of them, like Boots, are inquisitive. Appeals in dramatic interpretation lie in the characterizations of Axe, Shovel, and Walnut, including impromptu dialogue and voice patterns, and in the limitation of action to two impressive settings: (a) an enchanted forest, and (b) the king's courtyard. The plot is unusual in that the story experience belongs to Boots, whereas it first appears as if the problem is that of the kingdom. Boots' chief problem is being misunderstood by his lazy, dull brothers who mistake his curiosity for foolishness.

Once there were three brothers, Peter, Paul, and John. John was called Boots, of course, because he was the youngest, but chiefly because he was considered a foolish bumpkin by his brothers, who made him black their boots and wait upon them. The three brothers, who were near starvation, decided to try their luck at winning their fortune at the king's palace.

In the royal courtyard an oak tree had grown so stout and great that it kept the daylight from the palace windows. The king had sent messengers seeking a man who could fell the oak, but no man had yet been strong enough for that, for as soon as one chip of the oak's trunk fell off, two grew in its stead. The king also wanted a well dug which would hold enough water for a year, for all the water used at the palace had to be carried by servants. Many had tried digging, but the palace lay high on a hill and as soon as one began to dig he came upon solid rock. So it was that the king had offered the princess' hand in marriage and half the kingdom to whomever could dig the well and cut down the oak.

When Peter, Paul, and Boots thought of going to the palace the elder brothers discouraged Boots because of his foolishness, as they called it. But Boots, who was more curious than they, succeeded in getting them to allow him to join them. The brothers soon found themselves in a deep fir wood with a steep hill rising along one side. While the brothers rested they heard something hewing and hacking up on the hill among the trees. "I wonder now what it is that hews away up yonder?" said Boots.

"You're always so clever with your wonderings," said Peter in disgust.

"What wonder is it, pray, that a woodcutter cuts wood?" asked Paul sharply.

"Still, I must see what it is," said Boots.

"Well, we're going on to the palace and you'll have to run to catch us," said Peter stirring himself. Paul joined him and they were barely out of sight when Boots climbed hastily up the steep hillside above where they had rested. There, to his amazement, he saw an old axe. It stood hacking and hewing, all of itself, at the trunk of a fir.

"Good day!" said Boots, somewhat amused. "So you stand here all alone and hew, do you?"

"Yes," said Axe sharply. "Here I've hewed and hacked with every sunrise, waiting for the first curious man. Now, that must be you."

"Yes, here I am first and last," said Boots drolly. He pulled Axe off its haft and answered her curious questions as they walked down the hill together. As they came to the foot of the hill Boots stopped suddenly, for he heard a strange sound. "I wonder now?" said Boots to Axe. "Something digs and spades near here. Do you hear it?"

Before Axe could answer Peter called and bade Boots hurry. Axe gave a quick glance in the direction from whence Peter called as Boots answered, "Something digs and spades. I must find it for I wonder what it is."

"You're so clever with your wonderings," called Peter.

"We're going on to the palace," called Paul. "Go ahead and look. You'll probably find a woodpecker digging into a hollow tree."

"Well," said Boots to Axe. "I must see what it really is." So Boots searched through the trees and there, not far from where Axe waited, Boots saw a shovel digging into the earth.

"Good day" said Boots in surprise. "So you stand here all alone and dig and delve!"

"Yes, yes," said Shovel pleasantly. "I've done this with every sunrise, waiting for the first curious man, and that must be you."

"Yes, here I am first and last," said Boots humbly, with a smile. He took Shovel by its handle and answered its curious questions. It shoveled its way along until they came to Axe who listened keenly to their conversation. Boots introduced the two and was surprised by their unusually sharp greetings for one another. Axe and Shovel talked together about their good fortune in being found at last, and Boots, being thirsty, looked about for a stream. He found one nearby and was down on his knees having a cool drink when Paul came storming back into the clearing. He saw Axe and Shovel leaning against a tree and thought nothing of them but gave Boots a tongue lashing for his loitering. Boots appeared to be listening but when Paul finished speaking Boots asked, "Paul, this brook? Look. Wonder where all the water comes from?"

"I wonder if you're right in your head," Paul answered angrily. "Where the brook comes from indeed! Have you never heard how water rises from a spring in the earth?"

"Yes, but still I've a great fancy, a yearning it is, to see where *this brook* comes from," said Boots as he studied the surgings of the water.

"Well," said Paul. "Peter and I shall wait no longer for you. 'Twould be a disgrace in truth to admit we belonged to such a wondering bumpkin as you."

With that Paul ran ahead through the trees to join his brother Peter. As for Boots, he wandered in and out of the trees looking for the spring while Axe and Shovel watched curiously. Soon Boots realized he was wandering in winding circles, for the brook brought him at last to the very tree against which Axe and Shovel leaned. There at the foot of the mossy trunk of the tree the water trickled out of a great walnut.

"Good day!" said Boots in surprise as he removed his hat to speak to Walnut. "So you lie here, and trickle and bubble, and run down all alone?"

"Yes, yes," sang Walnut cheerfully. "Here I have trickled since the first sunrise and I've run this many a long year believing I would run into one curious man. Indeed, it must be you."

"Well, here I am first and last," said Boots curiously, for he was surprised to hear Walnut speak. He was more surprised to hear Axe and Shovel and Walnut greet each other, recalling earlier meetings. Boots invited Walnut to join them on their journey. When he learned that she had been waiting for this very invitation for years Boots took up a lump of moss and placed it carefully inside Walnut's shell. Then he took Walnut gently with his right hand, took Axe gently by the handle with his left hand. Axe, in turn took Shovel gently by her handle and the four of them set off merrily wondering what wonders awaited them as they wandered.

Banners fluttered in the courtyard at the palace. It was a hopeful day whenever anyone arrived to try his luck at solving the riddles of the kingdom. The king and the princess were seated on a large, golden dais near the great oak tree. On their right stood the courtiers and on the left stood the bold executioners.

"Two brothers wait without," announced the pages in a hopeful chant.

"Bid them enter," answered the king sternly.

Peter and Paul entered amidst a flurry of trumpets. They were taken aback by the magnificence of the colorful courtyard, but more so by the size of the great oak tree. They exchanged fearful glances, for in this moment each wished with all his heart that he had not come.

The ceremony started without delay. "I am the king of the land, and this is my fair princess. Tell me, in the fewest words possible, who you are, where you are from and why you are here."

Peter and Paul explained nervously. The king continued: " 'Tis a noble mission if you succeed. My daughter will explain." The beautiful princess explained that half the kingdom with her hand in marriage would be the reward for the one who was skillful enough to solve the riddles. As she spoke Peter and Paul wished that they had worked hard enough for their father so they might have grown strong, for each knew his strength was weak.

"My chief executioner will state the punishment that comes to those who fail in this mission," continued the king.

The executioner revealed his knowledge, "He who fails to fell the oak or dig the well will be put on a barren island. Both his ears will be clipped off."

Peter and Paul were uncomfortable throughout the ceremony. Peter, the eldest, was commanded to try his hand first. For every chip he cut out, two grew in its place. So the king's men seized him and held him while Paul tried his luck. He fared exactly the same, for when he had hewn two or three strokes everyone saw the oak tree begin to grow bigger. So the king's men seized Paul and started to march both of them away, when a trumpet sounded at the gate. The page announced that John, the youngest brother to these two, had arrived to try his luck. The king asked the page to tell John of the reward and punishment. Peter and Paul exchanged quick glances, for now each wished that he might warn Boots not to try. In no time at all Boots was escorted into the courtyard with the customary fanfare. As he viewed the courtyard he removed his hat, knelt before the king and princess, and addressed them with dignity and honor. Boots took pleasure in introducing his friends Axe, Shovel, and Walnut. The king, the princess and the courtiers were startled, yet pleased. Never had anyone arrived with such a refreshing and confident spirit. When Boots greeted his brothers the king spoke sternly. "Your brothers have tried and failed. If you *will* look like a marked sheep, we're quite ready to clip your ears at once and save both yourself and ourselves some bother."

"Your majesty," said Boots bowing, "it is altogether possible that you are right, but I am curious and want to try. I understand fully your impatience since from the first sunset no one has solved the riddles. With your kind permission I'd like to try before I surrender for the clipping, for, as I understand, ears do not grow as readily as the oak."

The king and courtiers laughed and gave him leave to try. Boots with much ceremony escorted Axe to the oak tree. "Hew away, good one," he said kindly. Away Axe hewed gently, making the chips fly so that it wasn't long before the mighty oak fell to the cobblestone courtyard. There was immediate amazement and acclaim. This was soon silenced when the king commanded Boots to dig the well. Boots, with ceremony, escorted Shovel to the rocky ledge in the courtyard. "Dig away, good one," he said kindly. Shovel dug gently and continued to dig and delve until the earth and rock flew out in great chunks and the great well was soon dug. When this was finished Boots escorted Walnut, with ceremony to the center of the well. Then, removing the moss, he said, "Trickle and run, good one." The water trickled and ran and bubbled until the well was brimfull in less time than it takes to tell about it.

The reward was given then and there to Boots. The princess and the king and courtiers were exceedingly happy. In his moment of greatest acclaim Boots wondered if his brothers might work and serve the king rather than to sit in idleness on Ear Clipped Island. The king, appreciating Boots' humor, granted his desire. From that day on the merriment in the castle was as refreshing as the water from the well. Boots saw to it that Axe and Shovel were given an honored place in the castle. On rare evenings Boots entertained the princess by inviting her to join himself, the king, the brothers and the courtiers. They gathered around the well and were entertained by Axe, Shovel and Walnut. The entertainment was filled with wonder and always the conversation was sharp, deep, and a little nutty.

THE HORNED WOMEN

Adapted by Geraldine Brain Siks from an ancient Irish legend

An eerie mood, superstitious beliefs, and characterizations of Horned Women motivate dynamic discussions when older children interpret this story dramatically. Empathy for the mother and son's danger is built quickly and becomes heightened by the intense, rhythmic weaving of the weird women. Original thinking comes in ideas for poisons, chants, wails, and dances, as well as in interactions between mother and son. This legend has been dramatized with enjoyment by beginning groups in pantomime to the background music of Stravinsky's *Firebird Suite*. It is perhaps enjoyed even more by experienced groups who respond to opportunities to interpret witch characters with impromptu dialogue.

Long ago a beautiful woman lived in an old castle with her only son. He was a brave young lad and hoped one day to become a knight as his father had been. He spent much of his time riding and jousting but now he had grown ill and his mother was deeply worried.

One night when darkness came early a storm blew up and raged over the hills and valleys. The wind rattled the weathered castle and the mother was troubled because her son's fever was raging. She made a bed for him in front of the fireplace, gave him warm tea and tried to comfort him.

"Mother, if only I had a drink of cold water from the spring, then I would be well again," he said desperately. "Water is the strangest thing in the world. It comes from a spring, a mysterious fountain in the earth. It will bring new life to me. Mother, let us go together to the spring for cold water."

"My son, you are so ill with fever that you know not what you say," said the worried mother. "To walk in the storm would mean your death, though what you say of water is true. Quite true."

As she spoke, a single knock was given at the door. A strange voice called, "Open, woman. Open for me."

"Who comes?" asked the startled mother.

"It is I, Witch of One Horn. Open at once, or I shall open for you."

The mother opened the door cautiously. There stood an ugly witch. One horn grew boldly from her forehead. The witch entered mysteriously, flew about the room as if searching for someone in the shadows. "Where are the others?" she asked. "Are they hiding in your castle? Speak woman."

"No, old one," said the mother. "No one is here, save my son. He is ill. I must close the door, for the wind blows cold upon him."

The boy and his mother were fearful. They watched closely as the Witch of One Horn waved the gnarled cane upon which she had entered. The waving of her cane produced skeins of yarn, although they were invisible to all save the witch.

"I make the mightiest thing in the world," Witch of One Horn said as she watched the mother huddle close to her son in fear. "Before the night is through you shall know what we do."

Two knocks sounded on the door. Witch with One Horn opened it. "Give me a place," said the second witch with two horns showing. She flew into the room in wild fashion, and waved her gnarled stick mysteriously. She spoke to her sister, "I weave with you the greatest thing in the world," she said smiling with her secret. "Know you that this is the very night we have waited for in this long year?"

"I know well," said Witch of One Horn. The two old witch sisters nodded their heads knowingly and sang an ancient wailing song.

One by one the knocks were sounded. The door was answered by the Witch of One Horn until twelve weird women had gathered in the castle room, the first with one horn, the last with twelve horns. Each old woman with her bony fingers worked with the others to weave a large invisible mantle.

Witch of One Horn spoke, "Silence. We must cook our cake before we finish the mantle." As she finished speaking she went to the fireplace and spoke in sharp command: "Woman, take the sieve from the shelf yonder. Fetch water for us from the well."

The mother thought of her son being alone with the weird women. "I dare not leave my son. He is ill with fever."

"If you care for him, you will go," she commanded.

"We shall watch him, we shall watch him well," chanted the old women together. "Well—well—well," they repeated eerily.

"I cannot bear to leave him," said the mother fearfully.

"Go, mother," whispered her son. "Bring water. Have no fear, I shall think of you every step of the way and you think of me—that way we will be together and everything will be all right."

The mother moved to the shelf and reached for an urn. "The seive! Take the seive," called the sisters.

"I shall be all night trying to carry water in the seive," said the anxious mother. The witches mumbled among themselves. This is what they had hoped for.

"Begone, woman," said Witch of One Horn as she opened the doorway. "Remember there are many horns among us."

The mother went out into the windy night. She looked back anxiously toward her son who watched her disappear into the night. He then sighed a heavy sigh and fell back into his covers to feign sudden sleep as he kept his mind on his mother. In truth as he closed his eyes he listened as well to every word the witches spoke.

"Look, the boy's fever has put him to sleep," said one of the witches. Little does he know that our mantle is woven from the evil poisons of the world. I brought poison on three snake tongues," she said with delicious pleasure. The other witches cackled with approval and each told of the poison she had brought to weave secretly into the mantle.

"Hark, sisters, my poison is different. A young lass in the village was jealous of another. I have brought the rage of jealousy and have woven it into the threads." The old witches laughed at the cleverness of evil.

"Silence," called Witch of One Horn. "The lad must not awaken, for we must replenish our witches' bundles."

"Aye," said another. "Once our bundles are replenished our work for another year is done. Nothing must prevent replenishing."

"Little does the lad know that it is heart—a human heart of a child —which will give life to our bundles," whispered One Horn.

This thought set all the witches to wailing. "A heart, a human heart!" They chanted as they circled round in evil rhythm.

"Silence," commanded Witch of One Horn. "Let us put the poison mantle over the lad while he sleeps. The mother may return soon. Make haste."

Together the old witches took hold of the invisible mantle. They moved toward the boy silently and mysteriously, while only the wailing of the wind disturbed the silence.

Suddenly a voice outside called, "Fire, Fire! Fire on Slievenamon Mountain." The old witches stopped and listened. When they heard the message a great and terrible cry broke from their lips, for Slievenamon Mountain was the home of these evil Fenian women. Witch of One Horn pulled the mantle in haste and carried it with her as she fled through the door. With weird shrieks and lamentations the others followed to fly to their mountain. When the old women were gone the boy sat up in his bed. He saw his mother hurry in through the open door carrying a sieve of water.

"Are you all right, my son?" she asked.

"I'm all right, but we must make haste and do something. The old women have a mantle of poison to spread over me to . . . ."

"Fear not, my son," interrupted the mother. "Do as I tell you, for there is not much time. Drink cold water from the spring to quench your fever thirst," she said as she put the sieve to his lips. The boy drank as if his thirst could bear it no longer. Then he stopped suddenly and asked, "Mother, how did you think of putting clay and moss on the sieve?"

"From the Spirit of the Water," she said as she quickly removed the blankets from the boy's feet. "A voice from the water seemed to speak and tell me what to do. You must drink no more. Here, my son, now put one foot at a time into the sieve of water."

The boy did not understand but he sensed that his mother was working in haste so he did as she bade him. At that moment wailing cries pierced the air. The witches were returning to the castle and calling for vengeance, for they had found that there was no fire on Slievenamon Mountain. This the mother knew. She had learned from the Spirit of the Water that the witches fear fire and water and she had planned this way to get the witches out of the castle.

"Open," called the wild voice of the Witch of One Horn but the mother stood silently behind the door holding the sieve of foot-water in her hand. The old witches pushed the door open and Witch of One Horn flew in. She carried the invisible mantle. She was followed by the sisters, each eager to replenish their witches' bundles. As the Witch of One Horn entered the mother dipped her hand into the sieve and hastily sprinkled water on the back of the old witch and on each witch who followed. As the water touched each woman she uttered a weird, pathetic cry. Each called out for help but each wilted slowly and became weak. Each woman hobbled from the castle, knowing she had little strength and time for her climb back to Slievenamon Mountain. When the Witch of One Horn, who was the last to leave, had gone through the door, the mother barred the door and hung an old witch cloak beside the door to ward off future evil. The mother then turned to her son. She was amazed to find that his fever had broken. She was greatly relieved for she knew he would soon be well. "Mother," he said excitedly, "Didn't I tell you that water was the greatest thing in the world. Remember I spoke of it before the old women came."

"I remember," said the mother. "There is a mystery in water, my son, but an even greater mystery helped us through this night. Think upon it. You will know—it is the greatest thing in the world."

SNOW-WHITE AND ROSE-RED

Adapted by Geraldine Brain Siks
from Margaret Hunt's translation of the Grimms' fairy tale

Literary authorities recognize this Grimm tale as one of the most appealing of fairy tales, for "it never fails to delight the listener of any age." Children respond to the theme of kindness, which is the core of the story. Dramatization falls into two acts set in: (1) the Cottage, and (2) the Forest. The cottage action reveals the protagonist characters (Snow-White, Rose-Red, Mother) and heightens the problem with the arrival of the bear (the antagonist). Initial action offers interpretation of domestic life with maternal and filial affection and kindness to animals. The forest action heightens the complication with the introduction of the dwarfs and leads directly to the unexpected resolution.

There was once a poor old widow who lived in a lonely cottage on the edge of a deep forest. In front of the cottage grew two rare rose trees which bloomed throughout the year. On one of the trees the roses were as white as snow, while on the other the roses were as red as fire. The widow had two daughters who were like the two rose trees. The older one was quiet and gentle and the mother called her Snow-White; the other was happy and spirited and was called Rose-Red.

The poor widow herself was old and unable to get about easily, so every day she sat and spun and watched her rose trees. She sang while she worked to cheer her daughters but in her heart she was deeply troubled, for she worried silently about what might become of them when she no longer lived. Snow-White and Rose-Red loved their mother as dearly as they loved each other. Every morning before she was awake they wove a crown of red and white roses for her to wear upon her head so she might be like the queen she had always dreamed of being. Snow-White stayed in the cottage to clean and cook and tend the gray lamb and white dove who lived with them, while Rose-Red went to the forest to fetch food, water, and wood for the fire place. Snow-White and Rose-Red were as good and happy, as busy and cheerful as ever two children in the world were, for little did they know of their mother's worry.

One winter evening while Snow-White and Rose-Red were spinning by firelight the mother took her spectacles and read aloud to them from a great book. While she read a knock came at the door. "Quick, Rose-Red," said the mother. "Open the door. It must be a traveler who seeks shelter far from his home this snowy night."

Rose-Red pushed back the bolt and opened the door curiously. Imagine her surprise! The traveler was a bear! As he stretched his broad, black head within the door Rose-Red screamed and sprang back. The lamb bleated; the dove fluttered; the mother hid herself behind the couch, but Snow-White went to the door. She looked closely at the bear and invited him to come in. The bear growled as he lumbered in by the fire. He tossed his head as if to tell Snow-White to close the door from the cold of winter. As she did so the bear began to speak in a hoarse, husky voice, speaking in words like a man. "Do not be afraid," he said. "I mean no harm. I am half frozen and want to warm myself beside your hearth."

"Good bear," said Snow-White kindly. "Lie down by the fire and take care that you do not burn your coat." The mother and Rose-Red looked at each other with quick glances, for they were anxious about the bear's presence in the cottage. The dove stayed perched in the rafters and cooed while the bleating lamb stayed near Rose-Red.

"The bear means no harm, mother," said Snow-White. "Come Rose-Red, we must sweep the snow from his coat. He is nearly frozen." Snow-White brought the broom and a heavy brush and together they swept the bear's furry coat clean while the mother studied the bear closely. The bear growled and seemed to thank them in his deep husky voice. He then stretched and lay down by the fire and was soon fast asleep.

"Listen, my daughters," whispered the mother. "The lamb and the dove are gentle creatures by nature, but a bear is a savage beast. At one moment he may be kind as this bear is but in the very next moment he may become a savage creature. I wonder if we are wise to let him sleep all night under our roof."

"This bear seems kind, mother," said the good Snow-White. "He speaks kindly and seems to be trying to tell us more than he speaks."

Rose-Red and the mother nodded with understanding and the mother opened the door to look out into the cold night. As she did so the cold air caused the bear to awaken. He roused himself and growled as he watched the family in the firelight. "It is our bedtime," said the mother kindly. "You may stay here by the fire if you promise not to harm any of us."

"I shall never harm you who are kind. Have no fear of me," spoke the bear. He then rolled over and went to sleep while the others went off to their beds, anxiety still with them.

As soon as day dawned Snow-White let the bear out and he trotted across the snow into the forest. Henceforth the bear came every evening at the same time, laid himself down by the hearth, and drank the fresh water which Snow-White always had ready for him. The widow and her daughters got so used to the bear that the doors were never fastened until their forest friend had arrived.

One morning when spring seemed to have come in the night and all outside was green, the bear said to Snow-White, "I must go away and cannot come back until the snow falls again."

"Where are you going, then, dear bear?" asked Snow White.

"I must go into the forest and guard treasures from the wicked dwarfs. In the winter, when the earth is frozen hard, they are obliged to stay below and cannot work their way through; but now, when the sun has thawed and warmed the earth, they break through and come out to pry and steal. Whatever gets into their hands and their caves does not easily see daylight again. Beware of little dwarfs who seem so harmless."

Snow-White was sorry that the bear was going away. She stood in the doorway and watched until he was out of sight behind the trees. The mother understood Snow-White's loneliness for the bear who had been so friendly. Rose-Red wanted to cheer her and she said suddenly, "Snow-White, I shall help you with the housework and as soon as we are through you shall come with me to gather wood and to fish in the forest stream. Perhaps we shall see the bear, for he cannot travel too far in so short a time."

Snow-White was happy with the thought and the sisters worked quickly to make the cottage clean and to feed the dove and lamb. They bid their mother a hasty goodbye and took each other by the hand as they hurried into the woods. As they walked along looking for the bear they found a big tree which lay felled on the ground. Close by the trunk they saw something which was jumping backward and forward in the grass, but they could not make out what it was. When they came near they were surprised to see a small dwarf. He had a furrowed old face and a snow-white beard which was more than a yard long. His beard was caught in the crevice of the tree and he jumped backward and forward like a dog tied to a rope. He did not know what to do to get himself free.

Snow-White and Rose-Red watched him curiously. He glared at them with his fiery, red eyes and cried, "Why do you stand there and gape? Can you not come here and help me?"

"What are you trying to do, little man?" asked Rose-Red.

"You stupid goose," answered the dwarf. "Can't you see? I'm trying to get my beard free. I was trying to split some wood for a fire so I could cook for my two brothers, and my beard got caught. I cannot free myself, and you silly, sleek, milk-faced things laugh and snicker. Ugh! How odious you are!"

"I will run and fetch our mother," called Snow-White.

"You senseless goose!" snarled the dwarf. "Why should you fetch another? Do it yourselves, you weaklings!"

At this moment a crashing of branches and a loud growl were heard in the trees. "Perhaps it is our bear," said Snow-White hopefully as she started into the woods.

"A bear!" screamed the dwarf with such fear that he stopped Snow-White in her tracks. "Cut off my beard then!" yelled the dwarf. Rose-Red took the scissors from her pocket and sniped off the dwarf's beard. As soon as the dwarf felt himself free he asked about the bear. When he found that the bear had followed a different path, the dwarf jumped up and down in rage and shook his fist at Rose-Red. "Uncouth human folk to cut off a dwarf's beard. Bad luck to you!"

With that the dwarf took up his heavy bag of gold which had been lying on the ground and he tramped off through the trees muttering to himself without so much as looking back at the children.

"I do not understand why he is so angry," said Rose-Red. "Surely his beard will grow again." She continued to watch him while Snow-White looked at the fallen tree.

"This log that the dwarf was cutting would be good for our hearth but it is too heavy for us to carry so far," she said.

"Look," Rose-Red replied as she turned from watching the dwarf. "A stream runs nearby. Perhaps we may catch a dish of fish for mother."

As Snow-White and Rose-Red came near the bank they saw something like a large grasshopper jumping toward the water, as if it were going to leap in. They ran to it. Imagine their surprise! It was another dwarf with a beautiful golden beard which was more than a yard long.

"Where are you going?" asked Rose-Red. "Surely you don't want to go into the water?"

"I am not such a fool," cried the dwarf. "Don't you see that the accursed fish wants to pull me in?"

The little man had been sitting on the bank fishing, and the wind had caught his beard and carried it into his fishing line; just then a big fish bit, and the feeble dwarf had not strength enough to pull it out. The fish kept the upper hand and pulled the dwarf toward him. He held on to the reeds and rushes, but it was of little use, for he was forced to follow the movements of the fish. He was in great danger of being dragged into the stream.

Snow-White and Rose-Red came just in time. They held him fast and tried to untangle his beard, but all in vain. Again, at this moment a crackling of branches and a loud growl were heard in the trees. "Perhaps it is our bear," said Snow-White hopefully as she looked into the woods.

"A bear!" screamed the dwarf with such fear that he frightened the girls. "Cut off my beard!" yelled the dwarf. So Rose-Red snipped off the beard and when the dwarf felt his chin he screamed, "Is that civil, you toadstool, to make me so ugly? Where is the bear that roamed through the trees?"

When he learned that the bear had followed a different path he jumped up and down in anger and said, "I wish you had been made to run the soles off your shoes!" Then he picked up a sack of pearls which lay in the rushes, and without saying a word more he sputtered as he dragged it away and disappeared in the trees.

While Snow-White and Rose-Red watched the dwarf, they were startled to notice a large eagle hovering in the air, flying slowly around and around above them. They watched the bird sink lower and lower and land at last on a rock not far from them. Directly afterwards they heard a loud, piteous cry. They ran up and saw with horror that the eagle had seized a third dwarf with a deep red beard at least a yard long. The eagle was carrying the dwarf off when the girls, full of pity, at once took hold of the dwarf's jacket and pulled against the eagle so long that at last he let his prey go. As soon as the dwarf recovered from his first fright he cried with shrill voice, "Could you not have been more careful? You dragged at my brown coat so that it is all torn and full of holes, you helpless, clumsy creatures." Then he took up his sack full of precious stones and slipped away under the rock into his hole in the ground.

Rose-Red and Snow-White, who could not understand the dwarf's temper, crossed the knoll and went back to the log again on their way home. There they were surprised to find the first dwarf sitting on the ground counting out his gold. "Why do you stand there gaping?" cried the dwarf, who was angered because he had been caught unawares. He was going on with his bad words when a loud growling was heard, and a black bear came lumbering out of the trees. The dwarf sprang up in fright, but he could not get to his cave under the log, for the bear was already close. Then with dread in his heart the dwarf cried, "Dear Mr. Bear, spare me, I will give you all my treasures."

The bear growled and held his sharp claws above the dwarf's head. "Grant me my life. Take these two wicked girls. They are tender morsels for you, fat as young quails. For mercy's sake, eat them!" The bear took no heed of his selfish words but gave the wicked creature a single cuff with his paw. The dwarf turned at once into stone!

Rose-Red and Snow-White had run away into the trees in fear, but the bear called to them, "Snow-White and Rose-Red, do not be afraid. Wait, I will come with you." Snow-White knew the bear's voice, and they waited. As he came to them his black bearskin fell off, and he stood there a handsome prince clothed in gold. "I am a king's son," he said. "I was bewitched by that wicked dwarf who had stolen my treasures. I have had to run about the forest as a savage bear until I was freed by his death. You have helped me to catch him. Now he has his well-deserved punishment."

There was great joy in the lonely cottage when the prince returned with Snow-White and Rose-Red. In the days which followed they went in a golden carriage to the prince's castle. In a year and a day Snow-White was wed to the prince and Rose-Red to his brother from a nearby kingdom. The mother and the white dove and gray lamb lived happily and peacefully with Snow-White and Rose-Red, half a year with one and half a year with the other. The mother planted two rose-trees, one in front of each castle. Every day one of the daughters made a fresh crown of roses for her mother and every day Snow-White and Rose-Red wore fresh roses in their golden crowns. Everyone who ever visited the castles spoke of the queens as being happy and kind, like the true queens one dreams about.

MOLLY WHUPPIE

Adapted by Geraldine Brain Siks
from Joseph Jacob's English Fairy Tales

This is a favorite tale for listening and playing. Bravery and wit (brain outwits brawn) become the central theme through the role of a heroine who overcomes a giant-killer. Characterization of Molly (protagonist) and the Giant (antagonist) hold particular appeal, for the drama is essentially between these two. Plot incidents of the changing of the necklaces, stealing of the giant's objects, and deception of the giant's wife motivate discussions and invite strong dramatic interpretations with suspense in action and reaction. Original thinking comes when children are challenged to decide how to create the illusion of a Bridge of One Hair.

Once upon a time there was a brave young lassie named Molly Whuppie. She was far braver and more beautiful than her two older sisters, who were as pretty as an English garden in spring. Because of her courage Molly Whuppie persuaded her sisters to go with her to seek their fortunes. They had trudged for many days and nights and the sisters were weary and discouraged, but not Molly Whuppie.

One night a storm came up quite suddenly. Molly led her sisters through the deep forest to a large, lonely-looking cottage where a candle shone in the window. Molly knocked. A large door opened. There stood a huge woman, a huge dog, and a huge cat. "Well, what do you want?" asked the woman.

"We would like to come in if you please," said Molly bravely. "We are cold and fearful in this storm tonight."

"I can't let you in," said the woman uneasily. "You see, my man is a giant. I fear he would be angry when he comes home."

The dog and cat agreed with the wife. The sisters were frightened and wanted to leave, but Molly persuaded the wife to let them come in. While they supped on broth and warmed themselves by the fire a sound louded than thunder was heard. It was the giant coming home. "Fee, fie, fo, fum, I smell the blood of some earthly one," he called as he knocked on the door.

Molly and her sisters watched as the wife answered his knock. There stood the mighty giant brandishing a sword and swinging a purse of gold. He couldn't believe his eyes, nor his nose as he stared at Molly and her sisters. Molly stared back at him but the sisters turned their eyes away from this mountain of a man. "Who have you here, wife?" he asked in his bold voice.

"Eh," she answered. "See for yourself—three hungry lassies who will soon be on their way. Ye won't touch 'em, man. Come eat your meat."

The giant hung his sword on the wall and put his gold in a huge chest. Then he sat down at the table and ate a mutton leg in three bites. He said nothing all the while, but stared at Molly, who stared right back. "Call my children to come to bed," commanded the giant to his wife. He then walked over to Molly and her sisters and said in a voice like thick marmalade, "You shall stay here this night and sleep in this bed with my chickabiddies. To show you I mean no harm I shall give you presents."

Then he went to the chest, opened it, and looked through it with eyes as sharp as carving knives. While he searched his daughters came in wearing their nightdresses. They were much younger than Molly and her sisters but they were very nearly the exact size. "Here, my darlings," said the giant as he gave a golden necklace to each of his daughters, and, pretending to be sorry that he had no more golden chains, he gave Molly and her sisters each a necklace made of straw. "Now to bed, my lassies. It grows late," he roared impatiently.

"Come," said the wife to Molly. "You and your sisters shall sleep here in this big bed with our daughters. I shall sleep in my bed by the fire, and I see my man has already settled down on his bed yonder."

All this Molly saw clearly. As soon as the wife snuffed out the candle, Molly lay awake listening. She listened for the snoring of the giant, the wife, the dog, the cat, and all the lassies. When she was certain that everyone was sleeping Molly slipped out of her bed, took off her own and her sister's straw necklaces and exchanged them very cautiously with the golden necklaces which the other lassies wore. Molly then lay down and pretended to be asleep. Soon the giant woke himself up with his snoring. Molly watched as she squinted through her half-opened eyes. The giant got up, took his sword, unbolted a big door which led to a bottomless dungeon, and stole quietly to the bed where the lassies slept. In the darkness he felt for the necklaces of straw. Unbeknown to himself he carried his own lassies, one by one, and dropped them through the dungeon door. With a gleeful chuckle he bolted the door, went back to bed, and soon snored heavily.

Molly, who had watched with her eyes half opened, now thought it time for her and her sisters to be on their way. She wakened them and they tiptoed silently out of the house. Once they were away from the giant's house they ran and ran and never stopped running until morning.

Suddenly a great palace loomed up before them. Between them and the palace was a deep chasm which seemed to reach downward for a thousand years. Across the chasm was a "Bridge of One Hair." Molly ran bravely over it, but the sisters were afraid. "Never look down, look up," said Molly encouraging them. But still the sisters were afraid. While Molly crossed back and forth over the bridge, the king from the palace rode to the bridge with his three sons and servants to see what the trouble might be. The king greeted Molly and her sisters. He was pleased to see a lassie as brave and clever as Molly, who succeeded in getting the sisters to cross the Bridge of One Hair.

Molly and her sisters told their story, but it was Molly's bravery that interested the king. "The giant keeps our kingdom in constant fear," said the king. "My sons, the princes, ride through the forests with their servants from dawn until darkness so no poor traveler will be harmed by this cruel giant."

"Your majesty," said Molly, curtseying before the king, "Your sons should tell the people they need not fear the giant, for though he is a huge man he must have a bit of a brain. Most anyone who keeps his wits about him could think faster than the giant."

This pleased the king. He smiled and spoke, "Molly, you are a clever girl, and you have managed well. If you would manage better, go back and take the giant's wicked sword and his purse of gold. It is with these that he does his harm."

"Is it, your majesty?" questioned Molly. "I know where he keeps them. If it will help your kingdom I shall try to get them from him."

"You shall be rewarded more than you dare to hope for," said the king. "Since you set out to seek your fortunes, I shall give my two eldest sons to your two elder sisters in marriage."

The king's sons were pleased. The sisters were pleased. Molly was very pleased. She crossed over the Bridge of One Hair and set out for the giant's cottage amidst the well-wishing and cheering of her sisters and the king and his party.

When night came Molly was outside the cottage. She waited until she heard loud snoring. Then entered slowly and saw that everyone was sleeping. She saw that the dog slept by the giant's bed and the cat slept by the wife's bed. Molly then tiptoed to the giant's bed as quiet as air. She reached over his head and got the sword from the wall. The sword rattled. Molly stood as still as a statue, ready for whatever might happen. The giant snored louder. The dog stretched and the cat stretched. The giant's wife turned over. Molly moved back to the bed and reached carefully under the giant's pillow. She found the purse of gold and tiptoed to the door. She opened it as carefully as she might with the purse in one hand and the sword in the other. The door creaked with a loud creak. The dog barked. The cat mewed. The wife shouted, and the giant jumped up and called: "Fee, fie, fo, fum, I smell the blood of that earthly one!"

Molly ran out the door, holding tightly to the sword and the purse of gold. The giant ran after her. They both ran for all their might and came in great haste to the Bridge of One Hair. Molly's sisters and the king and his party were waiting. They cheered for Molly as she ran over the bridge. The giant stopped. He was afraid of the bridge and the chasm below. He shook his fist and called: "Woe worth ye, Molly Whuppie! Never ye come again."

"Once yet, carle, I'll come again to Spain," called Molly, and the giant went away muttering. Great was the rejoicing as Molly knelt before the king to present the giant's sword and purse of gold. "Molly, ye've managed well," said the king. "I shall keep my promise, but if ye would manage better, take the giant's ring that he wears on his thumb. His ring reminds him of his power over others. If ye succeed my youngest son will be your husband."

The youngest son was pleased. The king and his party and Molly's sisters were pleased. Molly was pleased, but she was curious about how she could manage the ring. That night she managed to slip in where the giant and his wife were sleeping. The giant snored in anger over the happenings of the past two nights. Molly hid under his bed and crouched low, until, at last, the giant dangled his arm over the bedside. "Tuh, tuh, tuh," went Molly as she spat lightly upon the giant's thumb. Then she pulled and tugged gently on the ring. She held her breath as she did so. At last she got the ring off and put it in her pocket. While she was doing this the giant reached out and gripped her by the hand. Molly was surprised, but she did not shout. "I've caught you at last," thundered the giant holding her in the trap of his fist. "If I had done as much ill to ye, Molly Whuppie, as ye have done to me, what would ye do now?"

Molly answered bravely, "Why I would put you into a sack, and I'd put the cat inside wi' you, and the dog aside you, and a needle and thread and a shears and I'd hang you up upon the wall, and I'd go to the wood and choose the thickest stick I could get, and I would come home, and take you down, and bang you till you were dead."

"Well, Molly," said the giant, "I'll just do that to you." So he took a sack from off his pillow and put Molly into it with the cat and dog beside her, and a needle and thread and shears, and hung her up upon the wall and went to the wood to choose a stick. Molly began laughing, "Oh, if ye saw what I see!"

"Oh?" asked the giant's wife. "What do ye see, Molly?"

But Molly laughed and laughed. "Oh, if ye saw what I see!"

The giant's wife begged Molly to take her into the sack so she might see what Molly saw. So Molly took the shears, cut a hole in the sack, took out the needle and thread with her, jumped down and helped the giant's wife climb into the sack, and when she was in, Molly sewed up the hole.

The giant's wife saw nothing. She asked to get out, but Molly hid herself behind the door. Home came the giant with a great big tree in his hand, and he took down the sack, and began to batter it. His wife cried, "It's me, man"; but the dog barked and the cat mewed, and he did not know his wife's voice. Molly slipped out from behind the door and ran, but the giant saw her. She ran and he ran and they both ran until they came to the Bridge of One Hair. Molly ran over it bravely, but the giant stopped on the other side. He shook his fist over the thousand year chasm and cried: "Woe worth you, Molly Whuppie! Never you come again."

"Never more, carle," quoth she. "Never again will I come to Spain." And the giant never saw Molly, and Molly never saw the giant again. And never again were the people in the kingdom afraid. When Molly presented the giant's ring to the king there was great cheering and right then and there the king presented his three sons to Molly and her sisters. Away they went to the castle to celebrate three weddings and a Molly Whuppie who was not afraid of a giant or a Bridge of One Hair.

URASHIMA TARO

Adapted by Geraldine Brain Siks from a traditional Japanese tale

This beautiful fantasy has been enjoyed by generations of Japanese children. It was first introduced to the English-speaking world by Lafcadio Hearn and it is a tale which never fails to arouse wonder. It has appealed to children from seven through fifteen years of age for dramatic interpretation. Its theme evokes identification with the hero and its action stimulates discussions of kindness; youth and aging; and the mysteries of time, water, and life beneath the sea. The oriental background provides appreciation of customs and cultures. The action of the story falls into three clear acts: (1) Beach; (2) Sea; (3) Beach. Characters are distinctly divided into Human Beings and inhabitants of the deep. Younger groups have dramatized this tale entirely in pantomime to the music of Rimsky-Korsakoff's *Le Coq d'Or*. Older groups have been challenged to originate rhythmic interpretations of turtles, crabs, fish, mermaids, lobsters, and other water creatures with brief, appropriate dialogue. Strong appeal comes in opportunities to originate palace entertainment and seasonal activities which rotate with rhythmic swiftness to designate the passage of time.

Thousands of seasons past in the Land of the Rising Sun there lived a young fisherman named Urashima Taro. Early each morning he rowed out to sea in his small boat to fill large baskets with fish so he and his parents could sell them in the market place.

One day as Urashima pulled his heavy boat to shore he saw a group of children gathered around something on the beach. The children laughed and shouted to each other: "Strike him! Poke him! Watch him when I throw this stone!"

Urashima hurried to the children in time to stop a boy from throwing a heavy stone at a big, brown turtle which was struggling for its life there on the beach. Urashima, who was kindhearted, could not bear to see anyone being cruel. He spoke firmly to the children, "What's this you do? The turtle means no harm, so why do you want to harm him—a poor helpless creature?"

"He's ours," said one of the boys who was angered by the interruption. "What have you to say about a turtle on the beach?"

"Why can't we have a turtle when we find him?" asked another.

"Indeed, why not? Look at your baskets filled with fish."

"It is one thing to take the turtle if you are hungry," Urashima said fairly. "It is quite another thing to tease and harm for pleasure."

Some of the children felt ashamed. "Come, let us help the helpless creature," said Urashima as he and several of the children helped the turtle back into the water. While they watched, the turtle crawled into the water and swam out to sea. Urashima then offered the children fresh fish for their families. Some of them took the fish and thanked him and they all hurried away.

Urashima went on with his work. He hefted baskets of fish to the shore and looked for his father who came usually just before midday. As Urashima worked he heard an unusual voice. "Taro! Urashima Taro!"

He looked around but could see no one. As he listened to the calling he believed it to be a voice from the sea. "Who calls? Who calls Urashima Taro?" he asked curiously, as he looked out into the rising tide. There riding in on a wave he saw the big turtle. "It is I who speaks," called the turtle in a cheerful voice. "The one whose life you saved just now. You must have known those children almost ended me."

"Well, old turtle," said Urashima in surprise, "I am glad I came in time. You never quite know about children. You'd better stay in water when they are around, old fellow."

"Indeed," said the turtle. "But I've come now to counsel with you. How would you like to see the Princess who lives in the Palace of the Sea?"

"The Princess of the Sea!" Taro exclaimed in surprise as he looked around to see that no one was near. He answered quietly "I have wondered secretly about her many times when I've fished in deep waters. I've heard that the Sea Palace is more magnificent than any palace on earth."

"It is as beautiful as the mystery of water," said the turtle. "But would you like to decide about its magnificence for yourself?"

"There's nothing I like better than decisions," said Urashima, laughing. "But how could that ever be? I'm neither a fish nor a turtle you know."

"You will see," said the turtle. "Climb on my back and I can take you there in no time at all. Trust me, for I am a Royal Guard at Sea Palace."

Urashima looked at his baskets of fish. He knew his father would be coming soon. "I cannot stay for long," said Urashima. "But I have decided to accept your rare invitation." Urashima walked out into the water and climbed on the smooth back of the turtle. The turtle caught the tide and swam swiftly with it as each wave carried them farther out to sea. All at once Taro felt a swirl and a downward glide. It was a strange mystery of beauty and curiosity. Taro felt himself descending through the water, but he was not getting wet. The ocean floor was as colorful as an earth garden on the loveliest day of spring. Down, down, down they went, winding in and out, gliding swiftly among trees and flowers which bowed gracefully to Taro and the Royal Guard. Down, down, down they went, spiraling past fish and water creatures who honored Taro and the turtle with nods and salutes and amusing gestures. Taro felt more glorious than he had ever felt in a glorious dream.

Suddenly they came to a stop. Two silver swordfish guarded a coral gate. "Salutations," announced the guards to the turtle. "The Princess of the Sea awaits you. We shall announce your arrival." They bowed and sent a secret message to the palace, and almost at once the coral gates opened to Taro and the turtle.

Rows of fish in golden armor guarded the passageway leading to the magnificent crystal palace. Taro could see the throne on the open balcony and he saw the waiting princess as she called to him in a voice like music: "Welcome to the Palace of the Sea, Urashima Taro."

As Taro walked up the golden stairs the mermaid ladies bowed before him, fanning the water with tall sea flowers. The princess smiled as Taro came near. She was tall and graceful and wore a crown of emeralds and a gown which looked as delicate as pink sea foam. She gestured to a golden chair which stood beside her throne as she spoke, "Welcome, honorable one from the earth. Welcome, Urashima Taro. We celebrated this day in honor of your kindness to our royal subject. This is the first celebration of this nature we have had this century. Since you have shown rare kindness we invite you to stay with us forever."

Taro was surprised. He thought at once of his parents and the fish baskets on the shore. He knew that he was needed to help his father, who was very old. "You honor me," said Taro. "I thank you, but I must return soon to my mother and father, for they will wonder about me and become worried."

"I understand," said the princess. "It is natural that one who is thoughtful would feel as you do. Let us show you the peace and beauty of the sea. Perhaps, in time, you will see that your parents do not need you as you think they do. They are old; you are new. They are age—you are youth."

Taro was puzzled by the words of the princess. He watched her sound the coral bells with one clear "gong." At once her servants brought rare sea delicacies. Taro and the princess dined on delicious morsels, after which the princess repeated the invitation for Taro to remain forever in the everlasting waters. A sudden hush came over the sea as all of its inhabitants listened for Taro's reply. Like the princess, they were disappointed when he explained that his home was on the earth.

The princess sounded the coral bells with two clear "gongs." At once her servants announced the entertainment they had planned in Taro's honor. Around the balcony gathered mermaids, oysters, lobsters, swordfish, octupi and rare sea folk which Taro never before knew existed. All of the sea creatures entertained in turn. Taro laughed as he never before had laughed as he watched unusual sea chanteys, choirs, dances, quadrilles. He was even more impressed with the beauty of sea ballets, symphonies and solos. He was sorry to disappoint the princess but he had to be honest in his decision when she inquired for a third time whether he would stay.

When the princess realized that Taro was not yet ready to remain in the sea she sounded the coral bells with three clear "gongs." The Four Guardians of the Seasons appeared at once, each from a secret door in the sphere of ocean waters. Each guardian in turn opened the door of the season he guarded. As each door opened Taro and the princess and her court were enchanted by the magnificent beauty and happenings of each season—spring, summer, fall, and winter. The celebrations were so beautiful that the princess asked that they be repeated again, and again, and again. Taro was amazed at the swiftness in change from frosty winter to blossoming spring and on into bright summer and mellow autumn.

Urashima Taro felt that with such beauty he should perhaps be content but in his heart he longed for his rightful place. He realized he must speak what was in his heart. When the princess asked about his decision he answered, "You have been kind to me and I am happy here, but I long to go back where I belong and where I am needed. Will you please help me to get back to the earth to be with my family?"

"I will," said the princess sadly. "I understand. While you have been here our life has been happier, for we, too, have had greater purpose in our living. Will you come back to visit us again someday, Urashima Taro?"

"It will be a privilege, gracious princess. I would like to return."

"Very well," said the princess as she took a small, jeweled box from the crystal table. "This will remind you of the sea. It is sealed with a golden cord. Never break the seal or allow it to be broken if you desire to return to the Palace of the Sea. Do you understand what I mean?"

"I understand," said Urashima. "The cord is like a promise not to be broken. No matter what happens I will not open the box."

This pleased the princess. She called for the Royal Guard. As Taro climbed on the smooth back of the turtle, the princess and all her court bade him farewell. As the turtle swam down the passageway there was much fanfare in farewells. Taro waved to the mermaid ladies, the swordfish and the servants, but it was the princess that he watched for as long as he could see. He had grown to honor her deeply and he was sorry to bid her farewell. The turtle swam onward and circled the water currents to find one which spiraled upward. Then he caught a high tide, swam swiftly to shore, and stopped on the white sands where Taro always left his boat.

"Goodbye, old fellow," Taro said cheerfully as he jumped to the beach. "Thank you for the greatest adventure of my life."

"Goodbye," said the turtle. "Remember us whenever you hear the song of the sea." The turtle turned and swam away and Taro watched until the turtle was out of sight. Then Taro breathed deeply and walked on the beach to look for his fishing boat. He was puzzled as he looked about, for at first he seemed to be on a different beach. As he looked further he realized it was the same beach, but he was curious about the change which he realized had come about. He could not believe that so much could have happened so strangely in a single afternoon. He ran along the sands to find the thatched house where he lived, but the house itself had disappeared. He called to his parents and waited, but there was no reply. It was then that he saw an old woman coming down the beach. He hurried to her. "Good woman, something strange has happened. Will you please try to help me?"

"What's this you say?" asked the old woman, who saw at once that the boy was troubled and filled with questions.

"Tell me, please, where the parents of Urashima Taro might be? . . . What, pray, has happened to their house which stood here only this morning?"

The old woman looked at him, pondered on his questions, and asked him to repeat the names of his parents. She listened closely and shook her head as her memory slowly helped her to remember.

"Well, young fisherman, you asked about Urashima Taro and his parents. There is an old legend, I recall dimly, in which it is said they lived along this very beach long, long ago. The young son who was a fisherman was drowned at sea. As for his parents, they, like everyone on earth, lived for a space of time and then went on. . . ."

"Long, long ago, you say?" interrupted Taro as he tried to solve the riddle.

"That's the way I remembered the legend. The sea, like the earth has strange tales," said the woman. "But I must be on my way. My grandson is waiting for me to sell fish in the market place."

"Thank you," called Taro as he watched her trudge on toward the village. "How could this be?" he said to himself. "Here I am just as I was this morning, but the woman tells me that many years have gone by." As he looked at his hands and his clothes he shook his head in puzzlement. It was then that he remembered the jeweled box. "Perhaps the answer to this riddle lies within the box," he said as he opened it hastily.

As the cord broke and he removed the lid a wisp of white smoke puffed forth and swirled around him like a gentle wind. Taro peered into the box for an answer, but it was empty except for a mirror in the lid. Urashima looked in the mirror. It was then that he saw that his hair had grown as white as the sands. His face was as wrinkled as a withered pear, and his voice was as raspy as his heavy boat when shoved on sand. Urashima sat upon a stone and wondered.

"I must have stayed in the sea for many seasons. I never quite understood the beautiful princess while I was there," he said sadly.

Taro rose and looked longingly out to the ocean. He turned and looked toward the village. "I wonder if children ever play upon these sands. I wonder if children have changed much in these years. I wonder how they would treat a turtle . . . or an old man." Taro sat upon the stone. "I shall wait here—perhaps I shall see."

RAPUNZEL

Adapted by Geraldine Brain Siks from the Grimms' fairy tale

This has become one of the favorites for dramatic interpretation. Its appeals are several: the theme of love and the spiritual quality of the tale in which tears heal blindness; the development of Rapunzel's characterization as she endures and pursues; the evil and unexpected actions of Dame Gothel; and symbolism through fantasy. Even though children identify with Rapunzel and interpret her characterization with depth of feeling, most children find great satisfaction in interpretations of this particular witch. Limitation of characters to five essential ones appeals to some groups. Others have recognized opportunities to heighten the witch's character by introducing characterizations of Rampion and Thickets who interpret through original rhythmic movement under the evil spell.

Far away in a poor woodcutter's cottage on the edge of a deep forest lived a girl named Rapunzel. She was her father's only joy in his lonely world, and every day he chopped wood and sold it so he might bring food and surprises to his young daughter. In the eyes of her father Rapunzel was the most beautiful child under the sun. Her hair fell in soft curls, her voice was as sweet as music, and she was as kind and bright as she was beautiful.

Rapunzel was curious about her strange name. Whenever she spoke of it her father explained that it was another name for rampion or radish but when Rapunzel asked why she had been given such a name her father begged her to ask no further. Rapunzel wondered often about her mother who had died when Rapunzel was yet a babe, but whenever Rapunzel inquired about her mother, her father sighed and told her to only look into the mirror and she would see how beautiful her mother was.

Of all Rapunzel's wonderings it was an old gray castle which concerned her most. The castle rose high above the trees not far from the cottage and it was surrounded by a high stone wall which seemed to Rapunzel to be three times as high as the cottage itself. Whenever Rapunzel peeked through the cracks in the wall she saw a most beautiful garden, but her father had warned her to stay away from the garden and the wall because they belonged to a wicked witch.

On the morning of Rapunzel's twelfth birthday she walked with her father to the end of the path leading to the deep forest. As he bid goodbye he said, "Promise, Rapunzel, as you do each day, that you will not go near the stone wall."

"But father, I do not understand," replied Rapunzel. "Every day you bid me promise. When I have looked through the chinks I see that the garden is beautiful. Surely no harm could come from such a place of beauty. Why do you ask me to make such a promise?"

"It is for your own good that I bid you promise," said the father firmly. "On a day before you were born I entered the garden to get rampion for your dear mother who was tempted by its fragrance and her longing. It was that fateful trip, I fear, that caused your mother to die long before her time. As you know, we have been lonely these many years without her."

"Was it the rampion that caused her death, father?" asked Rapunzel anxiously.

"Ask no more," said the father sadly. "But be not tempted by the garden. It is not what it seems to be. Try to think yourself out of such temptation by finding a new thought."

At that moment a swallow flew near and warbled so clearly that Rapunzel and her father stopped to watch and to listen. "What message does the gentle swallow sing?" he asked cheerfully. "Think upon such a thought as this whenever you are tempted by a desire which gets hold of you." With this the father bid Rapunzel farewell and went on his way to the woods.

Hardly was the father out of sight than Rapunzel turned to the swallow. "Little bird, you fly so freely over the castle wall and you seem to sing to me. Tell me, do you sing of the beauty of the garden? —Or do you sing of a lonely prince?—Or—"

The swallow chirped and then flew upward. Rapunzel watched as the bird circled above her and then flew toward the wall. "I think the swallow invites me to the castle," she said as she ran straight to the stone wall and looked through a little chink. Rapunzel was amazed to find the garden so bright with blossoms. "Sometimes, like now, I do not understand my father," she said as she moved a secret stone to allow a hidden door to swing open. Now Rapunzel could see the garden clearly. "Oh," she exclaimed. "It is as radiant as my mother's opal ring which I wear upon my finger."

As Rapunzel stood in the doorway she was startled by what she believed to be voices calling her name.

"Who calls?" she asked as she listened. A chorus of voices seemed to answer, "Rampion—Rampion—Rampion."

"Why, that is my name too," Rapunzel said aloud. "Perhaps someone calls for me to help." As the voices continued to call in a luring tone Rapunzel moved carefully through the small doorway. She looked around cautiously but was amazed to find herself walking between two rows of rampion which seemed to grow taller as she watched them. The leaves reached out like long arms and beckoned mysteriously to her as they moved with the wind which seemed to call her name.

Suddenly a shadow fell over the garden and it grew as dark as the sky before a thunderstorm. Rapunzel started to run back to the garden door but was held at every turn by the rampion leaves. While she struggled to free herself she heard a wild cackle of glee. The rampion leaves opened the way for the wicked witch who swooped down from the sky and hobbled toward Rapunzel. Rapunzel screamed at the frightful sight, and drew back in fear as the witch approached her.

"Rapunzel, you are a rosy radish!" cackled the witch. "I am Dame Gothel, and you are my prize for twelve years of waiting."

The witched looked at Rapunzel closely. "You look as sweet as honey. I see my rampion has tempted you just as it did your mother and father. You simpletons!" the witch cackled as she flew down the row in a triumphant rage and waved her thorn stick at the door which swung closed. As she flew swiftly back to Rapunzel she said, "You are my prize radish. I am your Mother Gothel. I will keep you safe from the world up in the tower of my castle."

With this the witch waved her thorny stick in the air. She grabbed Rapunzel by the shoulder and they flew together on the whirling wind to the castle tower. They entered through an open balcony. "Look," said the witch. "You are high above the world. There are no doors, no stairways—only this window." She cackled. "Watch!" she commanded as she waved her stick over Rapunzel's hair and chanted wildly in mysterious fashion.

At once Rapunzel's hair began to grow. It grew long and longer and became the longest and most magnificent hair that either of them had ever seen. The witch commanded Rapunzel to drop her honey tresses out of the window. When the hair fell twenty ells down it reached the ground and the witch ended her mysterious chanting. "My golden ladder to my golden prize!" she cackled. "I shall climb up and down this golden ladder every night when I come to brings eels and radishes and secrets of blackness. Have no fear. Lower the ladder only for me."

With that the witch climbed down the golden hair and waited while Rapunzel pulled in her long tresses and closed the window for the night. While the witch hobbled away with triumphant cackling Rapunzel sat alone to think upon all that had happened since she bid farewell to her father that morning. All she could hear now was the wailing rampion calling with the wind.

Nights followed the days into a year. One morning the little swallow flew to the tower ledge and Rapunzel remembered her father's words about thinking a new thought. "Little swallow, what song do you sing," she asked as she listened to his song.

"Is it news of my father that you sing? Is it of the forest?" she asked, but she saw that the bird was ready to fly. "Little swallow, wait, I pray. Listen so you may sing my song to one who will hear."

The swallow listened while Rapunzel sang the lonely song within her heart. The bird then flew far beyond the castle wall until he found a lonely prince who had grown curious about the castle. On this morning when the prince heard the swallow's poignant song he listened curiously. He followed the swallow until by evening he found the secret door in the castle wall. He opened the door and entered. The little swallow led him through the thickets beyond the rampion garden until by nightfall he was near the castle. He hid in the thickets as he watched the swallow fly to the window ledge in the tower. He was startled to see Rapunzel on the balcony. The prince was ready to call to her when suddenly he heard the strange cackling of the witch. The prince watched from his hiding place as the ugly witch hobbled to the castle and called:

> Rapunzel, Rapunzel
> Let down your gold hair.

The prince was amazed when he saw the tresses of long golden hair drop from the tower window to the ground below. He was more amazed to see the witch climb up the golden hair as if it were a ladder. He crept nearer to the castle, being very careful not to make a sound, and just as he came near enough to listen to what was spoken he heard the cackling voice call:

> Rapunzel, Rapunzel
> Let down your gold hair.

The prince hid and saw the witch climb down and hobble off and out of sight. When he believed the witch had gone for the night he crept to the tower and called:

Rapunzel, Rapunzel,
Let down your gold hair.

Rapunzel was amazed to hear a strange voice and to see a prince standing on the ground below. She dropped her golden tresses down and urged the prince to climb upward before he might be seen by the evil witch. The prince hesitated for fear his climbing might hurt the maiden's head, but the wailing rampion and Rapunzel urged him on. When the prince reached the tower he was astonished at Rapunzel's beauty and bravery. He greeted her and explained how the little swallow had led him to the tower. He explained that the castle had once belonged to his father and he had been curious about the mystery which surrounded it. He promised to free Rapunzel and take her and her father to his own castle where they could find happiness.

"I must find a way to take you down from this prison," said the prince as he looked from the height of the tower and saw that thorns and thickets surrounded it.

"You cannot climb down on your own hair," he laughed as he wondered hastily what he might do to free Rapunzel.

"If the witch should find you here I would be afraid for both of us," said Rapunzel. "We must hurry, for she sometimes returns at midnight."

"I must think of a way for you to climb down from the tower," said the prince. "Perhaps I could find strong vines or skeins of silk in the forest and tie them together. It is one way, but there should be a better way."

While the prince tried to think of a way to get Rapunzel down from the tower they were startled by the witch's voice bidding Rapunzel lower her golden hair.

"Have no fear, Rapunzel," whispered the prince. "You must believe that we shall find a way to happiness, for we certainly will." The prince hid hastily in a dark shadow under the window hoping the witch would not see him.

Rapunzel, who was nervous over the happenings, chattered carelessly. "Tell me, Mother Gothel," she said, "How does it happen that you are so much heavier for me to draw up than . . ." Rapunzel stopped short, for she realized too late what she was saying. "Ah, wicked child!" cried the witch as she climbed through the window. "What do I hear you say? I thought I had separated you from all the world and yet if you speak so you have deceived me."

In her anger the witch searched through the tower and there she found the prince. He stepped forward and addressed her bravely, "Dame Gothel, I am a prince from the kingdom beyond the shadows. My father told me of you. I will explain my presence later, but I ask you to let mercy take the place of justice."

"Mercy, is it? Prince or no prince!" raged the witch. "As long as you are in my tower I have power to transform you. You shall be a prince of stone," she said as she waved her thorny stick and started her mysterious chant.

As the witch cackled and circled around him, the prince in desperation leaped from the tower window. He was saved from death by falling into thickets, but in the fall sharp thorns pierced his eyes, and he was blind. The witch with her green eyes which saw through darkness cackled gleefully, "Now you are blind forever! What good does princely blood do now? You shall suffer forever in punishment."

The angered witch then turned to Rapunzel. She clutched Rapunzel's beautiful tresses, wrapped them twice around her hand, snapped her bony fingers to seize a blade from the air and slash! Rapunzel's hair was cut off to the scalp and her golden hair lay on the ground below. Rapunzel cared not about her hair, but she was fearful for the prince and for what the witch might do to her. The witch waved the blade away and seized Rapunzel by the shoulder. She clutched her tightly and flew out through the tower window. They flew over the thickets and the witch called in revenge to tell the prince that Rapunzel would be lost to him forever on the desert sands at the end of the earth. As the witch flew away with Rapunzel the little swallow stayed near the prince who was deep in pain but deeper in despair over the fate of Rapunzel. The rampion wailed with the lonely wind.

Three years and a day later Rapunzel found herself in a deep forest. She had followed the faithful swallow's song. By running day and night whenever the bird was near she had wandered out of the barren deserts. Likewise, the blind prince had listened to the songs of the brave little swallow and the wailing rampion. He had worked his way out of the thickets, along the edge of the rampion garden, through the secret doorway of the stone wall and out into the deep forest. On this day he was startled to hear the singing of a human voice. It sounded to him like the voice of Rapunzel. He listened. He called her name. Rapunzel heard but she feared to believe what she had hoped for so long. She answered and followed his voice, until at last she saw him. His face was scratched and bleeding; his clothes were ragged and torn and he had neither shoes nor stockings on his feet. In his blindness he had become trapped by vines and was crawling on his hands and knees trying to free himself.

Rapunzel's heart was filled with compassion as she saw him. Tears came to her eyes as she worked to free him from the tangled vines, and two of her tears fell upon his face as he turned to speak to her.

At once his eyes opened and his sight grew clear. It was a moment of mystery. He could see again. When he saw Rapunzel he rose at once like the noble prince he was. He stepped back to get a clearer look at the ragged Rapunzel. Her hair had grown into soft curls, but it was her true beauty that shone through her raggedness. The prince was puzzled. He was afraid to believe that Rapunzel who stood before him was alive and not in a vision which he had dreamed a hundred times in his blindness.

Rapunzel and the prince stood apart and greeted each other like dear friends and yet like strangers who have been parted for many seasons. The little swallow chirped a cheerful song to break the silence of their meeting. They laughed with understanding, for now they knew they had found the happiness they had been seeking.

DUNIS AND THE THANKFUL FROG

A Latvian fairy tale translated by Charles J. Siks
and adapted by Geraldine Brain Siks[8]

This is a comparatively new tale for dramatization which appeals to older children. The tale offers freshness and a general Latvian flavor while it reflects the universal folk theme in which kindness is rewarded. Particular appeals of this tale for dramatization lie in the unusual characterizations of Dunis, the frog, and the white owl and in the sudden character transformations of royalty and attendants which lead to humor and imaginative response in actions and dialogue. The action takes place in three settings: (1) the turn of the road; (2) the castle gateway; and (3) the lake and shore.

Long ago in a small kingdom by the sea there lived a poor farmer who had three strapping young sons. The two older sons were known as Ansis and Janis and were considered to be handsome, hard-working youths. The youngest son was called Dunis and it was whispered among the royalty as well as the villagers that Dunis was a dunce.

In truth Dunis was the wittiest lad in the kingdom. He lived close to nature, studied Mother Nature's lessons and kept to his own counsel. It was for this very reason that he was considered a dullard. Dunis did not follow usual customs which to him seemed dull, but rather he thought for himself. He dressed differently from anyone else, as he put to good use such findings as feathers, fur, and flax. Dunis listened to squirrel chatter, whistled to larks, and conversed often with his wise friend, white owl, and with other forest birds and animals. In so doing Dunis became the laughingstock of the kingdom and was treated rudely by many, but particularly by his older brothers who were ashamed to be seen with him.

One day the father sent Ansis, Janis, and Dunis into the forest to cut wood. The two older sons drove off together, proudly, each with

[8] By permission of Charles J. Siks.

his own horse and cart, and left Dunis to walk along behind them. When Ansis and Janis came to a turn in the road they were surprised to see a large frog struggling to hop out of the dust ahead of them. Each brother pulled his horse to a stop to watch as the helpless frog croaked frantically. The brothers were startled when the frog's croaking turned to words, "Please—please," she croaked. "I must get over the ditch. Please—please; help me."

The brothers laughed at the frog mockingly. "Foolish frog! We are not our younger brother," shouted Ansis. "Get out of our way if you do not want to be crushed."

"We have no time to fool with a stupid frog," echoed Janis as he reined his horse and drove his cart forward through the dust. Ansis followed and drove right over the frog, but the creature hopped quickly to save herself from being crushed under the moving cart wheels.

As the frog struggled in the dust she stopped suddenly to listen to a shrill whistle. As she leaped upward she saw Dunis, who was walking down the road whistling merrily as he answered a lark. All at once Dunis saw the frog and he hurried toward it as she repeated her plea, "Please—please. Must get over ditch. Please—please. Help me."

"Well, what's this, old hopper?" Dunis inquired cheerfully as he put his axe down and knelt in the dust so that he might better understand the frog's croaking.

"Too weak to jump. Ditch too wide. Must get over," the frog croaked pitifully.

"Come," said Dunis kindly as he studied the situation. "I shall get you out of this dust, for you are nearly choked. 'Tis no wonder you are weak." Dunis helped the frog into the cool grass and brushed the dust gently from off her skin. He cupped water in his hands from the stream, gave her a drink and then helped her over the ditch as she had asked him to do.

"Thank you; thank you," croaked the frog. "When you need help, call me."

"What is this you say?" asked Dunis in surprise.

"To begin with," croaked the frog. "You will never carry wood again." Hardly had the frog finished croaking when an elegant white stallion trotted up the road from around the turn, pulling a bright red cart full of wood. The elegant stallion neighed in a friendly way, stopped when he came to Dunis and nuzzled him playfully. While Dunis turned to admire the horse the frog hopped through the tall grass and disappeared. When Dunis turned to thank the frog she was nowhere to be found, so he got into the cart and drove happily down the road, somewhat overwhelmed by the sudden happenings.

The princess and her attendants were in the castle garden when they heard the horse trotting down the road. They were startled to see such a striking sight as the white stallion and the bright red cart. The princess and her ladies hurried to the castle gate to see who the driver might be. When the princess recognized him as Dunis the dullard she laughed aloud and called to her ladies. "Can you believe it? Dunis, the country dunce, drives a handsome white horse! However did such a stupid one acquire such finery?"

Dunis was insulted at being laughed at and spoken of in such a cruel manner by the princess. He refrained from speaking as he took counsel with himself and then addressed the princess firmly, "Your highness, may I ask a single question?"

The princess laughed again unkindly, but her curiosity got the better of her. "What is your question, stupid one?"

"Why do you call me stupid?" Dunis asked, but in the very instant that the princess laughed again she disappeared into thin air. Puff! She was gone like candlelight snuffed out. Her ladies were astonished. So, too, was Dunis. He looked around curiously while the ladies called in sudden horror as they ran toward the castle. Their frantic cries brought the king and his guards at once from the castle. When the king learned that the princess had disappeared into air he was shocked. He called as he ran to learn who had put such a spell upon his daughter. As the king approached the gate, Dunis knelt, for he intended to explain just what had taken place. The king was horrified when he saw Dunis.

"Take this dunce and throw him into the lake," commanded the frantic king to his guards.

The guards seized the youth, carried him inside the gates, tied a stone to his feet and threw him into the deep lake near the castle. As the heavy stone pulled Dunis deeper and deeper into the water, Dunis ~~prayed~~ silently: "Frog, dear frog. I surely need your help now. Please, save me from drowning."

Instantly the frog swam to him and pulled him up and out to shore. Dunis was deeply grateful and as he freed himself from the heavy stone he thanked the frog.

"What else may I do for you?" asked the frog.

"Please, good frog, where is the princess?" asked Dunis, for he was fearful for what had happened to her. "Is the princess gone . . . ."

Before Dunis could finish speaking the princess stood before him on the steps of a golden stone castle. Dunis sensed that the castle was his, for the doors were opened by white owl. He announced that dinner was ready to be served to Dunis and the princess. Dunis bowed deeply before the princess and invited her to dine with him. He greeted white owl graciously as he escorted the princess inside the castle doors. Unusual music from the castle attracted the attention of the king's guards. Two guards rode in haste to learn from white owl that the honorable Dunis was lord of the golden stone mansion. When the guards returned with this news the king was furious. He ordered his company of soldiers to march to the castle, take it apart, stone by stone, and return his daughter without delay.

The soldiers marched in a beeline, straight to the castle of Dunis. They surrounded the castle in a complete circle. At a given signal from the captain each one started to work upon a stone. In this exact instant the frog croaked from the shore of the lake, and every soldier turned into a molehill.

The king and queen, who had been watching from behind a nearby tree, were filled with horror. The desperate king then ordered the queen to go to Dunis and beg for their daughter. The queen in her anger stamped up the golden steps. She stood at the door and demanded the release of her daughter. As she spoke her angry words to Dunis, the frog croaked on the shore. At this moment the queen turned into a spirited horse.

The king, who was watching from behind the tree, could not believe what had happened. When the horse stomped and charged toward him, he realized that now it was up to him to go to Dunis and beg for his daughter's release. The king considered this carefully as the charger charged off through the castle grounds. The king walked to the castle, went up the steps slowly, and inquired very politely from white owl if he might speak with Dunis, youngest son of the good, old farmer.

The owl winked and disappeared. The frog watched from the shore. Dunis appeared and greeted the king courteously.

"May I inquire, Dunis my lad, why my poor soldiers turned into molehills?"

Dunis smiled. "It is quite simple, your majesty. They came to me with anger in their hearts. As you know, anger always puffs one up until he is worth less than a molehill—except for a mole, that is."

The king agreed and then inquired softly with embarrassment, "Why was my wife, the queen, turned into a horse?"

"Do you not know?" inquired Dunis, pleased with the question. He spoke courteously. "The honorable queen stomped up the steps in a most unqueenly way, with anger surging from her heart."

The king spoke humbly. "You are most observing and honest, Dunis my lad. Never before have I talked with you and I find I cannot agree with the whisperings I have heard for many a year about you being a dullard. It would greatly please your king if with your wit and kindness of heart you could find a way to return the queen and soldiers to your kingdom."

"Indeed, I shall honor your request, good king," spoke Dunis. "But first may I finish what it was I wanted to tell you before you ordered your guards to drown me?"

Dunis then told the king exactly what had happened that day. The king was amazed and he forgave Dunis. At this moment the soldiers appeared and marched to the king's attention in front of the castle. The spirited horse charged back to the lake and as she approached the castle she changed, at once, into the spirited queen. Last of all the princess appeared in the castle doorway. Everyone cheered for her safe return. The princess announced with great joy that Dunis had asked for her hand in marriage. The queen lifted her eyebrows in sudden anger and was ready to speak. However, the king announced to the queen and everyone in attendance that he had realized on this very day that Dunis was not only the wittiest but the kindest lad in the kingdom and that he was delighted to have Dunis for his son-in-law. Great was the rejoicing by everyone except the puzzled queen as the king announced that they would celebrate this eventful day by feasting at his castle. As Dunis and the princess led the procession, Dunis waved to the winking white owl and to croaking frog who watched together from the lake shore.

THE UGLY DUCKLING

by Hans Christian Andersen[9]

It is probably because Hans Andersen told his own true story that children empathize with and love it so and feel a deep tug in their hearts when the scorned duckling becomes, at last, a stately swan. This story has become one which children from seven through fifteen years respond to for dramatic interpretation. The many episodes heighten sympathy and build duckling's characterization. However, for dramatization children generally prefer to select representative action from episodes in the following settings: (1) the canal in which ducks and duckling hatch; (2) the barnyard in which duckling suffers from cruel reactions of ducks, poultry, and children; (3) the swamp in which duckling encounters wild ducks, hunters, and dogs; (4) the peasant hut with treatment of woman, cat, and hen; (5) the forest in autumn, with duckling's response to beautiful birds; (6) the cottage in winter, with reaction to family and to hunger; (7) the garden in spring, with realization of true self. Music selected from Grieg's *Peer Gynt Suite* has been effective for groups who have interpreted the story entirely in pantomime.

[9] Reprinted from *Fairy Tales* by Hans Christian Andersen, The World Publishing Company.

It was glorious out in the country. It was summer, and the corn-fields were yellow, and the oats were green; the hay had been put up in stacks in the green meadows, and the stork went about on his long red legs, and chattered Egyptian, for this was the language he had learned from his good mother. All around the fields and meadows were great forests, and in the midst of these forests lay deep lakes. Yes, it was really glorious out in the country. In the midst of the sunshine there lay an old farm, surrounded by deep canals, and from the wall down to the water grew great burdocks, so high that little children could stand upright under the loftiest of them. It was just as wild there as in the deepest wood. Here sat a Duck upon her nest, for she had to hatch her young ones; but she was almost tired out before the little ones came; and then she so seldom had visitors. The other ducks liked better to swim about in the canals than to run up to sit down under a burdock, and cackle with her.

At last one egg shell after another burst open. "Piep! Piep!" it cried, and in all the eggs there were little creatures that stuck out their heads.

"Rap! rap!" they said; and they all came rapping out as fast as they could, looking all around them under the green leaves; and the mother let them look as much as they chose, for green is good for the eyes.

"How wide the world is!" said the young ones, for they certainly had much more room now than when they were in the eggs.

"Do you think this is all the world?" asked the mother. "That ex-tends far across the other side of the garden, quite into the parson's field, but I have never been there yet. I hope you are all together," she continued, and stood up. "No, I have not all. The largest egg still lies there. How long is that to last? I am really tired of it." And she sat down again.

"Well, how goest it?" asked an old Duck who had come to pay her a visit.

"It lasts a long time with that one egg," said the Duck who sat there. "It will not burst. Now, only look at the others; are they not the prettiest ducks one could possibly see? They are all like their father: the bad fellow never comes to see me."

"Let me see the egg which will not burst," said the old visitor. "Believe me, it is a turkey's egg. I was once cheated in that way, and had much anxiety and trouble with the young ones, for they are afraid of the water. I could not get them to venture in. I quacked and clucked, but it was no use. Let me see the egg. Yes, that's a turkey's egg! Let it lie there, and teach the other children to swim."

"I think I will sit on it a little longer," said the Duck. "I've sat so long now that I can sit a few days more."

"Just as you please," said the old Duck; and she went away.

At last the great egg burst. "Piep! piep!" said the little one, and crept forth. It was very large and very ugly. The Duck looked at it.

"It's a very large duckling," said she; "None of the others look like that: can it really be a turkey chick! Now we shall soon find it out. It must go into the water even if I have to thrust it in myself."

The next day the weather was splendidly bright, and the sun shone on all the green trees. The Mother Duck went down to the water with all her little ones. Splash she jumped into the water. "Quack Quack!" she said, and one duckling after another plunged in. The water closed over their heads, but they came up in an instant, and swam capitally; their legs went of themselves, and there they were all in the water. The ugly gray Duckling swam with them.

"No, it's not a turkey," said she; "look how well it can use its legs, and how upright it holds itself. It is my own child! On the whole it's quite pretty, if one looks at it rightly. Quack! quack! come with me, and I'll lead you out into the great world, and present you to the poultry yard; but keep close to me so that no one may tread on you, and take care of the cats!"

And so they came into the poultry yard. There was a terrible riot going on in there, for two families were quarreling about an eel's head, and the cat got it after all.

"See, that's how it goes in the world!" said the Mother Duck; and she whetted her beak, for she, too, wanted the eel's head. "Only use your legs," she said. "See that you can bustle about, and bow your heads before the old duck yonder. She's the grandest of all here; she's of Spanish blood—that's why she's so fat; and do you see, she has a red rag around her leg; that's something particularly fine, and the greatest distinction a duck can enjoy; it signifies that one does not want to lose her, and that she is to be recognized by man and beast. Shake yourselves—don't turn in your toes; a well brought up duck turns its toes quite out, just like father and mother, so! Now bend your necks and say 'Rap!' "

And they did so; but the other ducks round about looked at them, and said quite boldly:

"Look there! Now we're to have these hanging on as if there were not enough of us already! And—fie!—how that Duckling yonder looks; we won't stand that!" And one duck flew up immediately, and bit it in the neck.

"Let it alone," said the mother; "it does no harm to anyone."

"Yes, but it's too large and peculiar," said the Duck who had bitten it; "and therefore it must be buffeted."

"Those are pretty children that the mother has there," said the old Duck with the rag around her leg. "They're all pretty, but that one; that was a failure. I wish she could alter it."

"That cannot be done, my lady," replied the Mother Duck. "It is not pretty, but it has a really good disposition, and swims as well as any other; I may even say it swims better. I think it will grow up pretty, and become smaller in time; it has lain too long in the egg, and therefore is not properly shaped." And then she pinched it in the neck, and smoothed its feathers. "Moreover, it is a drake," she said, "and therefore it is not of so much consequence. I think he will be very strong: he makes his way already."

"The other ducklings are graceful enough," said the old Duck. "Make yourself at home; and if you find an eel's head, you may bring it to me."

And now they were at home. But the poor Duckling which had crept last out of the egg, and looked so ugly, was bitten and pushed and jeered, as much by the ducks as by the chickens.

"It is too big!" they all said. And the turkey cock, who had been born with spurs, and therefore thought himself an emperor, blew himself up like a ship in full sail, and bore straight down upon it; then he gobbled, and grew quite red in the face. The poor Duckling did not know where it should stand or walk; it was quite melancholy because it looked ugly, and was scoffed by the whole yard.

So it went on the first day; and afterward it became worse and worse. The poor Duckling was haunted about by every one; even its brothers and sisters were quite angry with it, and said, "If the cat would only catch you, you ugly creature!" And the mother said, "If you were only far away!" And the ducks bit it, and the chickens beat it, and the girl who had to feed the poultry kicked at it with her foot.

Then it ran and flew over the fence, and the little birds in the bushes flew up in fear.

"That is because I am so ugly!" thought the Duckling; and it shut its eyes, but flew on farther; thus it came out into the great moor, where the wild ducks lived. Here it lay the whole night long, and it was weary and downcast.

Toward morning the wild ducks flew up, and looked at their new companion.

"What sort of a one are you?" they asked; and the Duckling turned in every direction, and bowed as well as it could. "You are remarkably ugly!" said the Wild Ducks. "But that is very indifferent to us, so long as you do not marry into our family."

Poor thing! It certainly did not think of marrying, and only hoped to obtain leave to lie among the reeds and drink some of the swamp water.

Thus it lay two whole days; then came thither two wild geese, or, properly speaking, two wild ganders. It was not long since each had crept out of an egg, and that's why they were so saucy.

"Listen, comrade," said one of them. "You are so ugly that I like you. Will you go with us, and become a bird of passage? Near here, in another moor, there are a few sweet lovely wild geese, all unmarried, and all able to say 'Rap!' You've a chance of making your fortune, ugly as you are!"

"Piff! Paff!" resounded through the air; and the two ganders fell down dead in the swamp, and the water became blood-red. "Piff! paff!" it sounded again, and whole flocks of wild geese rose up from the reeds. And then there was another report. A great hunt was going on. The hunters were lying in wait all around the moor, and some were even sitting up in the branches of the trees, which spread far over the reeds. The blue smoke rose like clouds among the dark trees, and was wafted far away across the water; and the hunting dogs came —splash! splash!—into the swamp, and the rushes and reeds bent down on every side. That was a fright for poor Duckling. It turned its head, and put it under its wing; but at that moment a frightful great dog stood close by the Duckling. His tongue hung far out of his mouth and his eyes gleamed horrible and ugly; he thrust out his nose close against the Duckling, showed his sharp teeth, and—splash! splash!— on he went without seizing it.

"Oh, Heaven be thanked!" sighed the Duckling. "I am so ugly that even the dog does not like to bite me!"

And so it lay quite quiet, while the shots rattled through the reeds and gun after gun was fired. At last, late in the day, silence was restored; but the poor Duckling did not dare to rise up; it waited several hours before it looked around, and then hastened away out of the moor as fast as it could. It ran on over field and meadow; there was such a storm raging that it was difficult to get from one place to another.

Toward evening the Duckling came to a little miserable peasant's hut. This hut was so dilapidated that it did not know on which side it should fall; and that's why it remained standing. The storm whistled round the Duckling in such a way that the poor creature was obliged to sit down, to stand against it; and the tempest grew worse and worse. Then the Duckling noticed that one of the hinges of the door had given way and the door hung so slanting that the Duckling could slip through the crack into the room; and it did so.

Here lived a woman, with her Tom Cat and her Hen. And the Tom Cat, whom she called Sonnie, could arch his back and purr, he could even give out sparks; but for that one had to stroke his fur the wrong way. The Hen had quite little short legs, and therefore she was called Chickabiddy-shortshanks; she laid good eggs, and the woman loved her as her own child.

In the morning the strange Duckling was at once noticed, and the Tom Cat began to purr, and the Hen to cluck.

"What's this?" said the woman, and looked all around; but she could not see very well, and therefore she thought the duckling was a fat duck that had strayed. "This is a rare prize!" she said. "Now I shall have duck's eggs. I hope it is not a drake. We must try that."

And so the Duckling was admitted on trial for three weeks; but no eggs came. And the Tom Cat was master of the house, and the Hen was the lady, and always said, "We and the world!" for she thought they were half the world, and by far the better half. The Duckling thought one might have a different opinion, but the Hen would not allow it.

"Can you lay eggs?" she asked.

"No."

"Then you'll have the goodness to hold your tongue."

And the Tom Cat said, "Can you curve your back, and purr, and give out sparks?"

"No."

"Then you cannot have any opinion of your own when sensible people are speaking."

And the Duckling sat in a corner and was melancholy; then the fresh air and the sunshine streamed in; and it was seized with such a strange longing to swim on the water, that it could not help telling the Hen of it.

"What are you thinking of?" cried the Hen. "You have nothing to do, that's why you have these fancies. Purr or lay eggs, and that will pass over."

"But it is so charming to swim on the water!" said the Duckling, "so refreshing to let it close above one's head and to dive down to the bottom."

"Yes, that must be a mighty pleasure truly," quoth the Hen. "I fancy you must have gone crazy. Ask the Cat about it—he's the cleverest animal I know—ask him if he likes to swim on the water, or to dive down; I won't speak about myself. Ask our mistress, the old woman; no one in the world is cleverer than she. Do you think she has any desire to swim, and to let the water close above her head?"

"You don't understand me," said the Duckling.

"We don't understand you? Then, pray, who is to understand you? You surely don't pretend to be cleverer than the Tom Cat and the woman—I won't say anything of myself. Don't be conceited, child, and be grateful for all the kindness you have received. Did you not get into a warm room, and have you not fallen into company from which you may learn something? But you are a chatterer, and it is not pleasant to associate with you. You may believe me, I speak for your good. I tell you disagreeable things, and by that one may always know one's true friends! Only take care that you learn to lay eggs, or to purr and give out sparks!"

"I think I will go out into the wide world," said the Duckling.

"Yes, do go," replied the Hen.

And the Duckling went away. It swam on the water, and dived, but it was slighted by every creature because of its ugliness.

Now came the autumn. The leaves in the forest turned yellow and brown; the wind caught them so that they danced about, and up in the air it was very cold. The clouds hung low, heavy with hail and snowflakes, and on the fence stood the raven, crying, "Croak! Croak!" for mere cold; yes, it was enough to make one feel old to think of this. The poor little Duckling certainly had not a good time—One evening— the sun was just setting in his beauty—there came a whole flock of great handsome birds out of the bushes; they were dazzling white, with long flexible necks; they were swans. They uttered a very peculiar cry, spread forth their glorious great wings, and flew away from that cold region to warmer lands, to fair open lakes. They mounted so high, so high! and the ugly little Duckling felt quite strangely as it watched them. It turned round and round in the water like a wheel, stretched out its neck toward them, and uttered such a strange loud cry as frightened itself. Oh! it could not forget those beautiful happy birds; and so soon as it could see them no longer, it dived down to the very bottom, and when it came up again, it was quite beside itself. It knew not the name of those birds, and knew not whither they were flying; but it loved them more than it had ever loved any one. It was not at all envious of them. How could it think of wishing to possess such loveliness as they had? It would have been glad if only the ducks would have endured his company—the poor ugly creature!

And the winter grew cold, very cold! The Duckling was forced to swim about in the water, to prevent the surface from freezing entirely but every night the hole in which it swam about became smaller and smaller. It froze so hard that the icy covering crackled again; and the Duckling was obliged to use its legs continually to prevent the hole from freezing up. At last it became exhausted, and lay quite still, and thus froze fast into the ice.

Early in the morning a peasant came by, and when he saw what had happened, he took his wooden shoe, broke the ice crust to pieces, and carried the Duckling home to his wife. Then it came to itself again. The children wanted to play with it; but the Duckling thought they would do it an injury, and in its terror fluttered up into the milk pan, so the milk spurted down into the room. The woman clapped her hands, at which the Duckling flew down into the butter tub, and then into the meal barrel and out again. How it looked then! The woman screamed, and struck at it with the fire tongs; the children tumbled over one another in their efforts to catch the Duckling; and they laughed and screamed finely! Happily the door stood open, and the poor creature was able to slip out between the shrubs into the newly fallen snow; and there it lay quite exhausted.

But it would be too melancholy if I were to tell all the misery and care which the Duckling had to endure in the hard winter. It lay out on the moor among the reeds, when the sun began to shine again and the larks to sing: it was a beautiful spring.

Then all at once the Duckling could flap its wings: they beat the air more strongly than before, and bore it strongly away; and before it well knew how all this happened, it found itself in a great garden, where the elder-trees smelt sweet, and bent their long green branches down to the canal that wound through the region. Oh! here it was so beautiful, such a gladness of spring! and from the thicket came three glorious white swans; they rustled their wings, and swam and swam lightly on the water. The Duckling knew the splendid creatures, and felt oppressed by a peculiar sadness.

"I will fly away to them, to the royal birds! and they will kill me, because I, that am so ugly, dare to approach them. But it is of no consequence! Better to be killed by them than to be pursued by ducks, and beaten by fowls, and pushed about by the girl who takes care of the poultry yard, and to suffer hunger in the winter!" And it flew out into the water, and swam toward the beautiful swans: these looked at it, and came sailing down upon it with outspread wings. "Kill me!" said the poor creature, and bent its head down upon the water, expecting nothing but death. But what was this that it saw in the clear water? It beheld its own image; and, lo! it was no longer a clumsy dark gray bird, ugly and hateful to look at, but—a swan!

It matters nothing if one is born in a duck-yard, if one has only lain in a swan's egg.

It felt quite glad at all the need and misfortune it had suffered, now it realized its happiness in all the splendor that surrounded it. And the great swans swam round it, and stroked it with their beaks.

Into the garden came little children, who threw bread and corn into the water; and the youngest cried, "There is a new one!" and the other children shouted joyously, "Yes, a new one has arrived!" And they clapped their hands and danced about, and ran to their father and mother; and bread and cake were thrown into the water; and they all said, "The new one is the most beautiful of all! so young and handsome!" and the old swans bowed their heads before him.

Then he felt quite ashamed, and hid his head under his wings, for he did not know what to do; he was so happy, and yet not at all proud. He thought how he had been persecuted and despised; and now he heard them saying that he was the most beautiful of all birds. Even the elder-tree bent its branches straight down into the water before him, and the sun shone warm and mild. Then his wing rustled, he lifted his slender neck, and cried rejoicingly from the depth of his heart. "I never dreamed of so much happiness when I was still the ugly Duckling!"

DRAKESTAIL

Adapted by Geraldine Brain Siks from a French fairy tale

Children delight in opportunities to interpret the humanized animal and inanimate characterizations in this pungent tale. It is a rare story which offers a spirited hero in the character of a likeable, resourceful, persistent, and friendly little duck. He becomes a favorite literary character for many children once they are privileged to know him well. When children understand the maturity of Drakestail's personality they interpret this story with noticeable freedom, humor, and enjoyment. They respond to Drakestail's rhythm in walking, talking, and thinking. They recognize loyalty and uniqueness in his friendships. They enjoy opportunities to originate characterizations of Friend Fox, Lady Ladder, Friend River and Comrade Wasp's Nest to help Drakestail overcome his conflict with the selfish king. Action centers in three distinct places: (1) the roadway; (2) the castle with balcony above the poultry-yard below; and (3) the courtroom.

Drakestail was a very little duck. That is why he was called Drakestail. But tiny as he was, he had brains and spirit. It so happened that the king of the country had borrowed a hundred crowns from Drakestail and in the two years which had gone by Drakestail had not been paid. So one fine morning Drakestail, very spruce and fresh, dressed in his best, took to the road singing: "Quack, quack, quack! At last I shall get my money back!"

He had not gone far when he met Friend Fox, on his morning rounds. "Good day, neighbor," says Friend Fox. "Where are you off to so early?"

"I am going to the king for what he owes me."

"Oh! take me with thee!" says Friend Fox.

Drakestail said to himself as he thought, "One can't have too many friends." Aloud says he, "I will, Friend Fox, but going on all fours you will soon be tired. Make yourself quite small, get into my throat; go into my gizzard, and I will carry you."

"Happy thought!" says Friend Fox. He takes bag and baggage and presto! He is gone like a letter into the post.

Now Drakestail is off again, all spruce and fresh, still singing, "Quack, quack, quack! At last I shall get my money back!" He had not gone far when he met his lovely Lady Ladder, leaning on her wall. "Good morning, my duckling," says the lovely Lady Ladder. "Whither away so bold?"

"I am going to the king for what he owes me."

"Oh! Take me with thee!" says Lady Ladder.

Drakestail thought to himself, "One can't have too many friends." Aloud says he, "I will, Lady Ladder, but then with your wooden legs you will soon be tired. Make yourself quite small, get into my throat; go into my gizzard, and I will carry you."

"Happy thought!" says Lady Ladder. She takes her bag and baggage, and nimble! She is gone to keep company with Friend Fox. "Quack, quack, quack!" sings Drakestail, who is off again, all spruce and fresh. A little further on he meets his sweetheart, My Friend River, wandering quietly in the morning sunshine. "Thou my cherub," says River. "Whither so lonesome, with arching tail, on this muddy road this morning?"

"I am going to the king, you know, for what he owes me."

"Oh! take me with thee?" sings River.

Drakestail thought to himself. "One can't have too many friends." Aloud says he, "I will, My Friend River, but you who sleep while you walk will soon get tired. Make yourself quite small; get into my throat; go into my gizzard, and I will carry you."

"Happy thought!" says My Friend River. She takes bag and baggage and blou, glou, glou! She takes her place between Friend Fox and Friend Ladder. "Quack, quack, quack!" sings Drakestail, who is off again, all spruce and fresh. A little further on he meets Comrade Wasp's Nest, maneuvering his wasps in precision drills. "Well, good morning, friend Drakestail," said Comrade Wasp's-Nest. "Where are we bound, so spruce and fresh?"

"I am going to the king for what he owes me."

"Oh! Take me with thee!" says Wasp's-Nest.

Drakestail said to himself, "One can't have too many friends." Aloud says he, "I will, Comrade Wasp's-Nest, but with your battalion to bring along, you will soon be tired. Make yourself quite small; go into my throat; get into my gizzard, and I will carry you."

"By Jove! that's a good idea!" says Comrade Wasp's-Nest. And left file! He and his battalion take the same road to join the others. There is not much room, but by closing up a bit they manage.

Drakestail is off again, singing, and arrives in good spirit at the king's palace. The king sees Drakestail from a window of his courtroom. Remembering his loan, he orders the porter to admit Drakestail to the poultry-yard. Fancy how vexed Drakestail is when he finds himself in this yard with a flock of curious turkeys and chickens. "Quack, quack, quack!" calls Drakestail. "When shall I get my money back?"

"What is it he says? What does he want?" ask the curious poultry of one another as they look back at Drakestail. Finally, with a sign from the rooster, they rush at Drakestail all together to overwhelm him with pecks.

"I am lost!" says Drakestail to himself. Then he calms down and remembers his Friend Fox, and calls:

Reynard, Reynard, come out of your earth,
Or Drakestail's life is of little worth.

Friend Fox, who is waiting for these words, hastens out, throws himself on the wicked fowls, and quick! quack! he puts an end to them. In no time at all they are lying about the courtyard ready for the makings of a castle banquet. Drakestail, quite content, begins to sing, compellingly, "Quack, quack, quack! When shall I get my money back?"

The king, looking from the window, cannot believe what he sees. He orders the porters to throw this tail of a drake into the deep well there in the poultry-yard. It is done as the king commands. Drakestail is now in despair of getting himself out of such a deep hole, when he remembers his friend Lady Ladder.

> Ladder, Ladder, come out of thy hold,
> Or Drakestail's days will soon be told.

Lovely Lady Ladder, who is waiting for these words, hastens out and leans her two arms on the edge of the well. Drakestail climbs nimbly on her back, and hop! He is in the poultry-yard, where he begins to sing louder than ever. The king looks out from the balcony window and cannot believe what he sees. He becomes livid with rage. He commands that this tail of a drake be thrown into the furnace doors. It is done as soon as the king commands, but Drakestail is ready. He calls on his sweetheart, My Friend River.

> River, River, outward flow,
> Or to death Drakestail must go.

My Friend River hastens out, and errouf! She throws herself into the furnace which she floods. She then flows into the courtyard and into the hall of the palace. Drakestail, quite content, begins to swim and sing, compellingly, "Quack, quack, quack! When shall I get my money back?" The king looks out from the balcony window and cannot believe what he sees. He becomes more livid with rage. He commands that this tail of a drake be brought to the courtroom. Drakestail spruces himself up a bit while the two porters escort him to the courtroom as the king has commanded. "At last," says Drakestail, "he has decided to receive me."

Imagine Drakestail's terror when on entering the courtroom he sees the king as red as a turkey. Drakestail sees all the king's ministers attending him, standing with swords in hands. Drakestail thinks this time it is all up with him. Happily he remembers that there is still one remaining friend. He cries with dying accents:

> Wasp's-Nest, Wasp's-Nest, make a sally,
> Or Drakestail nevermore may rally.

"Bs, Bs, Bs—Bayonet them!" orders Wasp's-Nest as he rushes out with his battalion of wasps. They fly at the infuriated king and his ministers and sting them so fiercely that they jump pell-mell from the window and rest forever as statues on the cobblestones below.

Behold, Drakestail is much astonished, all alone with the wasps in the big throne room and master of the field. He cannot get over it. Nevertheless, he remembers shortly why he has come, and he examines the golden throne and velvet carpets. Meanwhile, people peering into the poultry-yard to see Drakestail's friends find the king and his ministers with their feet in the air. The people hurry into the palace to find out what has happened. On entering the throne room they see that there is already someone on the royal chair. They break out in cries of surprise and joy:

> The King is dead, long live the King!
> Heaven has sent us down this thing!

Drakestail, who is no longer surprised at anything, receives nobly the acclaim of the people and his many friends as if he had never done anything else in all his life. His friend, Lady Ladder, announces that Drakestail will make a rare king. His friends who know him reply that Drakestail is a more worthy king than the spendthrift who lies on the cobblestones below. With this the king's crown is rushed in by My Friend River and placed on the head of Drakestail. Oddly, it fits like wax. Thus Drakestail is crowned the king of the country. There is great cheering.

"And now," says Drakestail after the ceremony. "Ladies and gentlemen, and my very dear friend, let's go to supper. This has been a long two years. We are so hungry."

AN ARK IN THE WILDERNESS

Adapted by Geraldine Brain Siks
from The Holy Bible, King James version

Sir James G. Frazer explains: "Apart from all questions of its religious and historical import, the Bible is an epic of the world." A child's introduction to the Bible should be so satisfying that he will one day seek to read and discover for himself the rich heritage of great literature found in both the Old and New Testaments. The story of Noah appeals to children of all ages for dramatic interpretation. It is essentially a story of obedience to faith. Characterizations offer variety and opportunities for original interpretations. They fall into three areas: (1) Noah, his family and the "living things"; (2) the Voice of God; and (3) the witnesses. The action falls readily into the two settings of the wilderness and the Ark.

It came to pass on the face of the earth that men became as many as sands on the shore of a sea. God looked upon the earth and saw that the wickedness of man was great, and that every imagination in men's minds was continually that of evil.

God was sorry that He had made man to dwell upon the earth. It grieved Him to see hatred and wickedness among men, for He knew that only evil could come from evil. The voice of God spoke, "Behold, ye men of earth. I will destroy man whom I have created. I will destroy man and every living thing from the face of the earth; for I regret that I have made them."

In the midst of men's fighting and wickedness none heard the Voice save one old, listening man. He was named Noah. He was more than five hundred years old and, in the eyes of God, Noah was a good man, and his family, too, was good. Noah had a wife and three sons named Shem, Ham and Japheth, and each son had a wife.

Noah, who talked often with God, was not startled to hear God's voice, but he was startled to hear God's words. "Behold I will bring a flood of waters upon the earth to destroy the breath of life from all living things."

"From all living things?" asked Noah anxiously, for he was a righteous man, and he knew that the word of God was ever true.

The Lord spake again, "Noah, with thee I make a promise. Make an ark for thyself and thy sons and thy wife and thy sons' wives."

"An ark? Here in the wilderness—far from the sea?" Noah asked, for he wondered if he had heard correctly. He called to the wives and sons in the fields. As his family joined him, Noah told of the Lord's promise. While they stood in astonishment, Noah inquired of the Lord concerning the ark.

As the Lord spoke all heard clearly: "Make the ark of gopher wood and pitch it within and without. The length of the ark shall be three hundred cubits, the breadth of it fifty cubits and the height of it thirty cubits. A window thou shalt make in the top of the ark and there shall be rooms, and a lower, second and third stories."

Noah's wife and sons' wives were bewildered, but Noah and his sons set to work to make the ark according to the ways the Lord had commanded. While they worked curious men and women of little faith came to watch and to jeer at Noah and his sons. "What fools, what fools to build a ship upon the sands!" they repeated again and again in different ways with unruly tongues.

By the time the ark was built Noah was six hundred years old. Again the Lord spoke to Noah, "Of every living thing, of all flesh, bring two of every sort, male and female, into the ark, to keep them alive with you. Bring birds after their kind, cattle after their kind, and of every creeping thing of the earth after its kind. And take with you all food that is eaten and all seed and store it away."

Noah and his family did as God commanded. A crowd of evil merrymakers who camped in nearby tents to watch Noah's final preparations mimicked and jeered with rage and ridicule. Noah was sorry for these men but kept faithfully on with his work. When all was finished Noah and his family went into the ark. The onlookers shouted with scorn and laughed at Noah and his sons as they closed the door of the ark.

After seven days the windows of heaven suddenly opened. The fountains of the great deep sprung forth. Rain fell from a stormy sky. Water poured from above the earth for forty days and forty nights. As the waters increased the ark was lifted up and it went forth upon the face of the waters. Noah and all with him in the ark remained alive while the waters flooded the earth for an hundred and fifty days.

And in this time all the wickedness of the earth was destroyed as God had planned.

During the flood God watched over Noah and his family. At last He stopped the windows of heaven and the fountains of the deep. Rains ceased and the waters returned slowly from where they had come. As the waters went mysteriously away the ark rested upon the mountain of Ararat. Noah then opened the window and sent forth a raven which went to and fro and returned swiftly. Noah's son sent forth a dove but the dove found no rest for the sole of her foot, and she, too, returned. Noah knew then that the waters were yet upon the face of the whole earth.

After seven days the dove was sent forth again. She returned swiftly and in her mouth was a green olive leaf. Noah and his family rejoiced and the sons removed the door of the ark. When this was done God spoke saying: "Go forth from the ark. Bring every living thing that is with you of all flesh, birds and beasts and every creeping thing so they may multiply and grow abundantly upon the earth."

So Noah and his family and all living things went from the ark. They breathed the clean air. They rejoiced in the washed earth. They showed their thankfulness by building an altar and offering burnt offerings of clean birds and beasts. When the Lord smelled the sweet savor of the offerings He said: "I will never again curse the ground for man's sake, even though the imagination of man's heart is evil from his youth. Never again will I destroy all living things, as I have now done."

Noah and his family knelt down and thanked the Lord, for they both loved and feared Him. Amidst the rumblings of thunder the Lord spoke, "While the earth remains, seed time and harvest, cold and heat, summer and winter, and day and night shall not cease."

God then made a dark cloud to pass above the earth. "I do set my bow in the cloud," God vowed. "This bow of light shall be a token of my everlasting promise. No more shall waters become a flood to destroy man or life upon the earth."

Noah arose. He proclaimed aloud the glory of the Lord and His wonders to perform. As Noah spoke the bow brightened with light that lighted the darkness of the whole earth.

DAVID, THE SHEPHERD BOY

Adapted by Geraldine Brain Siks
from The Holy Bible, King James version

David's personality holds interest for almost everyone who studies it. His character appeals to children for dramatic interpretation, chiefly because of his strength in the Lord. When children are asked why David was probably chosen to be king, they mention most often his qualities of awareness, bravery, strength, kindness, and faith. Two distinct happenings in David's life are revealed in this story. David's action on the hillside provides understanding and motivation for the action which follows in the Bethlehem gathering for anointment.

David was a young shepherd boy. He was a good lad, strong in body, ruddy and good to look upon. He spent most of his time out in the open tending his father's sheep on the hillsides near Bethlehem. David was as brave as he was strong and he was ever watchful for wild beasts and birds of prey.

One morning as David practiced throwing stones in his sling he found that he could strike exactly the place for which he aimed. He was pleased with this reward for many seasons of practice, and he found joy in striking his mark again and again. At last he stopped to rest in the shade of a tree.

While he rested he gathered stones for his pouch. He picked up a black stone with a white streak around it. He looked at it closely as he wondered about a stone. He touched the earth. He marveled that it could bring forth grass and herbs and fruit trees like the flowering peach on the hillside. David knew that in time a peach flower would yield fruit from its seed. He looked to the sky and wondered about the great light shining there. Birds flew. David listened to their flight. He marveled that they were living creatures who could walk upon the earth and yet rise up with wings and fly through the air. Then he saw a butterfly. He smiled as he watched it swoop to the grass near a little creeping creature. David stood and looked out upon the beauty of the valley. "It is good," he said aloud. "God is great and greatly to be praised." He took up his harp and started playing. "I shall sing songs unto the Lord." As he played he praised the majesty of the morning.

At once David stopped his singing. He spoke aloud a deep thought which came often to him. "In the greatness of God's plan for grasses and all living creatures He must have a plan for every man. He must have a plan for me. But I do not understand it. Perhaps I too will be a soldier as my brothers are."

David looked at the grazing sheep, shook his head and spoke slowly as he thought, "My father grows old. Perhaps it is meant for me to always be a shepherd?"

David was so deep in thought that he did not hear the low roar in the thickets. He was alarmed by the sudden bleatings of the lambs. At once he saw a lion leap from the bushes, spring toward the flock and pounce on a little gray lamb. David rushed forward with his sling, took a stone from his pouch, aimed carefully and struck the lion on the head. The lion fell back stunned. David rushed forth, planning to strike the wild beast with his staff. The stunned lion sprang up, roared angrily and lunged toward David. But David's bravery and strength were with him. He struck the beast such a hard blow with his staff that the lion fell dead. The frightened lamb hurried to its mother. David looked at the savage beast and again at the flocks and said quietly, "I give thanks unto Thee."

David was startled at this moment to hear his father Jesse call to him. Looking toward the hillside, David saw that his father was dressed in his finest robes. With him was a neighbor. "Come, my son," Jesse called. "Our neighbor will watch the flocks. You must come as you are to Bethlehem."

"As I am? Behold the blood of the wild beast is upon me," David explained as he hurried toward Jesse.

"The prophet Samuel waits in the village. He comes to offer a sacrifice to the Lord and bids that all my sons be present," called Jesse sternly. "Your brothers have come from the king's army. The elders of the town are there. Come, we go in haste."

David was surprised at the news. He took up his harp, gave his staff to the neighbor as he thanked him, and then ran to join his father.

When David and Jesse came to the gathering the brothers smiled in greeting and David nodded in return, for he sensed the reverence which was upon the gathering. David was curious about the old prophet Samuel who stood apart from the others with a ram's horn in his hand and a young heifer beside him. Samuel studied the seven sons of Jesse and wondered which one he would anoint in the name of the Lord. Samuel nodded to Jesse and asked that he bid his sons pass by.

Eliab, the oldest son, was tall and noble looking. "Surely this handsome lad is the one whom the Lord would choose," Samuel said quietly as he questioned himself.

As Samuel wondered whether he should pour the oil upon Eliab's head, the voice of God spoke. Although the others did not hear, Samuel heard clearly, "Look not on his face, or on the height of his stature for the Lord seeth not as a man seeth. Man looketh on the outward appearance, but the Lord looketh on the heart."

Samuel bid Eliab pass by and the surprised elders looked at one another with question. Jesse called his next eldest son, Abinadab and bid him pass before Samuel. Again the Voice spoke, "Neither hath the Lord chosen this one." Samuel bid Abinadab pass by and the elders and the brothers exchanged glances of wonder. Jesse then called Shammah and his three younger brothers, and as each passed by, in turn, the voice spoke as before to Samuel.

Jesse then bid David pass by and Samuel heard the voice speak, "Anoint him, for this is he." Samuel took the horn of oil and poured it upon the head of David as he knelt down. "You shall be always a shepherd," said the prophet.

Jesse and the brothers and the elders were pleased, though they knew not the true meaning of that of which Samuel spoke. Only the wise prophet knew that the Lord had chosen David to be the next king of Israel. But David's soul sang with joy, for the Spirit of God came upon him and was with him from that day forward.

David rose and thanked Samuel and spoke to the others, "Let us rejoice and sing praises unto the Lord." As David played on his harp the others sang songs of His loving-kindness of the morning and of His faithfulness of the night.

David listened. He heard the mountains and hills and every living thing praising with song. He seemed at once to gain an understanding of the prophet's words. All listened in wonder as David struck the harp strings and sang a new song unto the Lord.

DAVID AND THE GIANT OF GATH

Adapted by Geraldine Brain Siks
from The Holy Bible, *King James version*

Children who dramatize earlier episodes of David's life look forward to David's heroic encounter with a giant armored in brass. David's characterization continues to hold strong appeal, chiefly because of his faith which brings bravery and action. For dramatization this tale is heightened by the unusual characterization of the giant and the contrast in reactions of the Philistines and the Israelites. Children never fail to respond to opportunities to develop the battle in this classic drama of faith. Older children enter into dynamic discussions as they plan characters, action, and reaction.

David kept his father's sheep for many seasons on the edge of the wilderness. During these days and nights he grew surer of his eye, surer of his aim, and his faith in God grew strong. David was troubled by the battles which took place between his people of Israel and their enemies, the Philistines.

There came a time when the Philistines gathered their armies on a mountainside for a battle with the Israelites at a place called Shochoh. King Saul and his men camped on the opposite hillside with a narrow valley separating the two camps. David's brothers were camped with

Saul's army, and as news of the battles reached David he was deeply troubled. He was puzzled about the giant Goliath of Gath who had joined the Philistines' camp. Goliath was a huge man, nine feet, nine inches tall and he wore a helmet of brass upon his head and heavy armor from his head to his feet. It was rumored too that a shield-bearer walked before him. The giant himself carried a huge spear twice as long and heavy as any man could carry.

David wished that he might go to battle, for he had no fear of any man. One morning he spoke aloud his thoughts: "If it be the will of the Lord, I shall someday see this giant of a man who is clothed in brass and swords, eager for killing."

That very day David was sent by his father to carry food to his brothers. David's heart beat fast as he hurried toward the soldiers' tents. He found his brothers talking with the captain on the ledge overlooking the enemy camp.

David called greetings and saluted as he approached. Eliab's anger was kindled at the sight of David. "Why do you come here?" he asked sharply. "With whom hast thou left those few sheep in the wilderness?"

David was surprised. "Our father sent me with parched corn and loaves of bread for you, my brothers. Here are cheeses, ten of them, some for the captain and his hungry men."

The captain was pleased and Eliab's anger was soothed. While David brought news of their father, the giant Goliath shouted from the opposite mountain, "I see you have set your battle in array. Choose a man, ye servants of Saul. Send him forth to fight with me."

The giant's thundering frightened Saul's men. Several fled in terror to their tents. The captain looked to see if any man stayed behind to accept the giant's challenge. When he saw their fear he called to the giant, "We wait for orders from our king."

"Let one of your men come this day to fight with me," shouted the giant. "If he kill me, the Philistines will be your servants. But if I should slay him, then ye shall be our servants.

David saw more of Saul's men hasten to their tents like frightened sheep running away from a roaring lion. David spoke to the fearful captain. "Who is this man that he should frighten the armies of the living God? Surely there must be one among us who shall slay this evil giant and taketh away the fear from Israel? Why does someone not go out and meet him?"

Eliab's fear turned to wrath. "Hark, how you speak, David. You begged to bring food to us, but you came only so you might see the giant. I know you."

David paid no heed to his brother's words, for he was more concerned about the giant and the fear of all the men. "O, captain, where is King Saul? I must speak with him."

"The king waits in yonder tent," the captain said as he turned to point out the tent to David. As the captain turned he was surprised to see Saul. "Behold, the king cometh," the captain said in honor.

David knelt as Saul approached. While the giant continued to shout, David spoke calmly. "Oh, King, let no man's heart fail because of a giant. I pray you, let me go and fight with this enemy. I have no fear, for the Lord is with me."

Saul's eyes measured David and the king spoke, "Thou art not able to go against this giant, for thou art but a youth. He is a man of war from his youth."

David stood upright and reached for his sling, "O, King, while I have kept my father's sheep in the wilderness I have grown strong and brave. With my sling and staff I have slain a lion and a bear. The giant shall be as one of them."

The king was curious about David's strength of body and spirit. "The giant is more than an animal. He is shrewd and trained for battle."

"Hear, O King, it was the Lord who delivered me out of the paw of the lion and out of the paw of the bear. I know in my heart that He will deliver me out of the hand of this giant."

Saul studied David and saw that the Spirit of God was with him. "Go then, my lad. Fear not, for I see that the Lord is with thee."

The captain and Eliab were amazed by the king's saying. They watched as Saul armed David with his helmet and armor. David girded himself with the king's sword and started forth. He stopped at once. "Hark!" called David to the king. "I cannot go with this sword and armor for I have not mastered them. They are yours. I must go in my own way."

David removed the armor, took his staff in his hand, and chose five smooth stones from the brook. He put them in his shepherd's bag, and with his sling in his hand he ran down the mountainside. He walked into the valley while Saul's men came from their tents to the hillside and watched in astonishment.

"What's this? What's this?" cried the captain to King Saul as he tried to persuade him to call David back. However, Saul called to the giant to let him know that they were answering his challenge. The giant strode downward to the valley with his shield-bearer going before him. When Goliath looked up and saw David running toward him, the giant was angered to see so young and fair a youth. "Am I a dog that thou comest to me with staves?" demanded the giant. "If thou should cross this stream to fight with me I will give thy flesh unto the fowls of the air and the beasts of the field."

David listened. He replied calmly, "Thou comest clothed in brass and with a sword and spear and shield. I come to thee in the name of the Lord of Hosts, the God of the armies of Israel."

The giant laughed in anger. "Lad, art thou mad? You speak of a god you cannot see. I speak of swords and spears."

The giant flourished his sword as David answered, "I have no fear of any sword. This day the Lord will deliver thee into mine hand. I will slay thee and take thine head from thee that all the earth may know there is a living God in Israel."

David looked at Saul and his armies on the hill above and then he looked at the many Philistines. He spoke as he raised his right hand and circled the hillsides in gesture. "Assembly of men, ye shall know that the Lord saveth not with sword and spear."

The wrathful giant came forward with his shield-bearer. David kept his eye fixed on the giant as he walked slowly backward to get a running start. David carefully placed a stone in his sling and ran suddenly forward as the giant lifted his spear to aim. David's eye was quick and his aim was true. David hurled the stone aimed at the giant's forehead. The stone struck its mark. The giant fell to the ground.

The two armies stood aghast as they watched the sudden happenings. As the shield-bearer stood helplessly, David took the giant's own sword and said, "I take thine head from thee, Goliath, in the name of the Lord."

As the Philistines watched they could not believe that their Giant of Gath was dead. They fled in haste, and the men of Israel, pleased with victory, arose and shouted as they ran after the Philistines.

David stood alone by the giant's body. As he listened to the fiery cries of battle David turned and looked to the high hills and called out unto the Lord.

JOSEPH THE DREAMER

Adapted by Geraldine Brain Siks
from The Holy Bible, King James version

Almost all children experience jealousy, faith, and dreams of self-esteem. These human traits, revealed so clearly in the conflict between Joseph and his brothers, motivate heated discussions when children are given opportunities to dramatize this and the following episode in this mighty drama. Children understand Joseph's faith and dreams, and they understand, also, the reason for the actions of Joseph's brothers. Many children are critical of the attitude and actions of Jacob as he seems to "spoil" and "favor" Joseph. In any event this tale tends to arouse respect for Joseph's innocence and faith. It motivates cogent dramatic interpretations. When older children dramatize events from Joseph's life they often read the story from the Bible, and the entire experience appears to reinforce a child's concept of divine faith. This episode provides another example of human drama in which acts of violence and deceit serve to produce suffering which leads gradually to compassion. Children talk about this story long after it has been dramatized.

Years ago there lived a lad named Joseph. He dwelt with his father

Jacob, his younger brother Benjamin, and his eleven older brothers. They lived in tents spread in a sheltered valley near Hebron in the land of Canaan. Joseph's older brothers were now young men who worked hard to tend the large flocks and herds which Jacob, the father, had gathered together. When the grass was fresh on the nearby hills the brothers herded the flocks near home, but at other times of the year they traveled to distant hills for greener pastures. Joseph spent much of his time caring for the littlest one, the babe Benjamin, since their mother was no longer living. At other times Joseph helped his father and brothers with planting and harvesting and working around the tents.

Joseph liked to work with his father, for then they could talk together about the Lord and his wondrous works. Of all his sons, Joseph seemed closest to Jacob's heart. There were many reasons, but above all Jacob saw that Joseph was good and faithful and thoughtful. Joseph looked often to the sky and the earth and exclaimed about the mystery of the Creator. Joseph's brothers scoffed at his wonderings but Jacob loved Joseph even more for his thoughts. "Deep calls unto deep," Jacob would tell the older sons whenever they grew impatient with Joseph. It seemed, too, that Joseph always did what was right, while at times his older brothers seemed bent on doing wrongful acts. Whenever Joseph asked his father why the brothers could not see the folly of their ways, the brothers grew angry. Over the years they became exceedingly jealous of Joseph.

One early morning as Jacob and his older sons were breaking bread together Joseph hurried from his tent. "I have dreamed two strange dreams," he called as he ran to join them. The brothers jeered, but Jacob saw that Joseph was radiant with astonishment. "Speak, my son, tell of your dreams," said the kind father.

Joseph was excited. As he spoke it seemed as if his dream was happening. "Look," he said, pointing to the grain fields. "Behold, we were binding sheaves, and lo, my sheaf arose. It stood upright, and behold, your sheaves stood upright. They gathered around and bowed down to mine."

The brothers looked at one another and flared up in fierce anger.

"Shalt thou, indeed, reign over us?" questioned Reuben, the eldest. "We bow down to you?" shouted Levi.

Judah scoffed as he thought upon the dream. "You be greatest among us in our father's family?"

Joseph answered kindly. "My brothers, I do not know. I only dream. But hark, I dreamed again. Behold I was standing alone in yonder field. Above in the morning sky the sun and the moon and eleven stars shone brightly. I looked upward and wondered at their daytime shining. And while I looked the sun and the moon and the stars bowed down to me."

The brothers were amazed at Joseph's boldness. Jacob was puzzled. He spoke out harshly. "What hast thou said, Joseph? You dream a dream of fools. Shall I and thy brethren come to bow down to thee? I do not understand, though I too dreamed in my youth." Jacob, immediately sorry for his harshness, walked straightaway to his tent and while he walked he thought. Levi and Simeon and the other brothers talked mockingly of the dreamer. Joseph walked slowly away from them and pondered all this in his heart, for he too wondered.

At this moment Jacob hastened from his tent. He carried a beautiful coat of many colors. His older sons watched as he walked toward them, but he called to Joseph. "Come, my son," Jacob said sternly. "Lo, I would honor you in the presence of your brothers. You see visions in your dreams."

Joseph was astonished as Jacob presented him with the coat of many colors. Joseph knelt down and thanked his father but this mark of favor angered the older brothers even more. Reuben spoke out for all the others as he rebuked his father. "You show favor to this dreamer, this sluggard who stays at home and never travels beyond the foothills? You would honor him above all the rest of us?"

"He will be honored. It is so willed," were the only words of the wise father.

The older brothers turned away in wrath and made haste to depart at once on their far journey with the flocks and herds, and they hated Joseph the more for his dreams and his honor. Joseph helped to round up the frolicking lambs. Joseph joined Jacob as the brothers started on their way. Joseph, who felt kindly toward them, called farewell and bid them a safe journey.

Jacob was troubled. He went into his tent to pray but Joseph stood on the hillside and watched his angry brothers depart. He understood their anger but he did not fully understand his dreams. He looked toward the hills and off to the holy mountain, for he knew he must talk with God.

TWENTY PIECES OF SILVER

Adapted by Geraldine Brain Siks
from The Holy Bible, *King James version*

Time passed. Jacob's older sons tended the flocks in a valley near Dothan which was ten days' journey on foot from Hebron. As the sun set the brothers gathered the flocks together and bedded them down while Reuben built a fire and made camp.

While the brothers came to warm themselves Simeon noticed a lone traveler walking toward them from a distance. The brothers shaded their eyes and peered curiously. It was not often that anyone journeyed on foot alone through the wilderness. "Hark," shouted the cruel Levi. "It is our blessed brother Joseph. He wears the coat of many colors."

"What, the dreamer?" asked Simeon as he squinted in the evening light.

Several of the brothers laughed sneeringly, revealing their quick annoyance at Joseph's arrival. "Behold the dreamer cometh!" Dan announced and the others chanted his words mockingly.

"Pray, why does he follow after us in his royal coat?" asked Simeon haughtily.

As the brothers watched Joseph hurry toward them their envy surged and they spoke their jealous thoughts with bitter tongues. "Hark now," said Simeon, building on their quick rebuffs. "Since our hearts are riled with jealousy and always will be, let us slay Joseph and be rid of him forever."

"Yea, yea!" shouted the brothers in quick agreement, all save Reuben, as they conspired against the dreamer.

"We will say some evil beast hath devoured him in the wilderness," Judah said, slyly winking to Simeon in enjoyment of his evil thought.

"Then, O then, we shall see what becomes of his mighty dreams," spoke the shrewd and generally silent Issachar.

Reuben was concerned. His strength was in his honor but he was as unstable as water. He wished he could reason with his brothers so they might see the evil in their plan, but he knew the wild power of jealousy. He seemed helpless in his desire. When Joseph was yet a short distance from them Reuben at last cried out. "My brothers," he said firmly. "If we should slay our brother we shall have his blood upon our hands forever. My black hair would change to white but my wicked thoughts would never change to good again. My heart would not let me sleep. I beg you. Let us not act hastily in that which we cannot right again."

"What's this? What's this, you coward? What would you do then?" came the sharp cries.

"Let us not be tempted here in the wilderness, away from sight of our father. Let us rather cast our brother into yonder pit," Reuben explained with a toss of his head. "Come, ye shall see what I mean."

The wrathful brothers followed Reuben to the nearby pit which was hidden by gnarled trees and vines. "Lo, it is bottomless," said Levi.

"Look," pointed Simeon. "It is dry and barren. There is neither water nor food in such depths, but room for bowing down. And for looking upward to the sun and moon and eleven stars!" The brothers laughed knowingly. Judah nodded. "Reuben speaks well. We shall cast the dreamer into this pit and leave him to his dreams.'

As the brothers talked among themselves Joseph ran down the rocky knoll and hurried toward them. "Greetings, my brethren," he called cheerfully. "You have traveled far. I bring bread and honey and news from our father, Jacob. He is well. He bids you start homeward."

The brothers listened to Joseph and accepted his gifts which he had carried on the long journey. Then, according to their hasty plan they talked Joseph out of his coat, tricked him into the pit and left him shouting from its depths as they strolled back to the fire to enjoy the gifts from their father.

Joseph was amazed. He called to his brothers and he listened. He then called to Reuben and asked him to think of their father. The brothers appeared not to listen to Joseph's pleadings but rejoiced in their cleverness as they feasted on bread and honey. Reuben and Judah could not bring themselves to join with the others. Judah sat silently looking into the fire, while Reuben wandered alone into the wilderness. Reuben planned to return in the darkness to help Joseph from the pit.

Suddenly the brothers stopped their laughing. They heard voices. They looked in the distance and saw a camel train coming down the hillside from Gilead.

"Behold, it is a company of Ishmeelites," said Levi. "No doubt they are traveling merchants carrying spicery and balm."

"Merchants," said Judah slowly with a sudden thought of Joseph. "Hark, my brothers, what profit is it if we leave our brother in yonder pit to die? Come, let us sell him to the Ishmeelite merchants. No doubt they will pay in silver."

"What's this? What's this? Sell him to merchants? Lo, what is this you say, Judah?"

Judah recognized their wrath. He answered their questions calmly. "Joseph is our brother. He is of our flesh. If he dies in yonder pit his death will be upon our heads forever. If we sell him into Egypt we will be free from him. Our hands will be clean. Our hearts will rest in peace."

"Lo, I understand," said Issachar. "He speaks of silver, my brothers. We shall have silver and be rid of the dreamer. Our heads will be as clear as the Nile."

Simeon and Levi nodded in quick agreement with Issachar as one after another rubbed his palms. The others agreed at once to Judah's plan. As the merchantmen on their camels drew close, Judah called to them. A bargain was made, and Joseph was sold for twenty pieces of silver. The merchants dropped a heavy rope into the pit and lifted

Joseph free. As Joseph mounted a camel's back he looked at his brothers and started to speak but shook his head and gestured in silent farewell. The brothers stood about uneasily and watched Joseph ride away toward Egypt.

As Judah shared the silver, darkness came quickly. Each brother gloated over his coins while they discussed the shrewd bargain. While they talked Reuben returned from the wilderness and stopped by the pit to secretly help Joseph. When Reuben called into the pit and there was no answer, a sudden terror came upon him. He shouted to his brothers in despair. "The child is not here. Our brother is dead or gone. How can we bear to tell our father?"

Reuben's brothers were calm in their secret knowledge of Joseph's whereabouts which they explained to him after they had enjoyed his misery. "Look," said Simeon. "We have Joseph's coat. We will take it to our father and tell him we found it in the wilderness as we returned homeward."

"Yea, we shall dip the coat in the blood of a young kid when next we kill one for our meat," said Levi.

Judah was cheerful. "Lo, Reuben, do you not understand? Goat's blood shall be on Joseph's coat. Joseph shall be safe in Egypt. We shall be free from thoughts of him. A seal be upon our lips forever."

Reuben nodded and the brothers relished their plan. They settled down by the fire while Reuben kept watch upon the night. He folded Joseph's coat gently. He looked eastward as he pondered on the trouble of the day and of the long night.

After ten days the brothers returned with the flocks to the vale of Hebron where Jacob waited anxiously. He saw them in the evening light and walked to meet them. Reuben hurried ahead carrying Joseph's coat. "This coat we have found in the wilderness," Reuben called, for his conscience nagged him. "Know you whether it be the coat of our brother Joseph? Pray where is he?"

Jacob was alarmed. He looked hastily at the coat and examined it. "It is my son's coat," he said fearfully. "An evil beast hath devoured him as he journeyed to you at my bidding."

Jacob wept. In his terrible grief he rent his garments. He could not be comforted. As the brothers listened to their father's sorrow, each one examined the truth within his heart. Yet each kept a seal upon his lips for fear of the others.

As the sun went down Jacob went into his tent. While the brothers watched him they suffered from the pangs of his grief and from stabs of jealous guilt for their wrongful deeds. Their heads which were once so high were withered now like grass. Thoughts of Joseph were with them and would be with them forever.

PROMETHEUS

Adapted by Geraldine Brain Siks from a Greek myth

> Prometheus, teacher in every art, brought the fire that
> hath proved to mortals a means to a mighty end.
> AESCHYLUS

Prometheus, the Fire-Bringer, has become a champion of man. He has become, also, a champion of children and youth whenever they have been guided into creative dramatizations of his story which reveals his heroism for the sake of man. Children sense the magnitude of Prometheus' character when they interpret the following episodes: fashioning of men; bringing fire to men; and receiving everlasting punishment. Children's imaginations are stirred when they decide how they may create the belief that they are formless earth, fashioned into statues of men to come alive to explore untouched frontiers.

Children have responded to the imaginative challenge of interpreting "the first blizzard and the first fires on earth." Excerpts from Richard Wagner's *Ring of the Nibelung* provide effective mood and rhythmic background for dramatic interpretation.

Years ago on Mount Olympus in the land above the sky lived the Greek gods and goddesses. They were ruled by the mighty Zeus, chief of all the gods. For many years, the Greek gods had been at war with the Titans, but now, once again, peace and happiness reigned on Mount Olympus. The Greeks had defeated the Titans who were sent to an everlasting prison in the nether world, below the earth.

Prometheus, a wise and gracious young Titan god, had recognized that the Greeks were fighting for the rights of beauty and goodness, whereas his Titans were fighting for power and might. Because of this Prometheus had joined Zeus and was a strong force in helping the Greeks defeat the Titans.

One morning Zeus and his sister Athena, the goddess of wisdom, strolled through the beautiful Olympus gardens. They enjoyed the trees and flowers in fresh blossom when Athena's quick eye suddenly caught sight of Prometheus. He was climbing on the Milky Way, which led from Olympus down to the earth.

"Prometheus," commanded Zeus. "Wait where you are. We must speak with you."

Prometheus was surprised at the command. "Indeed, your honor," he called and waited obediently on a star for Zeus and Athena to reach the Milky Way.

"We have watched you for several days," said Zeus. "Always you come out here."

The wise Athena spoke kindly, "We are curious to learn what interests you in the stars."

" 'Tis not the stars," Prometheus said honestly. "It is the earth below. Out here I can see the earth more clearly. Look, it is vast. No one seems to move about."

Zeus smiled with peculiar pleasure. "Athena and I have talked about your interest in the earth. We have considered a proper reward for your part in our victory over the Titans." Zeus nodded to the goddess to continue.

Athena spoke with conviction. "We recognize that you are wise as well as strong, Prometheus. You have shown, too, that you are kind."

With a triumphant gesture Zeus announced, "Prometheus, we have chosen you to go to the earth and fashion men from the soil."

Prometheus, who had been gifted with forethought, was astonished, and yet curious. "Your majesty, did I understand you to say that I was to fashion men from the soil? This is a great responsibility as well as an honor."

"Indeed, Prometheus. Mark me well," said Zeus mightily. "There are to be only men on earth—no women, no children. Do you understand?"

"I understand," Prometheus said slowly as he thought and looked below, for he was eager to be on his way to the place he had watched so often.

"Perhaps Athena has advice for you before you begin this important mission," Zeus said, wanting to impress Prometheus with the responsibility which he had been given.

"I have only this suggestion," said Athena. "Create man with a strong body, a strong mind and a gentle heart. Perhaps then, he will see the wisdom in beauty as well as in other necessities for living."

Prometheus listened closely and was ready to agree, but Zeus commanded further. "You may give man any gift except the gift of fire. Fire belongs to the gods alone. It must be kept here on Olympus. Remember this."

"I will remember," Prometheus nodded.

Zeus gestured. "Go, Prometheus. When you have created the men I will come and blow the breath of life into them."

Prometheus climbed swiftly down the stars and stepped to the earth. He walked around and looked for water. Then he knelt down and touched the soil. In his godlike way he worked with great speed to mix water and soil. With deft strokes he fashioned the first man. He gave him an upright stature so he could lift his head upward, rather than downward, as animals do. As Prometheus finished he spoke to his first clay statue. "I fashion you, Man the Builder."

Prometheus put grains of corn into the hands of his second creation and spoke, "I fashion you, Man the Sower and Reaper." Prometheus then looked around the earth and saw the deep forests. He fashioned a third statue. "You will be Man the Hunter," he said, putting a stone in the statue's hand.

Once again Prometheus scanned the earth, and he listened. He recalled Athena's words of wisdom. Deftly he made another statue. "You shall be Man the Musician. And you," he said as he fashioned another, "You shall be Man the Thinker."

Prometheus was pleased. He stepped outward to see the five men he had fashioned from clay. "They look like good men," he said. "I will seek the great Zeus to give them life."

From out of the nearby mist came a voice. "I am here, Prometheus." Zeus spoke as he and Athena walked into the clearing. "We have been watching and we are pleased."

The mighty Zeus blew the breath of life into the statues of man. In the silent mystery each man came slowly to life. Each moved and walked and discovered the power of his body and his mind. Zeus and Athena were pleased. They nodded approval to Prometheus and left him to enjoy mankind on earth.

Prometheus grew to care for them. He helped the hunter to make crude weapons and tools from bones and stones. He admired the patience of the builder, the industry of the sower, the bravery of the hunter, the sensitivity of the musician, and the curiosity of the thinker.

Days and months went by. One day high in sky there was a changing of seasons on Mount Olympus. Snow and wind came blizzarding down to earth. As it continued to storm the men grew cold, for Builder's stone house had no roof on it. The men ran through the forests looking for shelter. Prometheus saw that the men were in great distress. They were bitterly cold and hungry, for the snow had covered the harvest. The musical instruments were silent; man was too cold to think of anything except the cold chill of his body.

Prometheus watched the hungry men huddle behind tree trunks, out of the wind. Prometheus felt compelled to help them. "Man needs fire. Man cannot live without fire," he said quietly. He called out in desperation. "Athena, goddess of Wisdom, I ask for help. What shall I do for the men who suffer?"

Athena spoke from the sky. "I see, Prometheus. I have watched and realize that man needs fire to warm himself and cook his food."

"But fire has been forbidden by the mighty Zeus. Remember his words?"

"Tell me, Prometheus. How much do you care about these men?" asked Athena.

"I care with all my heart. I care so much what happens to them," said Prometheus with great compassion.

"Do you care enough to accept the punishment which the mighty Zeus will surely bring upon you?"

"Indeed, I care that much," called Prometheus. "I must help them, for I made them. I will be punished."

"Very well," said Athena. "Know full well that Zeus will be fiery in his wrath, but I will help you find fire if you so desire."

"I must bring fire for them," said Prometheus as he hastened to join Athena. The storm raged on. The men ran from the trees to an icy cave and huddled together to keep warm. Prometheus, spurred by his compassion returned with godlike speed. From the sun he brought a torch of fire which he carried in a hollow wand. In great haste he gathered leaves and branches and lighted the first fire on earth. "This is fire!" called Prometheus to his men as the flame caught and began to blaze. The men were puzzled. They stayed in the cave and watched. They could not understand how the fire could spring from dead branches and leap into flowers of light.

"Come, warm yourselves," called Prometheus. The men came closer but they were afraid, for the fire seemed mysterious. Prometheus beckoned to them to come closer. The men obeyed and found that the fire was warm and yet it had a sharp bite. "It is fire. It comes from the sun in the sky," explained Prometheus as he gestured. "Come closer. It will help you and yet it will harm you. You must learn to use fire with care."

Soon the men began to enjoy the fire with its peculiar warmth and friendly glow. They brought branches while Prometheus lighted new fires. Prometheus worked in haste. He taught the men how to use the fire. With his godlike power he showed them how to cook food, to place fire inside the stone cave, to melt the hollow wand to make a plowshare.

Suddenly the winter storm stopped but a greater storm shook the earth. It was the storm of Zeus. He was furious in his wrath against Prometheus. He strode into the clearing where the fires were flaming. With him came Hephaestus, the blacksmith of the gods, and his two giant servants, Might and Force. They carried a heavy chain, a forge, and hammers.

"You have disobeyed," thundered Zeus.

"Yes," answered Prometheus. "I ask your pardon, mighty Zeus. I wronged you because I love mankind and could not let the men suffer. Punish me as you will."

Zeus replied. "Once a gift has been given it cannot be taken away. Man shall always have fire. As for you, Prometheus, you are a god and cannot die. You shall be bound with a chain to yonder crag. You will be bound forever. You will freeze with the snows of winter and burn with the suns of summer. You will serve as a sentinel to those who dare to disobey the sacred laws. Go, Prometheus, to suffer for your wrongdoing."

Prometheus spoke forthrightly to Zeus. "I take my punishment for my mind and heart are now at peace."

Zeus strode away to the sky. The men watched silently, in agony because they were helpless against the power of the gods. Their hearts were filled with loving-kindness for Prometheus as they watched Hephaestus lead the great Prometheus on his way.

PANDORA

Adapted by Geraldine Brain Siks from a Greek myth

This story was suggested by Barbara Salisbury.[10] Mrs. Salisbury says: "This story has an impact which reaches eight-year-olds and on through adulthood. Whether it is integrated with a unit on mythology or played just because it is a good story, the powerful drama it sets forth is inescapable. Here is a story full of challenges which children like to meet: to create the penetrating forces of evil, tightly imprisoned and suddenly released; the single shaft of Hope which can render evil powerless; the gods with their very human characteristics; and to answer the provocative question raised by Zeus at the end. The depth of understanding and the detail with which this story is interpreted is limited only by the level of maturity of the participants in

[10] Mrs. Salisbury is a creative dramatics teacher in the School of Drama, University of Washington, Seattle, Washington.

combination with the guidance by the teacher. Selections from Moussorgsky-Ravel's 'Pictures at an Exhibition' provide appropriate background mood for dramatic interpretation."

Zeus, the mighty ruler of the Greek gods, was troubled. His was the agonizing trouble of envy. As he sat upon his throne in the clouds and looked down to earth his heart was heavy. He saw Epimetheus, the brother of Prometheus, showing the men new uses for fire, the gift which Prometheus had stolen from the gods. Zeus pondered, as he had for many months, on a plan which might serve to lessen man's interest in this rare mystery of fire. At last Zeus came to a decision about his plan.

On this particular morning he called Hephaestus out to the cloud for a secret meeting. Hephaestus, blacksmith of the gods, came with giant swiftness and was greeted by Zeus in a jovial mood.

"In my mind, I have imagined a most glorious thing," said Zeus cunningly. "It is a gift for the men on earth. It is new, the like of which has not yet been seen by gods or men. I ask you, Hephaestus, to use your utmost skill, for you are to fashion this idea which waits to be born."

"An idea?" questioned Hephaestus. "Of what shall it be fashioned?"

"Of all the beauties of the earth," Zeus answered. "You shall mix together all things lovely, good, and kind. But mark me, as you mingle each beauty you shall mix therein the exact opposite of each. This law must be honored. Each beauty must be balanced with its opposite."

Hephaestus nodded with enjoyment as Zeus explained further and confided quietly the remainder of his plan. "Mighty Zeus, your plan is magnificent! Shall I go to earth this day to fashion this glorious mystery?" inquired Hephaestus.

"Aye, go in haste. Go far away from Epimetheus and his men. Epimetheus is different from his brother. Prometheus is gifted with forethought while Epimetheus is gifted with after thought. If Epimetheus should watch you and think too long about this unusual gift, he might not accept it so willingly. He thinks slowly, but nonetheless he thinks."

Hephaestus nodded and summoned his servants Might and Force. They came at once, listened to Hephaestus' command, and the three of them strode down the milky way to the beautiful earth. Hephaestus bid his servants gather at once the fairest of the fair, along with their exact opposites. While the servants searched with godlike speed, Hephaestus started to mingle the earth's black soil with fresh, white snow. His servants returned with such opposites as a storm's violence and the gentleness of a butterfly, the industry of an ant and the laziness of the locust, and a peacock's squall and the music of rippling water. As his servants continued to bring opposites Hephaestus mixed all substances together and molded them into the shape which Zeus had described secretly. Hephaestus' work was done as swiftly as a flame leaps upward. His servants stood by in amazement to see what Hephaestus had fashioned, but Hephaestus was puzzled by the outcome.

Suddenly Zeus appeared as planned. With him came his delegation of cheerful gods and goddesses escorted down from Mount Olympus by Hermes with his winged sandals. The two goddesses were Aphrodite, goddess of Love, and Athena, goddess of Wisdom, with her dazzling owl. As Zeus admired the new creation, Hephaestus spoke, "Mighty Zeus, it is no new thing we have fashioned here. It appears as if we have made a young Athena."

"Nay," called Zeus knowingly. "It is not a goddess. Rather, it is the first young woman on earth. A child she seems to be. She is as beautiful as a lily that bloomed this morning in the cloudy mist on Olympus."

Hermes and the goddesses were curious. They agreed with Zeus that Hephaestus had created a beautiful delight. They watched in amazement as Zeus blew the breath of life into the statuesque form. "Behold! The first young woman on earth! I shall call her name Pandora, the All-Gifted!"

As the goddesses and Hermes cheered for Pandora's moment of

birth, the young Pandora awakened slowly and look curiously at those who called, and then she looked at the beauties of the earth around her.

The shrewd Zeus suggested that each one present a gift to the young Pandora on this day of her birth. The suggestion was accepted favorably and Hephaestus took a flowering branch from a nearby tree, fastened it into a crown and wafted it into a jeweled tiara for Pandora. Aphrodite gave a rare gift which she found on the earth to symbolize love, while Athena and her owl presented a gray feather with dazzling light. Hermes found an appropriate gift to symbolize the quality of swiftness. Zeus concluded the ceremony by presenting the gift of curiosity, symbolized in a small wooden chest which he had carried with him. The chest aroused curiosity, for it had two serpents carved into its wooden lid and it was tied with a golden cord in a double knot. After Pandora had examined the chest, Athena asked if she might see it. As Pandora handed the chest to Athena her first words were those of appreciation for the gifts, followed by words of curiosity about the chest.

Zeus, alert to Athena's wisdom and not wanting his shrewdness to be disturbed in any way, announced his decisive plan with gusto: "Pandora shall be sent at once as a gift to Epimetheus. Although we punish Prometheus for taking our gift of fire we bear no malice toward Epimetheus and the men he teaches. We send the beautiful Pandora as a token of our friendship. Hermes, you shall escort Pandora to Epimetheus without delay."   •

Hephaestus, Aphrodite, and Hermes were pleased, but Athena and her owl wondered about Zeus' plan. Hermes took Pandora gently by the hand. Pandora nodded kindly to thank Zeus and the others and bid them farewell as she mounted upward with Hermes and disappeared swiftly in flight. Zeus and the others chanted farewells and good wishes—all save Athena, who remained silent as she wondered on what was yet to be.

Epimetheus was resting in the open courtyard of his cottage when Hermes arrived with Pandora. Epimetheus was so startled to see the beautiful Pandora that he did not notice when Hermes disguised himself as an old man. Epimetheus listened closely to explanations which the old man brought from Zeus. Epimetheus was deeply impressed by the rare gift of Pandora and was impressed, too, by the warning Hermes gave concerning the carved chest which Pandora carried. "It comes as a dowry with Pandora but it shall remain closed forever. Open never. Open never." Hermes warned in his voice as old as ages past.

Epimetheus was astonished when the old man disappeared as mysteriously as he had come, but Epimetheus' interest turned entirely to Pandora. Although he did not know that she had been given the gift of curiosity he noticed that she looked and listened to the beauties of the earth which surrounded the cottage. He watched as Pandora fashioned plates and cups from broad leaves. He saw her arrange fruit and berries upon the plates. He saw her make music by blowing on reeds. He saw her dance gracefully as she followed blue butterflies in flight.

Suddenly Pandora's curiosity led her back to seek the chest in the courtyard. She picked it up to examine it closely. As she tugged at the knot, Epimetheus reminded her of the old man's warning. Epimetheus saw that it was difficult to explain to the young woman, for the more he spoke the more curious Pandora was to open the chest. Epimetheus, who seemed to be wise when it was too late, realized now that this gift could bring no good. He regretted that he had accepted it, for Pandora's curiosity would not ease. "Do you not long to know what gift it is that the ruler of the gods has bestowed upon us? Surely it is no ordinary gift. Come, let us open the chest together," Pandora insisted.

Epimetheus spoke kindly. "You cannot imagine how lonely it has been here on this vast earth with only men and fire. You are a bringer of happiness. Since we have been warned not to open the chest, it causes me to believe that we may be punished for disobedience as my brother Prometheus was. To have our happiness disappear almost as soon as it has come causes me to think we should bury the chest deep in the ground and forget about it forever."

Pandora laughed at his suggestion. "Bury it? Bury that which may bring us even greater enjoyment than all the mysteries which surround us?"

Epimetheus wanted to persuade Pandora to forget her determined desire. "Come, Pandora," he called as he started through the trees to a spring of water. "Bring the cups which you have fashioned. There is cool water bubbling forth from the earth."

Hardly was Epimetheus out of sight when Pandora laid her hands upon the chest. As she looked at it wondering what she should do, she believed she heard faint voices calling from within. A small voice and then another seemed to call to her, "Open—Pandora. Open—open."

Pandora's curiosity mounted. She moved back in surprise. She looked anxiously to see if Epimetheus were in sight. Then she hurried back to the chest and reached for the golden cord. Again she listened. She heard the voices call again: "Open, Pandora, open. Free us. Free us."

Pandora was exceedingly curious. Who could be calling her? What could be in the chest? What had Zeus, the greatest of the gods, placed there for her to find? Who cried to be free? As the voices continued to call, Pandora tugged at the cord. She untied the knot which seemed to give way easily to her eager fingers. She remembered the words of Epimetheus and of the old Hermes. She then decided she would not open the box, even if the cord were untied. Again the voices called. Suddenly Pandora knew what she would do. She would take one quick peek inside the lid to satisfy her curiosity. Then she would close it, join Epimetheus and forget about it forever.

Pandora raised the lid slowly. Suddenly it sprang open! Out flew a swarm of black-winged creatures. They swarmed around Pandora swiftly and sharply, buzzing and shrieking. As they flew at her with their stinging and biting Pandora cried out in fear and pain. She called to Epimetheus as she tried to fight them off, but when they did not go away she crouched down, covering her head as she tried to ward them off. Pandora's cries brought Epimetheus running back to the courtyard. The creatures left Pandora for a moment to strike at him in their wild rhythmic swarming. As the creatures flew out into the courtyard they changed in size from small winged sprites with venom in their tails into huge, shadowy figures. Each changed into a particularly gruesome form.

"Who are you?" Pandora shrieked in fear. Epimetheus joined her by the chest for he, too, was frightened.

"We are Troubles!" called a bold one. "Troubles!" echoed the others in a wild chant.

"We take up our dwelling here on earth. We remain forever." "Forever," echoed the others as they circled Pandora and Epimetheus in a frenzied rhythmic dance.

"Who did you say you were?" questioned Pandora again, for her curiosity would give her no rest.

As each trouble called out his name, Pandora shuddered to think of such evils on earth as Disease, Sorrow, Pain, Hate, Poverty, Poison, Prejudice, Deceit, and Death. As each one spoke the others cheered with fury. "We have been sent by Zeus to dwell with men forever," spoke the bold leader. "We shall leave you now to seek all men," he laughed as he joined with the others in eager frenzy. "We shall follow man, for we are his everlasting troubles."

The shadowy evil figures danced wildly and chanted as they followed their bold leader in search of man. When Pandora saw the ugly troubles move out into the beautiful earth she cried tears of shame, for she realized that she had brought trouble to the earth. Epimetheus tried to comfort her, not from the snarling stings, but from the deeper pain which was in her heart.

In the midst of her suffering Pandora was startled to hear a soft voice. It called from inside the chest. Epimetheus heard and was puzzled too. They listened closely while the pleading voice called clearly, "Open, Pandora. Open."

Epimetheus wondered whether it would be wise to have the earth burdened with even one more trouble, but Pandora, in her curiosity, insisted that she could recognize a gentleness in the pleading voice. They listened carefully as it called again and again. At last with Epimetheus' consent Pandora lifted the lid of the chest.

Out fluttered a small-winged creature, of delicate, frail beauty. The ugly troubles hovered back to see the creature. They screamed and fled in haste at the sight of her as she flew after them somewhat like a butterfly. "Who are you?" called the curious Pandora.

The creature returned to the courtyard to speak to them.

"I am Hope. I come by the wisdom of Athena," said the small winged creature. As she spoke she grew into a shadowy figure of radiance and majesty.

"I will dwell on the earth forever," she said. "Hope will always be near in the midst of trouble," she said with understanding. "There will be times when you and your fellow men will think I have vanished. But if you believe, I shall find you when you least suspect it. When you need me, believe in me. I may be far away but I shall come at last and show you the faint glimmer of my wings. This is my way—the way of Hope."

Hope, in her mysterious strength, ventured forth upon the earth. She followed after the Troubles who had gone ahead of her, for that was ever to be her way. As Pandora and Epimetheus watched in silence a new feeling came into their hearts.

High on his cloud on Mount Olympus, Zeus was puzzled. As he looked down he could not understand how it had happened that Hope had appeared on earth to dwell forever in the hearts of troubled men.

DEMETER AND PERSEPHONE

Adapted by Geraldine Brain Siks from a Greek myth

Children are impressed by the imaginative explanation of the seasons of summer and winter as set forth in this ancient Greek myth. Strong response comes in children's 'dramatic interpretations of Mother Demeter, Persephone, Hades, Hermes, and the water nymph. Children have expressed freely through dance the different forces of nature in symbolic emotions of joy, sorrow, grief and happiness. Response has revealed imaginative interpretations of rain, wind, rivers, shadows, ghosts, famine, frost, sun, and light. Excerpts from Stravinsky's *Rite of Spring* provide effective mood and rhythmic background for dramatic interpretation.

On an island in the bluest of seas lived the goddess Demeter. She was the mother of every growing thing, and had majestic power over the tallest of trees and the smallest of grasses. It was the kind Demeter who caused the lands to flower and the fields to harvest.

Demeter had one daughter named Persephone. She was as fair and beautiful a maiden as ever dwelt upon the earth, and Demeter loved her dearly. Persephone was known throughout the lands as the Maiden of Spring, for everywhere she went she brought a spirit as fresh as first violets after snow.

One day when the sun was high in the sky Demeter escorted Persephone and her maiden companions to a flowery glen among the trees and rocky ledges. "This is a secret glen," said Demeter. "You will be safe from all harm here, my daughter."

"It is beautiful and fragrant," Persephone called as she and her friends admired its rare beauty. "Never have I seen white flowers that looked like stars before! And look—golden lilies by the bluest of lakes!"

Demeter was pleased to hear Persephone and her friends exclaim over the beauty she had created for them. "The stars are called narcissus," spoke Demeter. "They are for you and your friends, Persephone. You may gather flowers while I hasten to the other side of the earth where fields lie barren. When I return we shall feast on nectar and ambrosia."

"Thank you, thank you!" called Persephone and her companions. As Demeter went swiftly on her way Persephone and the maidens filled baskets and their skirts with beautiful flowers. They called to one another to see and to smell rare flowers which were new to them.

Suddenly a sound like thunder shook the silence of the glen. Persephone and the maidens were startled and ready to run, but just as suddenly the earth near the ledges opened before them. Charging upward from the chasm came four shiny black steeds pulling a golden chariot. Riding in the chariot was Hades, Ruler of the Region of the Dead from the Underworld. Persephone and the maidens were astonished to see the bold Hades and they watched curiously. He wore shining silver armor and a silver crown over his long black hair. He circled the glen in his chariot and then drove straight toward Persephone. As the steeds charged toward them, Persephone and the maidens screamed and then ran hastily in every direction. The bold Hades reached outward to catch Persephone by the wrist and pulled her into the chariot. As she screamed for help Hades held her wrists with one hand and with the other he drove his fiery steeds straight through the earth, which opened before them. The lovely Persephone disappeared into the Underworld.

Persephone's cries for Demeter echoed through the silence of the glen as the maidens hurried out from the trees to look at the earth which had mysteriously opened and closed for the chariot. They were fearful for Persephone and even more fearful of Demeter. "Mother Demeter will be angry with us, for she loves Persephone more than any living thing on earth," said one of the maidens.

"We must not be here when she returns," said another. "She has power over all life." The maidens hurried to hide in a faraway cave, while the cries of Persephone continued to echo.

Far away Demeter heard. She returned to the glen with the swiftness of wind. She looked anxiously and called for Persephone as she hurried through the glen. Demeter called aloud to the birds, sky, and earth, entreating anyone who might know to tell her why Persephone cried for help. Demeter listened. There was no reply except faint echoes and the silent wilting of flowers, trees, and all living things in the outdoor world.

Suddenly the waters of the lake stirred and bubbled. A little blue nymph leaped out and onto the bank. "Demeter, great mother, I am the Water Nymph. I come from the depths of the earth. I saw your daughter seated on a throne at the dark king's side. She is beautiful in splendor, but her face is white like the the star flowers at your feet."

The little nymph answered quickly the many questions Demeter asked. "Good mother, I must return to the water," the nymph said hastily. "I can stay on earth no longer."

At once the nymph leaped into the lake and swam away. Demeter was beside herself with fear for Persephone. She sat on a large stone and thought aloud in her helplessness, for a deep sorrow filled her heart. "I must find a way to get Persephone back to earth if it takes the time of all seasons."

Demeter wept. The evening sky wept gently with her in her sorrow.

Meanwhile down in the Underworld the shrewd god Hades tried to win the heart of Persephone so that he could proclaim her queen of the dark region. Every day for more than three months he had tried different ways. This day Persephone was seated on an ebony chair on a silver dais in an open clearing among leafless trees. Surrounding the dais were shadows, ghosts, and souls waiting for punishment or paradise. Just beyond the dais flowed three rivers—the River of Woe, the River of Wailing, and the River of Fire.

Hades commanded each one—shadows, souls, and rivers—to speak to Persephone. Each spoke, in turn, and entreated her to stay and bring her brightness into everlasting darkness.

Persephone was understanding. "Darkness always brings loneliness," she said. "You honor me by wanting me to be your queen of light and enlightenment. I could learn to be happy here were it not for the rightness of life's honorable laws. You see, my mother Demeter loves me as all good mothers love their children. I could not be happy here, for I know my mother is unhappy there."

Hades was cunning in his response. "Very well, Persephone," he said patiently. "We shall feast. Perhaps we will find a way one day to convince you that your mother does not long for you. All children must leave their parents and forget them. You cannot stay with your mother forever."

Persephone wanted to challenge his thought but realized the wisdom of silence. Servants brought silver trays of beautiful fruit to Persephone and Hades. Persephone had not eaten any food since coming to this region, and the sight of fresh fruit made her hungry. "Eat of the beautiful pomegranate," said the sly Hades. "It is radiantly red like your beautiful lips."

Persephone examined the pomegranate closely to see that its outer skin had not been pierced, for she did not completely trust this proud god. She then peeled off the skin, loosened four pomegranate seeds and ate them slowly. Persephone looked up to see Hermes, the messenger of the gods, who had arrived mysteriously with the music. Hermes explained that he had been sent from Zeus, ruler of all gods. Hermes was to bring Persephone back to Demeter on this very day. "Famine rules the frozen earth," said Hermes. "No seed springs forth. Fields are idle. Demeter grieves day and night. Zeus commands that Persephone return this day."

Persephone was both happy and sad with Hermes' news of her mother. Hades was angered. "Persephone cannot return. She has eaten food of the Underworld."

"What food did she eat?" asked Hermes.

"Pomegranate," said Hades, pointing to the tray.

"Only four seeds, good Hermes," said Persephone.

"I see," said Hermes uneasily, as he thought to himself. Acting in the name of Zeus, he commanded, "Persephone will return to earth with me, but because she has eaten four seeds she shall come back to this region for four months of each year."

"'Tis a fair agreement," said Hades, for he knew it had to be.

"I shall return when the dark season is come," said Persephone as she rose and bid farewell to Hades and souls, shadows, and running rivers.

Hermes and Persephone traveled as swiftly as the sun back to the earth. Demeter hurried forth to meet her daughter and as Persephone sprang into the arms of Demeter, light brighter than sunlight radiated her happiness. Demeter called to every growing thing to awaken and rejoice. Grasses, leaves, and flowers appeared as silently beautiful as a rainbow follows a storm. Fresh violets lifted their heads above melting snows and birds and rivers sang songs of joy throughout the land.

THE DEATH OF BALDER

Adapted by Geraldine Brain Siks from a Norse myth

The ancient Norse explanation of winter and summer is among the most magnificent in all mythology. It is a story which all children should hear when they become curious about the seasons and other phenomena of nature. This version has been dramatized by groups of older children experienced in creative dramatics. Unusual interpretations have been motivated by the following episodes: (1) Balder's revelation of his dream; (2) Frigga's ceremony of promise; (3) Balder's enjoyment of the weapons' sport; (4) Loki's disguise with Frigga and Hode; and (5) the Aesir ceremony of tribute to the dead. Excerpts from Richard Wagner's *Ring of the Niebelung* have been effective in heightening dramatic interpretations.

High in the blue of the sky dwelt the Norse gods and goddesses in their beautiful land known as Asgard. Odin was their wise All-Father and Frigga the good Queen Mother.

Balder was Queen Frigga's youngest and dearest son and he was the best-loved god in all Asgard. He was known as the god of spring and light, the god of peace and beauty. Wherever the golden haired Balder went his happy spirit brought a freshness of springtime, not alone to the gods but to all nature.

One warm summer morning, every living thing awakened with the sunrise and waited anxiously for Balder to awaken and stroll in the wide courtyard overlooking the broad outdoors. They waited for him to come and greet the new day with his particular salutation. It was the third morning that Balder had been in deep sleep and failed to awaken and arise with the sun. King Odin and Queen Frigga, who sensed that Balder was not his usual cheerful self, waited for him on the golden benches in the open courtyard of Valhalla.

At last a sudden singing of the birds and sudden calling of the animals announced Balder's arrival. Flowers and trees swayed gracefully as he strolled out of the castle with vigor and enjoyment to rejoice in the newness of this day. He greeted his father and mother and the wise Odin studied him closely as he saluted the beauties of the morning. "All is not well with you, my son," spoke Odin kindly.

"I find a deep sadness in your eyes. Pray tell us what troubles you, for together we may find a way to ease your sorrow," said the anxious Mother Frigga.

Balder hesitated. He did not want to worry them but he was deeply fearful. However he spoke with honesty. "I did not plan to tell you, but since you have inquired I shall call for Nanna, my gentle wife. Then I will tell what troubles me."

As Balder spoke he gestured to the anxious Nanna who was waiting inside the castle. She came in haste, for she, too, was concerned.

Balder spoke. "There is a heavy shadow on my heart."

"A shadow?" asked Queen Frigga in alarm.

"What kind of shadow, pray?" Nanna asked.

"Explain what you mean, my son," spoke the All-Father.

It was then that Balder told of his three strange dreams. So vivid was his telling that the three listening believed they were seeing that which had frightened the brave Balder as he slept. On the first night a dark cloud moved over Asgard and covered the sun. It was a never ending cloud that would not drift away. All Asgard was shrouded in a lonely mist. In Balder's second dream the cloudy mist remained and the sun no longer smiled upon Asgard. Flowers and trees withered. Birds, beasts, and fish were fearful and still, and throughout Asgard there was weeping and sadness. In his third dream Balder found that the cloud mist grew black and the awful loneliness spread with a wind which wailed a weird message:

> The sun is no more
> The spring is no more
> Joy is no more
> Balder the Beautiful
> Has journeyed to Hela.

Odin was shocked and angered but Queen Frigga, who loved Balder, was more frightened than Balder himself. "This cannot be," said the queen calmly. "You shall not die, my son. You are dear to all Asgard. I shall command every living thing to protect you."

"However shall you do this, good mother?" asked Balder.

"This will be impossible," King Odin said, for he knew the way of evil. But Frigga was a queen of action. She sounded commands to her servants to call all the gods and goddesses, all living things from the sky, the earth, and the sea to come to the great courtyard at Valhalla.

She commanded, too, that all stones and metals, air, fire, and water, all kinds of weather and all illness come in haste to the courtyard.

Frigga's commands spread like winds through Asgard. Representatives came out of obedience and curiosity. Balder and Nanna watched them assemble on the open courtyard. When all had gathered, Queen Frigga told of Balder's dreams. She pleaded with the gods and goddesses to give their promise that nothing should injure her son. Thor, the eldest son, was first to shout his faithful promise. A great shout arose from all the gods and goddesses as they pledged a solemn oath. They continued to chant with spirit: "Balder, our Balder. Never shall we harm him."

Queen Frigga then spoke to the earthly creatures—beasts, reptiles and insects. They promised willingly that they would never harm the good Balder. "Not with claws or teeth or poison fangs or stings will we touch Balder," answered their spokesman.

The good queen spoke next to the birds of the air and the fishes of the sea. "We promise. We will never harm Balder. Not with beak or talon, bite or sting will one of us touch him," they chanted.

Frigga spoke next to the things of the earth—trees, plants, stones and metals. "We promise! We promise!" echoed the things of the earth. "Never, in any way shall we harm Balder."

Queen Frigga spoke next to the mysteries of gods and men. "Fire, water, air, weather, and disease, you have heard my plea. What is your answer?" And the mysteries, too, promised never to harm Balder. A massive cry came from each and everything as the ceremony came to an end. "Long live Balder! Long live the god of spring and life!" they chanted.

Balder was hopeful. In his kind way he thanked them, for he was deeply moved by their compassion. Queen Frigga thanked them as they moved slowly away from Valhalla and back to their places in Asgard. The queen then spoke to Balder, "I will travel throughout Asgard, step by step, I will get a further promise from anything I may have missed. Nothing shall pass my notice. Then, at last, we will again have peace within our hearts."

The anxious mother set forth and traveled step by step for days and nights. From everything she received the same ready promise.

Upon her return there was great rejoicing on Ida Plain. The gods had gathered together on their great playground to celebrate their love for Balder. They invented a game which offered rare sport to prove that Balder was safe from the bite of death. Balder stood on a high mound in the center of the plain. The gods stood around him in a great wide circle, each god with a supply of weapons. Each, in turn, threw an axe, hurled a stone, shot an arrow, hurled a spear or struck a sword straight at Balder's heart. The sport brought great delight when each weapon fell as if bewitched and never so much as touched him. Laughter drew a crowd of onlookers. Hode, the blind brother of the gods, sat beneath a tree on the edge of the playground to listen to the merriment. Frigga watched the game with peculiar interest from a tower window. The gods were roused to cheering when Thor threw his mighty hammer at Balder and it glanced from Balder's shoulders as if it were winged.

While the merriment was at its height, Loki, the god of mischief, arrived. He edged his way into the crowd of onlookers to watch the proceedings. In truth Loki was a giant, an enemy of the gods, but he had forced himself among the gods so often that he was considered by many to be one of them. Loki was a sly, merry fellow, full of pranks and jests, not always kindly ones. He could be so downright jolly and clever that Odin accepted him for the challenge of danger which he ever offered. As Loki watched the merry sport his eyes twinkled with excitement but his heart pounded with jealousy. He saw how everyone and everything loved Balder and he seethed with envy. Loki was the only one in all Asgard who hated Balder secretly and longed for his death. Balder had done Loki no harm but the wicked Loki's mind was filled with seeds of hate and he could not bear for anyone to be loved.

Loki watched the sport with a particular purpose. As he sized up the situation an evil plan ripened in his mind. He proceeded with care to carry out his secret. He made a particular point of greeting Father Odin and of commenting on Balder's health and the brilliance of Frigga's Ceremony of Promise. Loki inquired about the whereabouts of the queen and learned that she was viewing the merriment from a tower window. Loki then sought Hode, the strong blind brother of Balder. "Pray, why do you sit here alone, my good Hode?" inquired the sly Loki.

"I honor my brother Balder with my presence," said Hode. "Would that I could see to aim a weapon, for gladly would I honor him as other gods do."

"What's this?" asked Loki. "You care for your handsome brother who appears to have everything, while you who cannot see appear to have so little?"

"Ah, you do not know? Balder, my good brother, sees for me. He alone tells me of the beauties of Asgard. Often we walk and talk together when everyone else seems to be too busy to be with me."

"I see, I see," said Loki. "You do well to sit here and listen. Balder will enjoy hearing what you, alone, have heard. Farewell to you, listening Hode." Loki made haste as he strode through the trees. When he was certain he was out of sight of every eye he stopped. Quickly he took the contents from his bag and disguised himself as an old woman. He wore a wig of long, gray hair, and a brown gown with a tattered shawl over his shoulders. He found a crooked branch which he used for a cane. Then he hobbled in pursuit of Queen Frigga in the palace tower.

"Good day to you, beautiful queen," greeted the old crone in a raspy voice. "Pray, what is happening on the plains of Asgard?"

"Who are you, old mother, that you do not know?" asked the queen in surprise.

"I have been ill and sleeping for these many days," quoth the old woman hastily. "Pray, tell me. Why do the gods throw all manner of weapons at our beautiful Balder? Will they not harm him?"

"Indeed, you must have been sleeping," said the queen. "They throw weapons to prove the promise which all things have given me —the promise never to harm or touch my son Balder."

"A strange promise, but a noble one. Balder is the dearest loved, and rightly so. He is honorable."

"You speak the truth, wise mother," said the queen, pleased to hear this thought voiced.

"Tell me," said the sly crone. "Has everything sworn to guard Balder from all harm?"

"Yes," said Frigga. "Everything except one little plant called mistletoe. It grows in a meadow in the heart of Valhalla. It is such a tender sprig of a young plant that I did not think it necessary to bid it promise."

The old woman assured the queen that she was right. Bidding the queen goodday, the old crone explained that she wanted to watch the merriment. She hobbled away until she was out of sight. She then gathered up the skirts of her gown and ran in giant steps to the meadow of Valhalla, plucked a sprig of mistletoe, and was soon back at the side of Hode. The old crone touched Hode's arm, greeted him, and inquired slyly why he did not join the sport. Hode put his hand to his eyes to explain his blindness and added that he longed with all his heart to do so to honor his brother. At once the old crone offered to help him. It was in this way that she tricked him into throwing the little green sprig of mistletoe which she held in her hand. Hode, believing all was well, followed the old woman and did as he was told.

Hode threw the arrow of mistletoe which flew through the air and went straight to Balder's heart. At once Balder fell dead upon the field. A black cloud rose out of the sky and a gray mist spread itself over all Asgard. Spring and sunshine went suddenly away, for Balder's dream was coming true. At once flowers began to fade. Animals were silenced and birds ceased their singing. "Balder the beautiful is dead," the wind wailed and echoed mournfully.

Queen Frigga blamed herself for her son's death. "If only I had sought the promise of the littlest sprig of mistletoe," she said again and again in deep regret. Father Odin was silent in his grief, for he understood clearly the impending doom. In Balder's death he foresaw the fall of the gods at the hands of the giants—an everlasting darkness for Asgard.

Balder's brothers, as was the custom, lifted Balder's body upon their shields and carried him on their shoulders to the shore of the sea. Balder was to be sent to Hela, Queen of Death, with the trio of treasures he loved best. Above all, he loved Nanna, his dear wife. He loved, also, his beautiful horse, and his ship, Hringhorni. Nanna held the horse and stood with great courage by the body of Balder as they waited for his ship which was stranded far up the beach. "Even the giants bore no ill-will to Balder," said Father Odin. "The winds do not rage. All is gentle in honor. Let us bury our hatred and send to Jotunheim to the giants for help to move the good ship Hringhorni."

Odin sent a messenger to the giantess Hyrrockin, the hugest of the Frost Giants. In haste Hyrrockin came riding upon a giant wolf. She was followed by great throngs of huge frost giants and multitudes of little frost dwarfs, all coming to mourn for Balder. Hyrrockin was as mighty as forty gods and it took four gods to hold her wolf-steed while she strode out to the great ship and seized it by the prow. With one easy effort Hyrrockin caused the ship to leap upward with such force that sparks flew from beneath it as it struck against flint rock and the whole world trembled. Thor was angered by Hyrrockin's strength and started after her with his hammer but was held back by other gods. The great ship floated out to the open sea, eager, it seemed, to be upon its voyage of mystery. Hyrrockin waded into the deep sea until the water was above her waist. She caught the ship and pulled it ashore with her left hand.

The ship was made ready with a gift from the dwarfs, a beautiful cloth of gold designed with sunbeams and ice. Frost Giants carried gifts of furs, and the gods and goddesses presented rare silks of every color found in flower gardens. Father Odin took the hand of Nanna and escorted her to the ship, while Mother Frigga led Balder's beautiful horse. Nanna held the horse bravely, while Balder's brothers bore his body aboard the ship he loved. At the sight of Balder, who appeared to be sleeping, Nanna could bear her grief no longer. As she wept her heart broke. The gods laid her gently in the beautiful silks beside Balder so they might journey to the Valley of Death together. King Odin removed his golden ring Daysmir and placed it upon Balder's finger. "Take this with you, my son," he said, "Do not forget us. We shall be ever mindful of you as we wander through lonely mist."

When King Odin and Queen Frigga were back on shore the horse neighed knowingly. Thor then touched the ship with his hammer. Lightning flashed to start the ship to burning. Firelight revealed the faces of Balder and Nanna who seemed to sleep peacefully in glory. As the fiery ship sailed majestically on its last voyage all Aesir watched silently from the shore. They were united in sorrow as the ship sailed beyond the horizon. The final sunset came to Asgard as Balder journeyed onward with the mystery of death.

THE KNIGHTS OF THE SILVER SHIELD
by Raymond Macdonald Alden[11]

Suggested by Winifred Ward.[12] Miss Ward says: "Here is one of the rare stories which glorify moral courage above physical bravery. Most valuable for the players' growth in character study and delineation are the incidents with the three people who tempt Sir Roland to leave his post. Because they have strong and plausible arguments for his doing so, they cause an inner struggle in the young knight before each decision to remain steadfast. Children like to create a play from the story because of its dramatic action and it wonderfully impressive climax."

There was once a splendid castle in a forest, with great stone walls and a high gateway, and turrets that rose away above the tallest trees. The forest was dark and dangerous, and many cruel giants lived in it; but in the castle was a company of knights who were kept there by the king of the country, to help travelers who might be in the forest and to fight with the giants whenever they could.

Each of these knights wore a beautiful suit of armor and carried a long spear, while over his helmet there floated a great red plume that

[11] From *Why the Chimes Rang and Other Stories* by Raymond Macdonald Alden, by permission of the Bobbs-Merrill Company, Inc. Copyright 1906, 1908, the Bobbs-Merrill Company, Inc.

[12] Winifred Ward is Professor Emeritus of Children's Drama, Northwestern University, Evanston, Illinois, and author of *Playmaking with Children* and *Stories to Dramatize*.

could be seen a long way off by anyone in distress. But the most wonderful thing about the knights' armor was their shields. They were not like those of other knights, but had been made by a great magician who had lived in the castle many years before. They were made of silver, and sometimes shone in the sunlight with dazzling brightness; but at other times the surface of the shields would be clouded as though by a mist, and one could not see his face reflected there as he could when they shone brightly.

Now, when each young knight received his spurs and his armor, a new shield was also given him from among those that the magician had made; and when the shield was new its surface was always cloudy and dull. But as the knight began to do service against the giants, or went on expeditions to help poor travelers in the forest, his shield grew brighter and brighter, so that he could see his face clearly reflected in it. But if he proved to be a lazy or cowardly knight, and let the giants get the better of him, or did not care what became of the travelers, then the shield grew more and more cloudy, until the knight becamed ashamed to carry it.

But this was not all. When any one of the knights fought a particularly hard battle and won the victory, or when he went on some hard errand for the lord of the castle and was successful, not only did his silver shield grow brighter, but when one looked into the center of it he could see something like a golden star shining in its very heart. This was the greatest honor that a knight could achieve, and the other knights always spoke of such a one as having "won his star." It was usually not till he was pretty old and tired as a soldier that he could win it. At the time when this story begins, the lord of the castle himself was the only one of the knights whose shield bore the golden star.

There came a time when the worst of the giants in the forest gathered themselves together to have a battle against the knights. They made a camp in a dark hollow not far from the castle and gathered all their best warriors together, and all the knights made ready to fight them. The windows of the castle were closed and barred; the air was full of the noise of armor being made ready for use; and the knights were so excited that they could scarcely rest or eat.

Now there was a young knight in the castle named Sir Roland, who was among those most eager for the battle. He was a splendid warrior, with eyes that shone like stars whenever there was anything to do in the way of knightly deeds. And although he was still quite young, his shield had begun to shine enough to show plainly that he had done bravely in some of his errands through the forest. This battle, he thought, would be the great opportunity of his life. And on the morning of the day when they were to go forth to it, and all the knights assembled in the great hall of the castle to receive the commands of their leaders, Sir Roland hoped that he would be put in the most dangerous place of all, so that he could show what knightly stuff he was made of.

But when the lord of the castle came to him, as he went about in full armor giving his commands, he said: "One brave knight must stay behind to guard the gateway of the castle, and it is you, Sir Roland, being one of the youngest, whom I have chosen for this."

At these words Sir Roland was so disappointed that he bit his lip and closed his helmet over his face so that the other knights might not see it. For a moment he felt as if he must reply angrily to the commander, and tell him that it was not right to leave so sturdy a knight behind when he was eager to fight. But he struggled against this feeling, and went quietly to look after his duties at the gate. The gateway was high and narrow, and was reached from outside by a high, narrow bridge that crossed the moat, which surrounded the castle on every side. When an enemy approached, the knight on guard rang a great bell just inside the gate, and the bridge was drawn up against the castle wall so that no one could come across the moat. So the giants had long ago given up trying to attack the castle itself.

Today the battle was to be in the dark hollow in the forest, and it was not likely that there would be anything to do at the castle gate except to wach it like a common doorkeeper. It was not strange that Sir Roland thought someone else might have done this.

Presently all the other knights marched out in their flashing armor, their red plumes waving over their heads, and their spears in their hands. The lord of the castle stopped only to tell Sir Roland to keep guard over the gate until they had all returned, and to let no one enter. Then they went into the shadows of the forest and were soon lost to sight.

Sir Roland stood looking after them long after they had gone, thinking how happy he would be if he were on the way to battle like them. But after a little he put this out of his mind and tried to think of pleasanter things. It was a long time before anything happened, or any word came from the battle.

At last Sir Roland saw one of the knights come limping down the path to the castle and he went out on the bridge to meet him. Now, this knight was not a brave one, and he had been frightened away as soon as he was wounded.

"I have been hurt," he said, "so that I cannot fight any more. But I could watch the gate for you if you would like to go back in my place."

At first Sir Roland's heart leaped with joy at this, but then he remembered what the commander had told him on going away, and he said:

"I should like to go, but a knight belongs where his commander has put him. My place is here at the gate, and I cannot open it even for you. Your place is at the battle."

The knight was ashamed when he heard this, and he presently turned about and went into the forest again.

So Sir Roland kept guard silently for another hour. Then there came an old beggar woman down the path to the castle, and asked Sir Roland if she might come in and have some food. He told her that no one could enter the castle that day, but that he would send a servant out to her with food, and that she might sit and rest as long as she would.

"I have been past the hollow in the forest where the battle is going on," said the old woman while she was waiting for her food.

"And how do you think it is going?" asked Sir Roland.

"Badly for the knights, I am afraid," said the old woman. "The giants are fighting as they have never fought before. I should think you had better go and help your friends."

"I should like to, indeed," said Sir Roland. "But I am set to guard the gateway of the castle, and cannot leave."

"One fresh knight would make a great difference when they are all weary with fighting," said the old woman. "I should think that, while there are no enemies about, you would be much more useful there."

"You may well think so," said Sir Roland, "and so may I; but it is neither you nor I that is commander here."

"I suppose," said the old woman then, "that your are one of the knights who like to keep out of fighting. You are lucky to have so good an excuse for staying at home." And she laughed a thin and taunting laugh.

Then Sir Roland was very angry, and thought that if it were only a man instead of a woman, he would show him whether he liked fighting or no. But as it was a woman, he shut his lips and set his teeth hard together, and as the servant came just then with the food he had sent for, he gave it to the old woman quickly and shut the gate that she might not talk to him any more.

It was not very long before he heard someone calling outside. Sir Roland opened the gate and saw standing at the other end of the drawbridge a little old man in a long black cloak. "Why are you knocking here?" he said. "The castle is closed today."

"Are you Sir Roland?" asked the little old man.

"Yes," said Sir Roland.

"Then you ought not to be staying here when your commander and his knights are having so hard a struggle with the giants, and when you have the chance to make of yourself the greatest knight in this kingdom. Listen to me! I have brought you a magic sword."

As he said this, the old man drew from under his coat a wonderful sword that flashed in the sunlight as if it were covered with diamonds. "This is the sword of all swords," he said, "and it is for you, if you will leave your idling here by the castle gate and carry it to the battle. Nothing can stand before it. When you lift it the giants will fall back, your master will be saved, and you will be crowned the victorious knight—the one who will soon take his commander's place as lord of the castle."

Now Sir Roland believed that it was a magician who was speaking to him, for it certainly appeared to be a magic sword. It seemed so wonderful that the sword should be brought to him that he reached out his hand as though he would take it, and the little old man came forward as though he would cross the drawbridge into the castle. But as he did so, it came to Sir Roland's mind again that that bridge and the gateway had been intrusted to him, and he called out "No!" to the old man, so that he stopped where he was standing. But he waved the shining sword in the air again and said: "It is for you! Take it and win the victory!"

Sir Roland was really afraid that if he looked any longer at the sword, or listened to any more words of the old man, he would not be able to hold himself within the castle. For this reason he struck the great bell at the gateway, which was the signal for the servants inside to pull in the chains of the drawbridge, and instantly they began to pull, and the drawbridge came up, so that the old man could not cross it to enter the castle, nor Sir Roland to go out.

Then, as he looked across the moat, Sir Roland saw a wonderful thing. The little old man threw off his black coat, and as he did so he began to grow bigger and bigger and bigger, until in a minute more he was a giant as tall as any in the forest. At first Sir Roland could scarcely believe his eyes. Then he realized that this must be one of their giant enemies, who had changed himself into a little old man through some magic power, that he might make his way into the castle while all the knights were away. Sir Roland shuddered to think what might have happened if he had taken the sword and left the gate unguarded. The giant shook his fist across the moat that lay between them, and then, knowing that he could do nothing more, he went angrily back into the forest.

Sir Roland now resolved not to open the gate again, and to pay no attention to any other visitor. But it was not long before he heard a sound that made him spring forward in joy. It was the bugle of the lord of the castle, and there came sounding after it the bugles of many of the knights that were with him, pealing so joyfully that Sir Roland was sure they were safe and happy. As they came nearer, he could hear their shouts of victory. So he gave the signal to let down the draw-bridge again, and went out to meet them. They were dusty and blood-stained and weary, but they had won the battle with the giants; and it had been such a great victory that there had never been a happier home-coming.

Sir Roland greeted them all as they passed in over the bridge, and then, when he had closed the gate and fastened it, he followed them into the great hall of the castle. The lord of the castle took his place on the highest seat, with the other knights about him, and Sir Roland came forward with the key of the gate to give his account of what he had done in the place to which the commander had appointed him. The lord of the castle bowed to him as a sign for him to begin, but just as he opened his mouth to speak, one of the knights cried out:

"The shield! The shield! Sir Roland's shield!"

Everyone turned and looked at the shield which Sir Roland carried on his left arm. He himself could see only the top of it, and did not know what they could mean. But what they saw was the golden star of knighthood, shining brightly from the center of Sir Roland's shield. There had never been such amazement in the castle before.

Sir Roland knelt before the lord of the castle to receive his com-mands. He still did not know why everyone was looking at him so excitedly, and wondered if he had in some way done wrong.

"Speak, Sir Knight," said the commander, as soon as he could find his voice after his surprise, "and tell us all that has happened today at the castle. Have you been attacked? Have any giants come hither? Did you fight them alone?"

"No, my Lord," said Sir Roland. "Only one giant has been here, and he went away silently when he found he could not enter."

Then he told all that had happened through the day.

When he had finished, the knights all looked at one another, but no one spoke a word. Then they looked again at Sir Roland's shield to make sure that their eyes had not deceived them, and there the golden star was still shining.

After a little silence the lord of the castle spoke.

"Men make mistakes," he said, "but our silver shields are never mistaken. Sir Roland has fought and won the hardest battle of all today."

Then the others all rose and saluted Sir Roland, who was the youngest knight that ever carried the golden star.

WHERE LOVE IS, GOD IS

Adapted by Hazel Brain Dunnington[13]
from a tale by Leo Tolstoy

Mrs. Dunnington says, "Not only does Martin, the selfless shoe-maker in this story, strongly communicate love for one's neighbor, he even 'infects' with brotherhood those who become involved in the story and especially those who enter into the dramatization of his character. Martin's unselfishness projects concretely whether the entire story or just the Stepanich and vision scenes are dramatized. Dialogue also offers appealing challenge to sixth through ninth grade individuals and groups who have had some dramatic experience. Provocative discussions have led to imaginative interpretations of the vision episode with music and voice reinforcing the theme: 'Inasmuch as ye have done it unto one of the least of these my brethren, ye have done it unto me.' "

A blustery, chill winter night shut swiftly down in the little Russian village where Martin, a kindly old shoemaker, lived. Looking up through the high window of his basement dwelling, Martin removed his spectacles and rubbed his eyes as if to clear them of the snow blur outside. He nodded to the lamplighter passing by. Martin's eyes followed the peaceful halo of light surrounding the lantern until the lamplighter passed quietly out of sight. Martin set aside the shoe on which he had been working and put away his tools.

Taking his little lamp and lighting it, he sat heavily in a chair near his reading table. He picked up his beloved Book. Then he sat read-

[13] By permission of Hazel Brain Dunnington. Mrs. Dunnington is Assistant Professor of Speech and Drama, Central Washington State College, Ellensburg, Washington.

ing, nodding approval at the sacred words. Soon he lifted his head and spoke out musingly, "If unto me the Master came, how should I welcome him?" He pulled thoughtfully at his beard, wondering aloud, "Should I be selfish like the Pharisee? Nyet! Ah, nyet, I say. And yet, who is to know?" He shrugged his shoulders wearily and settled his head in his arm upon the table. Very soon the good shoemaker was slumbering gently.

"Martin," he heard a low voice call. He started; he looked toward the door but not anyone was there. "Martin," the soft voice continued, "Tomorrow, I will come. Expect me. Look out upon the street for me."

A gust of chill wind rattled at the door, and Martin roused and rubbed his eyes. "I dreamed," he mumbled. But half glancing up at the window he stumbled off to bed.

However, next morning as he worked, he kept watching the window. And at every passer-by in unfamiliar boots, he even stooped down that he might see the face of him who wore the boots. Aloud he wondered, "Were those dream words I heard last night or were they not, I say?"

A house-porter passed in new felt boots; then a water-carrier. Presently an old soldier of Nicholas' reign came near the window, spade in hand. Martin knew him by his boots, which were shabby old felt ones, galoshed with leather. The old man was called Stepanich; a neighboring tradesman kept him in his house for charity, and his duty was to help the house-porter. He began to clear away the snow before Martin's window. Martin glanced at him and then went on with his work.

"I must be growing crazy with age," said Martin, laughing at his fancy. "Stepanich comes to clear away the snow, and I must need imagine it's the Master coming to visit me. Old dotard that I am!"

Yet after he had made a dozen stitches he felt drawn to look out of the window again. He saw that Stepanich had leaned his spade against the wall and was either resting himself or trying to get warm. The man was old and broken down, and had evidently not enough strength even to clear away the snow.

"What if I called him in and gave him some tea?" thought Martin. "The samovar is just on the boil."

He struck his awl in its place, and rose, and putting the samovar on the table, made tea. Then he tapped the window with his fingers. Stepanich turned and came to the window. Martin beckoned to him to come in and went himself to open the door.

"Come in," he said, "and warm yourself a bit. I'm sure you must be cold."

"May God bless you!" Stepanich answered. "My bones do ache to be sure." He came in, first shaking off the snow, and lest he should leave marks on the floor he began wiping his feet, but as he did so he tottered and nearly fell.

"Don't trouble to wipe your feet," said Martin; "I'll wipe up the floor—it's all in the day's work. Come, friend, sit down and have some tea."

Filling two glasses, he passed one to his visitor, and pouring his own out into the saucer, began to blow on it.

Stepanich emptied his glass, and, turning it upside down, put the remains of his piece of sugar on the top. He began to express his thanks, but it was plain that he would be glad of some more.

"Have another glass," said Martin, refilling the visitor's glass and his own. But while he drank his tea Martin kept looking into the street.

"Are you expecting anyone?" asked the visitor.

"Am I expecting anyone. Well, now, I'm ashamed to tell you. It isn't that I really expect anyone; but I heard something last night which I can't get out of my mind. Whether it was a vision, or only a fancy, I can't tell. You see, friend, last night I was reading the Gospel, about Christ the Lord, how he suffered and how he walked on earth. You have heard tell of it, I dare say."

"I have heard tell of it," answered Stepanich; "but I'm an ignorant man and not able to read."

"Well, you, I was reading of how he walked on earth. I came to that part, you know, where he went to a Pharisee who did not receive him well. Well, friend, as I read about it, I thought how that man did not receive the Master with proper honor. Suppose such a thing could happen to such a man as myself, I thought, what would I not do to receive him! But that man gave him no reception at all. Well, friend, as I was thinking of this I began to doze, and as I dozed I heard a voice saying, 'Expect me; I will come tomorrow. . . .' This sank so into my mind that, though I am ashamed of it myself, I keep on expecting him, the dear Lord!"

Stepanich shook his head in silence, finished his glass and laid it on its side; but Martin stood it up again and refilled it for him.

"Here, drink another glass, bless you! And I was thinking, too, how he walked on earth and despised no one, but went mostly among common folk. He went with plain people, and chose his disciples from among the likes of us, from workmen like us, sinners that we are. 'He who raises himself,' He said, 'shall be humbled; and he who humbles himself shall be raised.' 'You call me Lord,' He said, 'and I will wash your feet.' 'He who would be first,' He said, 'let him be the servant of all; because,' He said, 'blessed are the poor, the humble, the meek, and the merciful.' "

Stepanich forgot his tea. He was an old man, easily moved to tears, and as he sat and listened he fisted the tears from his cheeks.

"Come, drink some more," said Martin. But Stepanich crossed himself, thanked him, moved away his tumbler, and rose.

"Thank you, Martin Avdeyich," he said, "you have given me food and comfort both for soul and body."

"You're very welcome. Come again another time. I am glad to have a guest," said Martin.

As Stepanich went away, Martin poured refreshment for himself and glanced again at the window. Finishing his tea, he stitched at the back seam of a boot, but he watched as he worked. Several soldiers went by, the master of a neighboring house in shining galoshes, and then a baker with his huge basket, and as they passed, Martin remarked knowingly on the boots they wore, on qualities and workmanship and the like. Then came a woman in heavy peasant-made shoes who stopped, leaning heavily against the wall. Looking upward at her face, Martin saw that she was a stranger and that she carried a babe in her arms. Both were poorly dressed against the cold. The mother, back against the wind, was trying to wrap the child more warmly even though she had hardly anything at all to wrap it in.

Martin went quickly out his door and out and up the steps to the street above. He brought the woman with the baby in to his little fire and gave her food. While she ate, he took the babe to give the mother rest. He did his best to make the tiny baby smile. When the mother finished her cup of soup, she took the child again. She dipped some bread in milk and fed the little one warm milk, and soon both were warmed and fed. Then the woman rose to go, saying, "May the good Master bless you, sir."

Martin looked at the scanty clothing of mother and child. He questioned gently, "But your wraps, have you no more than these?" Whereupon the young woman explained that since her soldier husband had been transferred to a new post, she had not received the money he always sent. Because of the delay, she had pawned her shawl the previous afternoon.

Martin got up, rummaged among some things hanging on the wall and returned with an old cloak. "Here, wrap the little one about with this," he said. Then he groped under the bed, pulled out an old trunk and fumbled around inside.

The woman spread out the cloak under the baby and struggling with tears murmured, "May the Lord bless you, sir. Surely the Master himself has sent us here or we should have frozen."

Martin smiled humbly as he gave her the shawl he had found. Then he told the woman of his dream and of how he had heard the Master's voice promising to visit him that day.

As the woman picked up the baby, and drew the shawl about them both, she spoke softly, "All things are possible." Then Martin saw her up into the street again, and she took her leave of him.

He sat to his work once more, watching the passers-by until night fell. Once again he lit his lamp and took the Book. As he prepared to read, he stopped now and then to look up at the window, but it was too dark to see anyone save the lamplighter who again passed by with shining light and then was gone.

Light flooded Martin's soul as he opened the good Book. He noted the morocco marker's place, but opened the gospels at a place other than the one he had marked the day before. As he reached for his spectacles to read, he seemed to hear a rustling sound behind his chair. He turned slowly, peering about and said ponderingly, "Did— did something move in that far corner?" A soft voice answered him, "Martin, Do you not know me, Martin?"

He half rose in his chair as he peered closer, asking, "Who spoke yonder?"

"It is I," replied the voice and out into the light of the little lamp stepped old Stepanich, smiling and nodding. Then he was gone as in a cloud and another voice called gently, "It is I." Out of the darkness this time stepped the woman with the baby in her arms. The woman smiled and the baby laughed as they too vanished.

Martin looked after them a moment, crossed himself, put on his spectacles and began reading from the page he had just turned to. As he read, heavenly voices seemed to join his words: "Inasmuch as ye did it unto one of these my brethren, even these least, ye did it unto me."

And at the bottom of the page he read: "I was an hungered, and ye gave me meat; I was thirsty, and ye gave me drink: I was a stranger, and ye took me in."

Martin understood then that his dream had come true. The Master had really come to him that day, and he had welcomed him.

KING OF THE GOLDEN RIVER

Adapted by Hazel Brain Dunnington[14] from a story by John Ruskin

Mrs. Dunnington says: "Children of ten through thirteen or fourteen years take great delight in dramatizing aspects of mystery surrounding the King and the South-West Wind as they develop these fantasy characters, and the older brothers afford challenging character contrast. The folktale quality enables children to consider with artistic detachment the theme that truthfulness with kindness is rewarded.

[14] By permission of Hazel Brain Dunnington. (See note 13.)

Thus triteness is avoided and the theme has added impact for children. There is also a medieval atmosphere that gives dialogue satisfactions in the use of such words as 'bless me,' 'naught,' 'farewell,' 'kin,' and the like. Groups have enjoyed working out selected scenes; other groups have dramatized the entire story in this simplified form. One group, presently, is contemplating a music dramatization or 'opera' of this story. Music from Smetana's *The Moldau,* from Sibelius' *Finlandia,* and from Grofé's *Grand Canyon Suite* are being considered by that group as mood-building background materials."

There came a season in the ancient land of Styria when all the valleys except fertile Treasure Valley were so ravaged by storm that they yielded no harvest. People came then to beg food from the three brothers who owned this valley watered by the great golden stream called the Golden River.

But the two older brothers, Schwartz and Hans, were greedy and mean. They stored away the apples, grains, grapes, honey and the like even before people began coming for food and sent all persons away without giving even so much as a crust to a little child. The youngest brother, Gluck, about twelve years of age, honest and sweet-tempered, longed to give to these unfortunates. However, he was helpless to do so against the tyranny of his older brothers, Schwartz and Hans. Since the parents' deaths these two greedy brothers had dismissed all servants but a sadly mistreated drudge or two, and they saw to it that Gluck did the scrubbing and the cooking and the fetching, with only scraps, slops and hard words in return.

At first there were only whispers of "Black Brothers" as Schwartz and Hans turned the hungry away, but as nothing at all was given to anyone the term came to be more loudly applied. Even so, naught was given, even when those who came pleaded piteously in the names of starving elders and crying children.

One late autumn day as the wind bellowed mournfully through the chimney, the two older brothers decided to leave their dismal house for the village tavern. They gave Gluck harsh orders to mind the leg of mutton roasting on the spit, and departed.

Gluck sat alone as the wind smacked rain against the windows, and as he turned the meat, he tried to understand his brothers' greed. Suddenly over the noise of the storm, he heard a sort of double knock at the great door. When it came again and yet again, he investigated. He discovered a strange and curious little gentleman outside, dripping wet from his tall hat to his boots, and begging shelter. Gluck hesitated momentarily, but his tender-heartedness prevailed over the fear of his brothers' wrath and he unbolted the door. As the strange fellow stepped inside the room, a great blast of wind shuddered through the house and shook the chimney. The little man drew close to the hearth and water ran in such streams from his great cloak as to nearly put out the fire. Gluck had a time of it, trying to catch the water in pots and pans and to wipe up all around.

When the fellow begged food, Gluck feared greatly to serve him lest the brothers miss the food. Nevertheless he did set about cutting off the one slice which the brothers had promised might possibly be Gluck's own share. But before he could serve it up, his brothers returned.

They were furious indeed, even though Gluck quickly fitted the slice back into its place. They also harangued Gluck's boldness in opening the door. They even reviled the strange fellow for dripping great streams of water everywhere about.

Then, as first Hans, then Schwartz, attempted to thrust the strange gentleman out the door, they found themselves confronting a peculiar power. This force not only prevented them from laying hands on the stranger, but also sent them reeling and spinning into the far corners of the room. The little gentleman, seeming to understand the sad state of affairs, gathered the great wet folds of his cloak about him with dignity. He drew himself up to his full height with deliberate calm. From inside the folds of his great cloak, he took out his calling card. He placed it on the table with grace and flourish. Then with great control of his mounting anger he bowed and advanced to the door. He turned then to speak, "Farewell, I shall depart, as you wish; I shall not return, nor indeed any of my kin. Henceforth, not any of us will come to Treasure Valley!" As he stepped outside into the night, wind and rain beat fiercely in. Above the ravaging of the storm, the brothers heard these final words, "Come, devastating storm! Come! Come, I say!"

The brothers shuddered in the wind drafts that shook the house. Hans roused himself, stumbled to the table and read from the card, gruffly, "Southwest Wind." Schwartz fiercely snatched the card away and laughed hollowly and loudly.

Already the great storm was upon the valley, however, and as young Gluck ran to his own room, a great gust of wind began to loosen the roof over the brothers' heads. The candle was snuffed out, and the brothers called out wildly to one another as rafters came crashing about them.

The storm continued throughout the night, and Treasure Valley was laid in ruins. In the weeks following, the stored-up wealth of the brothers dwindled until finally only the last of some gold remained. The two older brothers melted this into coin, trickily combining the gold with copper. Even so it did not last long and finally the only gold at hand was that of Gluck's greatly cherished drinking mug. Gluck cherished the mug not so much for its precious metal as for the gift it was from his parents and the expressive face and eyes in the design. He implored his brothers, "Please, please, only let me keep the mug! I'll work somewhere and give to you. . . ." But Schwartz laughed rudely and cuffed him, and Hans snatched up the mug. He tossed it into the melting pot with a laugh, and the two brothers left for the tavern commanding that Gluck finish the coin work, and quickly as well.

Gluck looked at his dear old friend in the melting pot. The flowing hair had melted, but the sparkling eyes appeared sharper than ever. He turned away in sadness, walking over to the window that looked out onto the mountains and the Golden River. It was the close of day and the approaching sunset heightened the golden look of the river as it fell from rock to rock. Watching, he mused, "If only the river were really gold, how nice it would be. How nice . . ."

He was interrupted as a voice very near replied, "No, it would not." Gluck jumped in surprise.

"Bless me!" called Gluck, leaping up and looking everywhere about, even behind himself several times. However, finding nobody he went again to the window, wondering if he had, or had not, heard anything after all. He looked out at the golden haze that had spread over Treasure Valley.

"No, it wouldn't, Gluck," the voice said even louder than before.

"Bless me!" Gluck called out again, and he twirled about again and again in trying to look ever more quickly behind himself.

Then the voice began a gay sort of chanting song, "La la-lira lira la." Gluck ran here and there, back and forth, from the window to other parts of the room and finally traced the voice to the fire; then to the melting pot on the fire. He was thinking to pull out the pot and look in. However, when the voice called out clearly, "Hello! Hello, Gluck," he froze in fright. Finally, blinking his eyes and setting his jaw, he summoned all his courage, pulled the pot from the fire and—looked.

The gold was all melted. Meeting his glance from beneath it were the sharp eyes of his old friend of the mug, a thousand times sharper than ever he had seen them before. "I'm all right. Get me out, Gluck," the voice called. But Gluck was too astonished to move. "I said you must get me out!" This time the voice was commanding, but still Gluck couldn't move. The voice became angry and shouting, "Gluck, take me out; I'm too hot!" Gluck with great caution reached down into the pot. He felt the clutching, squirming hand of the creature inside, and he pulled the little fellow to an upright position.

As the creature climbed out, Gluck backed off in wonder. He stared at the curious stretching and twisting of neck, arms and legs as the little fellow checked the working order of his body. Finally the creature steadied a piercing gaze on Gluck with the words, "No, Gluck, my boy, it wouldn't be nice at all to have the river be really gold."

"Would—would—wouldn't it, sir?" asked Gluck very, very humbly.

"No, it would not! It would not! It would not!" repeated the dwarf creature, who was dressed in cloth of gold. And to emphasize what he said, he strode forcefully about, himself looking out at the river at every turn made on the window side of the room. As the tempo of the fellow's strides decreased, Gluck ventured a delicate question. "Please, sir, were—were you my mug?"

The creature stopped, turned abruptly and drew himself up with great dignity. "I am the King of what you mortals call the Golden River," he said, fastening a very sharp eye on Gluck.

In the silence that followed, Gluck felt compelled to say something. "I hope that your majesty is very well," he said politely.

"Listen well," commanded the little man, making no reply to this courtesy. "You have freed me from an evil power. For long I have watched you and your brothers. From what I have seen, I'll do no business with your brothers, but I am willing to serve you. Therefore, listen well. For him who shall climb to the top of that mountain from which you see the Golden River issue and shall cast into the stream at its source three drops of holy water, and for him only, the river shall turn to gold. But no one failing in his first can succeed in a second attempt; and if anyone shall cast unholy water into the river it will rise over him, and he will become a black stone." Having so said, the little man walked with fierce dignity straight into the fire and disappeared in a brilliance of flame.

Gluck stared, then ran to look up the chimney, calling out, "My mug! Oh, my mug! It's gone!" Nothing at all happened, so he settled himself on the hearth. He was still there looking wonderingly into the fire when the brothers returned. Upon finding no coin, they beat him until they were tired. Then they flung themselves down for a rest, still demanding gold pieces.

When Gluck told of the evening's happenings, they beat him again for the untruthfulness of such a tale. All the same, both Schwartz and Hans began planning how they might follow the strange fellow's directions. The very next day the two older brothers went unaccustomedly to the church. They took some holy water when no one was looking and went quarreling along, up the mountain.

Gluck waited anxiously. When neighbors and the village priest stopped by early one morning Gluck told them of how he hurried home each night from his work at the goldsmith's hoping to find his brothers. But there was always only the empty house. So it was that Gluck finally decided to go to the mountain himself. The priest blessed him in his concern for brothers who had treated him so badly and gave the boy a flask of holy water. Gluck packed some bread in a basket, fastened the flask of holy water on his belt, and started off for the high mountains of Treasure Valley.

He hurried over the low hills in his eagerness. Suddenly ahead of him, there appeared a great glacier where he had never known one to be before.

But he hesitated only slightly and then began picking his way carefully over the slippery ice and around the deep chasms with their rushing water and weird sounds. Even so he had several bad falls and lost the basket. Thus he was altogether exhausted when he reached the firm soil of the mountain, and he lay down to rest. When he felt himself recovered enough to go on his way, he found himself climbing in the very hottest part of the day.

Thus a great thirst overtook him, and he lifted the flask to drink. At the same time he saw an old man come half stumbling down the path. The fellow leaned heavily on a stick and feebly called out, "My son, I am faint. Give me water." Gluck quickly did so, but cautioned all the same, "Only, sir, please don't drink it all." Nevertheless the man returned the flask two-thirds empty, thanked Gluck and continued down the mountain greatly refreshed.

Gluck noticed that his own way grew easier now and he felt merrier as he went along. Shortly again, however, so great was his thirst, that he felt compelled to drink. This time as he raised the flask he discovered a feeble child at the side of the path. He shared the water. The child drank, smiled, got up and ran down along the path smelling the flowers which now bloomed all along the way. Now only a few drops of the precious water remained, and Gluck decided he must bear his own thirst. As he climbed on, again the way under his feet became less difficult.

However, after another short while, Gluck's thirst became dreadful indeed. He looked at the flask, and he saw that there were only five or six drops left. Even though his throat was aching, he decided that he dare not drink. As he was hanging the flask at his belt again, he saw a little dog barely able to lift its head as it panted feebly for breaths of air.

He remembered the strange little King's words, ". . . no one can succeed except in his *first* attempt." He was about to pass by when the dog looked up at him and moaned piteously. "Poor little fellow. He'll be dead when I come down again if I don't help him," he said, and so he opened the flask and poured all the water into the dog's mouth. In a bright flash of light the dog disappeared; then before Gluck stood his old acquaintance, the King of the Golden River.

"Thank you," said the King. "But why didn't you come before? Had you done so, you could have saved me the trouble of turning those wicked brothers of yours into stones."

"Oh, have you really turned my brothers into stone? You are cruel!" cried Gluck, quite forgetting himself. Then he added more politely, "I am sure, sir, your Majesty, I mean, sir, they did get the water from the church."

"Very probably," replied the King, "but," and his face grew stern as he spoke, "the water which has been refused to the cry of the weary and dying, is unholy, though it had been blessed by every saint in heaven; and the water which is found in the vessel of mercy is holy, though it had been defiled. . . ."

So saying, the dwarf stooped and plucked a lily that grew at his feet. On its white leaves there hung three drops of clear dew. The dwarf shook them into the flask which Gluck held in his hand. "Cast these into the River," he said, "and descend on the other side of the mountains into the Treasure Valley. And so goodspeed."

The figure of the dwarf dimmed into a mist of light; the mist diffused; the King was gone.

Gluck went on to the designated place. When he cast the three drops of dew into the stream, he watched. The drops descended into a small whirlpool from whence came now a musical noise. He obeyed his friend and started down toward Treasure Valley. As he went, he heard the music of the water in a new place, directly under him, it seemed. Then he saw that a new river was springing from a new break in the rocks. It was flowing, down into Treasure Valley, and as it flowed in the afternoon sun, it took on a golden hue. As Gluck gazed, fresh grass sprang up beside the river and little flowers and vines appeared. So it was that Treasure Valley became once again a garden, and the "land which had been lost by cruelty was won again by love."

JO MEETS APOLLYN FROM LITTLE WOMEN
by Louisa May Alcott[15]

Louisa Alcott's understanding of children and youth is penetrating. When older children dramatize this episode they are motivated to discuss such vital concerns as anger, revenge, and forgiveness. Dramatizations begin, generally, with a brief scene between Amy and Meg to establish the essential conflict. When children are guided to recognize the effectiveness of a happy mood to contrast with Jo's angry mood they frequently include a group of townsfolk to skate happily at the river and on down the bend before Jo and Laurie arrive. The concluding episode is the favorite.

The little women are the four March sisters. Lady-like Meg is sixteen, Tomboy Jo is fifteen and tall and thin. She has the uncomfortable appearance of a girl who is rapidly shooting up into a woman, and doesn't like it. Elizabeth, or Beth, as everyone calls her, is a rosy, bright-eyed girl of thirteen. Amy, though the youngest, is a most important person, at least in her own opinion. Laurie, seventeen, is the boy next door. As this episode opens Jo is deeply disturbed with Amy and will not accept her forgiveness because Amy, in revenge, burnt Jo's manuscript.

Jo still looked like a thundercloud, and nothing went well. It was bitter cold in the morning. . . . "Everybody is so hateful, I'll ask Laurie to go skating. He is always kind and jolly, and will put me to rights, I know," said Jo to herself, and off she went.

Amy heard the clash of skates, and looked out with an impatient exclamation: "There! She promised I should go next time, for this

[15] Reprinted from *Little Women*, by Louisa May Alcott, Grosset & Dunlap, Inc. Copyright, 1947, by Grossett & Dunlap, Inc.

is the last ice we shall have. But it's no use to ask such a crosspatch to take me."

"Don't say that; you *were* very naughty, and it *is* hard to forgive the loss of her precious little book; but I think she might do it now, and I guess she will, if you try her at the right minute," said Meg. "Go after them; don't say anything till Jo has got good-natured with Laurie; then take a quiet minute, and just kiss her, or do some kind thing, and I'm sure she'll be friends again, with all her heart."

"I'll try," said Amy, for the advice suited her; and, after a flurry to get ready, she ran after the friends, who were just disappearing over the hill.

It was not far to the river, but both were ready before Amy reached them. Jo saw her coming, and turned her back; Laurie did not see, for he was carefully skating along the shore, sounding the ice, for a warm spell had preceded the cold snap.

"I'll go on to the first bend, and see if it's all right, before we begin to race," Amy heard him say, as he shot away, looking like a young Russian, in his fur-trimmed coat and cap.

Jo heard Amy panting after her run, stamping her feet and blowing her fingers, as she tried to put her skates on, but Jo never turned, and went slowly zigzagging down the river, taking a bitter, unhappy sort of satisfaction in her sister's troubles. She had cherished her anger till it grew strong, and took possession of her, as evil thoughts and feelings always do, unless cast out at once. As Laurie turned the bend, he shouted back.

"Keep near the shore; it is not safe in the middle."

Jo heard, but Amy was just struggling to her feet, and did not catch a word. Jo glanced over her shoulder, and the little demon she was harboring said in her ear: "No matter whether she heard or not, let her take care of herself."

Laurie had vanished round the bend; Jo was just at the turn, and Amy, far behind, striking out toward the smoother ice in the middle of the river. For a minute Jo stood still, with a strange feeling at her heart; then she resolved to go on, but something held and turned her round, just in time to see Amy throw up her hands and go down, with the sudden crash of rotten ice, the splash of water, and a cry that made Jo's heart stand still with fear. She tried to call Laurie, but her voice was gone; she tried to rush forward, but her feet seemed to have no strength in them; and, for a second, she could only stand motionless, staring, with a terror-stricken face, at the little blue hood above the black water. Something rushed swiftly by her, and Laurie's voice cried out: "Bring a rail; quick, quick!"

How she did it, she never knew; but for the next few minutes she worked as if possessed, blindly obeying Laurie, who was quite self-possessed, and, lying flat, held Amy up by his arm and hockey, till Jo dragged a rail from the fence, and together they got the child out, more frightened than hurt.

"Now then, we must walk her home as fast as we can; pile our things on her, while I get off these confounded skates," cried Laurie, wrapping his coat round Amy, and tugging away at the straps, which never seemed so intricate before.

Shivering, dripping, and crying, they got Amy home; and, after an exciting time of it, she fell asleep, rolled in blankets, before a hot fire. During the bustle Jo had scarcely spoken; but flown about, looking pale and wild, with her things half off, her dress torn, and her hands cut and bruised by ice and rails, and refractory buckles. When Amy was comfortably asleep, the house quiet, and Mrs. March sitting by the bed, she called Jo to her, and began to bind up the hurt hands.

"Are you sure she is safe?" whispered Jo, looking remorsefully at the golden head, which might have been swept away from her sight forever under the treacherous ice.

"Quite safe, dear; she is not hurt, and won't even take cold, I think, you were so sensible in covering and getting her home quickly," replied her mother cheerfully.

"Laurie did it all; I only let her go. Mother, if she *should* die, it would be my fault"; and Jo dropped down beside the bed, in a passion of penitent tears, telling all that had happened, bitterly condemning her hardness of heart, and sobbing out her gratitude for being spared the heavy punishment which might come upon her.

"It's my dreadful temper! I try to cure it; I think I have, and then it breaks out worse than ever. Oh, mother, what shall I do? What shall I do?" cried poor Jo, in despair.

"Watch and pray, dear; never get tired of trying; and never think it is impossible to conquer your fault," said Mrs. March, drawing the blowzy head to her shoulder and kissing the wet cheek so tenderly that Jo cried harder than ever.

"You don't know, you can't guess how bad it is! It seems as if I could do anything when I'm in a passion; I get so savage, I could hurt anyone, and enjoy it. I'm afraid I *shall* do something dreadful someday, and spoil my life, and make everybody hate me. Oh, mother, help me, do help me!"

"I will, my child, I will. Don't cry so bitterly, but remember this day and resolve, with all your soul, that you will never know another like it. Jo, dear, we all have our temptations, some far greater than yours, and it often takes us all our lives to conquer them. You think your temper is the worst in the world; but mine used to be just like it."

"Yours, mother? Why, you are never angry!" and, for the moment, Jo forgot remorse in surprise.

"I've been trying to cure it for forty years, and have only succeeded in controlling it. I am angry nearly every day of my life, Jo; but I have learned not to show it; and I still hope to learn not to feel it, though it may take me another forty years to do so."

The patience and the humility of the face she loved so well was a better lesson to Jo than the wisest lecture, the sharpest reproof. She felt comforted at once by the sympathy and confidence given her; the knowledge that her mother had a fault like hers, and tried to mend it, made her own easier to bear and strengthened her resolution to cure it; though forty years seemed rather a long time to watch and pray, to a girl of fifteen.

"Mother, are you angry when you fold your lips tight together, and go out of the room sometimes, when Aunt March scolds or people worry you?" asked Jo, feeling nearer and dearer to her mother than ever before.

"Yes, I've learned to check the hasty words that rise to my lips; and when I feel that they mean to break out against my will, I just go away a minute, and give myself a little shake, for being so weak and wicked," answered Mrs. March, with a sigh and a smile, as she smoothed and fastened up Jo's disheveled hair.

"How did you learn to keep still? That is what troubles me—for the sharp words fly out before I know what I'm about; and the more I say the worse I get, till it is a pleasure to hurt people's feelings, and say dreadful things. Tell me how you do it, Marmee dear."

"My good mother used to help me—"

"As you do us—" interrupted Jo, with a grateful kiss.

"But I lost her when I was a little older than you are, and for years had to struggle on alone, for I was too proud to confess my weakness to anyone else. I had a hard time, Jo, and shed a good many bitter tears over my failures; for, in spite of my efforts, I never seemed to get on. Then your father came, and I was so happy that I found it easy to be good. But by and by, when I had four little daughters around me, and we were poor, then the old trouble began again; for I am not patient by nature, and it tried me very much to see my children wanting anything."

"Poor mother! What helped you then?"

"Your father, Jo. He never loses patience—never doubts or complains—but always hopes, and works, and waits so cheerfully that one is ashamed to do otherwise before him. He helped and comforted me, and showed me that I must try to practice all the virtues I would have my little girls possess, for I was their example. It was easier to try for your sakes than for my own; a startled or surprised look from one of you, when I spoke sharply, rebuked me more than any words could have done; and the love, respect, and confidence of my children was the sweetest reward I could receive for my efforts to be the woman I would have them copy."

"Oh, mother, if I'm ever half as good as you I shall be satisfied," cried Jo, much touched.

"I hope you will be a great deal better, dear; but you must keep watch over your 'bosom enemy,' as father calls it, or it may sadden, if not spoil your life. You have had a warning; remember it, and try with heart and soul to master this quick temper, before it brings you greater sorrow and regret than you have known today."

"I will try, mother; I truly will. But you must help me, remind me, and keep me from flying out . . ."

Jo saw that her mother's eyes filled and her lips trembled . . . . "Speaking of father reminded me how much I miss him, how much I owe him, and how faithfully I should watch and work to keep his little daughters safe and good for him."

"Yet you told him to go, mother, and didn't cry when he went, and never complain now, or seem as if you needed any help," said Jo, wondering.

"I gave my best to the country I love, and kept my tears till he was gone. Why should I complain, when we both have merely done our duty and will surely be the happier for it in the end? If I don't seem to need help, it is because I have a better friend, even than father, to comfort and sustain me. My child, the troubles and temptations of your life are beginning and may be many; but you can overcome and outlive them all if you learn to feel the strength and tenderness of your Heavenly Father as you do that of your earthly one. The more you love and trust Him, the nearer you will feel to Him, and the less you will depend on human power and wisdom. His love and care never tire or change, can never be taken from you, but may become the source of lifelong peace, happiness, and strength. Believe this heartily, and go to God with all your little cares, and hopes, and sins, and sorrows, as freely and confidingly as you come to your mother."

Jo's only answer was to hold her mother close, and, in the silence which followed, the sincerest prayer she had ever prayed left her heart without words. . . .

Amy stirred, and sighed in her sleep, and, as if eager to begin at once to mend her fault, Jo looked up with an expression on her face which it had never worn before.

"I let the sun go down on my anger; I wouldn't forgive her, and today, if it hadn't been for Laurie, it might have been too late! How could I be so wicked?" said Jo half aloud, as she leaned over her sister, softly stroking the wet hair scattered on the pillow.

As if she heard, Amy opened her eyes, and held out her arms, with a smile that went straight to Jo's heart. Neither said a word, but they hugged one another close, in spite of the blankets, and everything was forgiven and forgotten in one hearty kiss.

PROLOGUE TO THE MERRY ADVENTURES OF ROBIN HOOD

by Howard Pyle[16]

These adventures have been celebrated in ballad and story for centuries, and Howard Pyle's vigorous telling holds as much favor with modern children as it did with their forebears. The prologue, characteristic of Pyle's style, is told in dramatic form and invites dramatization when shared with adventure-minded boys and girls. This episode explains how Robin, the rightful Earl of Huntingdon, became an outlaw. It provides a forcible conflict between Robin and the king's foresters. Children admire Robin Hood for his qualities of courage, kindness, and daring in support of the poor, as well as for his rare skill at archery. When characterizations are understood, dramatizations are always enjoyed, particularly when children interpret with vigor in outdoor settings on schools grounds or at camp.

In merry England in the time of old, when good King Henry the Second ruled the land, there lived within the green glades of Sherwood Forest, near Nottingham Town, a famous outlaw whose name was Robin Hood. No archer ever lived that could speed a gray goose shaft with such skill and cunning as his, nor were there ever such yeomen as the sevenscore merry men that roamed with him through the greenwood shades. Right merrily they dwelt within the depths of Sherwood Forest, suffering neither care nor want, but passing the time in merry games of archery or bouts of cudgel play, living upon the King's venison, washed down with draughts of ale of October brewing.

Not only Robin himself but all the band were outlaws and dwelt apart from other men, yet they were beloved by the country people

[16] From *The Merry Adventures of Robin Hood* by Howard Pyle, Charles Scribner's Sons. Copyright, 1946, by Charles Scribner's Sons.

round about, for no one ever came to jolly Robin for help in time of need and went away again with an empty fist.

And now I will tell how it came about that Robin Hood fell afoul of the law.

When Robin was a youth of eighteen, stout of sinew and bold of heart, the Sheriff of Nottingham proclaimed a shooting-match and offered a prize of a butt of ale to whomsoever should shoot the best shaft in Nottinghamshire. "Now," quoth Robin, "will I go too, for fain would I draw a string for the bright eyes of my lass, and a butt of good October brewing." So up he got and took his good stout yew bow and a score or more of broad clothyard arrows, and started off from Locksley Town through Sherwood Forest to Nottingham.

It was at the dawn of day in the Merry May-time, when hedgerows are green and flowers bedeck the meadows; daisies pied and yellow cuckoo buds and fair primroses all along the briery hedges; when apple buds blossom and sweet birds sing, the lark at dawn of day, the throstle cock and cuckoo; when lads and lasses look up each other with sweet thoughts; when busy housewives spread their linen to bleach upon the bright green grass. Sweet was the greenwood as he walked along its paths, and bright the green and rustling leaves, amid which the little birds sang with might and main: and blithely Robin whistled as he trudged along, thinking of Maid Marian and her bright eyes, for at such times a youth's thoughts are wont to turn pleasantly upon the lass that he loves the best.

As thus he walked along with a brisk step and a merry whistle, he came suddenly upon some foresters seated beneath a great oak tree. Fifteen there were in all, making themselves merry with feasting and drinking as they sat around a huge pasty, to which each man helped himself, thrusting his hands into the pie, and washing down that which they ate with great horns of ale which they drew all foaming from a barrel that stood nigh. Each man was clad in Lincoln green, and a fine show they made, seated upon the sward beneath that fair, spreading tree. Then one of them, with his mouth full, called out to Robin, "Hulloa, where goest thou, little lad, with thy one penny bow and thy farthing shafts?"

Then Robin grew angry, for no stripling likes to be taunted with his green years.

"Now," quoth he, "my bow and eke mine arrows are as good as thine; and moreover, I go to the shooting-match at Nottingham Town, which same has been proclaimed by our good Sheriff of Nottingham; there I will shoot with other stout yeomen, for a prize has been offered of a fine butt of ale."

Then one who held a horn of ale in his hand, said, "Ho! listen to the lad! Why, boy, thy mother's milk is yet scarce dry upon thy lips, and yet thou pratest of standing up with good stout men at Nottingham butts, thou who art scarce able to draw one string of a two stone bow."

"I'll hold the best of you twenty marks," quoth bold Robin, "that I hit the clout at threescore yards, by the good help of Our Lady fair."

At this all laughed aloud, and one said, "Well boasted, thou fair infant, well boasted! and well thou knowest that no target is nigh to make good thy wager."

And another cried, "He will be taking ale with his milk next."

At this Robin grew right mad. "Hark ye," said he; "yonder, at the glade's end, I see a herd of deer, even more than three-score rods distant. I'll hold you twenty marks that by leave of Our Lady, I cause the best hart among them to die."

"Now done!" cried he who spoken first. "And here are twenty marks. I wager that thou causest no beast to die, with or without the aid of Our Lady."

Then Robin took his good yew bow in his hand, and placing the tip at his instep, he strung it right deftly; then he nocked a broad cloth-yard arrow, and, raising the bow, drew the gray goose-feather to his ear: the next moment the bowstring rang and the arrow sped down the glade as a sparrowhawk skims in a northern wind. High leaped the noblest hart of all the herd, only to fall dead, reddening the green path with his heart's blood.

"Ha!" cried Robin, "how likest thou that shot, good fellow? I wot the wager were mine, as it were three hundred pounds."

Then all the foresters were filled with rage, and he who had spoken the first and had lost the wager was more angry than all.

"Nay," cried he, "the wager is none of thine, and get thee gone, straightway, or, by all the saints of heaven, I'll baste thy sides until thou wilt ne'er be able to walk again."

"Knowest thou not," said another, "that thou hast killed the King's deer, and, by the laws of our gracious lord and sovereign, King Harry, thine ears should be shaven close to thy head?"

"Catch him!" cried a third.

"Nay," said a fourth, "let him e'en go because of his tender years."

Never a word said Robin Hood, but he looked at the foresters with a grim face; then, turning on his heel, strode away from them down the forest glade. But his heart was bitterly angry, for his blood was hot and youthful and prone to boil.

Now, well would it have been for him who had first spoken had he left Robin Hood alone; but his anger was hot, both because the youth had gotten the better of him and because of the deep draughts of ale that he had been quaffing. So, of a sudden, without any warning, he sprang to his feet, and seized upon his bow and fitted it to a shaft. "Ay," cried he, "and I'll hurry thee anon"; and he sent the arrow whistling after Robin.

It was well for Robin Hood that that same forester's head was spinning with ale, or else he would never have taken another step; as it was, the arrow whistled within three inches of his head. Then he turned around and quickly drew his own bow, and sent an arrow back in return.

"Ye said I was no archer," cried he aloud, "but say so now again!"

The shaft flew straight; the archer fell forward with a cry, and lay on his face upon the ground, his arrows rattling about him from out of his quiver, the gray goose shaft wet with his heart's blood. Then, before the others could gather their wits about them, Robin Hood was gone into the depths of the greenwood. Some started after him, but not with much heart, for each feared to suffer the death of his fellow; so presently they all came and lifted the dead man up and bore him away to Nottingham Town.

Meanwhile Robin Hood ran through the greenwood. Gone was all the joy and brightness from everything, for his heart was sick within him, and it was borne in upon his soul that he had slain a man.

"Alas!" cried he, "thou hast found me an archer that will make thy wife to wring! I would that thou hadst ne'er said one word to me, or that I had never passed thy way, or e'en that my right fore-finger had been stricken off ere that this had happened! In haste I smote, but grieve I sore at leisure!" And then, even in his trouble, he remembered the old saw that "What is done is done; and the egg cracked cannot be cured."

And so he came to dwell in the greenwood that was to be his home for many a year to come, never again to see the happy days with the lads and lasses of sweet Locksley Town; for he was outlawed, not only because he had killed a man, but also because he had poached upon the King's deer, and two hundred pounds were set upon his head, as a reward for whoever would bring him to the court of the King.

TRAGEDY IN THE GRAVEYARD,
FROM THE ADVENTURES OF TOM SAWYER
by Samuel L. Clemens[17]

Suspense is always enjoyed in dramatic pantomime when Tom listens to night sounds while he waits in bed beside Sid for Huck's whistle; then sneaks out the window to join Huck in curing warts at the cemetery. The gloomy atmosphere of the graveyard is changed to intense fear when the two boys become secret witnesses of a murder. Rich humor and insight into character cause this adventure to be a favorite for dramatization. "Cloudburst" from Grofé's *Grand Canyon Suite* provides an appropriate background for mood when this adventure is dramatized in pantomime.

At half past nine, that night, Tom and Sid were sent to bed, as usual. They said their prayers, and Sid was soon asleep. Tom lay awake and waited, in restless impatience. When it seemed to him that it must be nearly daylight, he heard the clock strike ten! This was despair. He would have tossed and fidgeted, as his nerves demanded,

[17] Chapter IX from *The Adventures of Tom Sawyer* by Samuel L. Clemens. Reprinted by permission of Harper & Row, Publishers, Inc.

but he was afraid he might wake Sid. So he lay still, and stared up into the dark. Everything was dismally still. By and by, out of the stillness, little, scarcely perceptible noises began to emphasize themselves. The ticking of the clock began to bring itself into notice. Old beams began to crack mysteriously. The stairs creaked faintly. Evidently spirits were abroad. A measured, muffled snore issued from Aunt Polly's chamber. And now the tiresome chirping of a cricket that no human ingenuity could locate, began. . . . Then the howl of a far-off dog rose on the night air, and was answered by a fainter howl from a remoter distance. Tom was in an agony. At last he was satisfied that time had ceased and eternity begun; he began to doze, in spite of himself; the clock chimed eleven, but he did not hear it. And then there came, mingling with his half-formed dreams a most melancholy caterwauling. The raising of a neighboring window disturbed him. A cry of "Scat! you devil!" and the crash of an empty bottle against the back of his aunt's woodshed brought him wide awake, and a single minute later he was dressed and out of the window and creeping along the roof of the "ell" on all fours. He "meow'd" with caution once or twice, as he went; then jumped to the roof of the woodshed and thence to the ground. Huckleberry Finn was there, with his dead cat. The boys moved off and disappeared in the gloom. At the end of half an hour they were wading through the tall grass of the graveyard.

It was a graveyard of the old-fashioned western kind. It was on a hill, about a mile and a half from the village. It had a crazy board fence around it, which leaned inward in places, and outward the rest of the time, but stood upright nowhere. Grass and weeds grew rank over the whole cemetery. . . .

A faint wind moaned through the trees, and Tom feared it might be the spirits of the dead, complaining of being disturbed. The boys talked little, and only under their breath, for the time and the place and the pervading solemnity and silence oppressed their spirits. They found the sharp new heap they were seeking, and ensconced themselves within the protection of three great elms that grew in a bunch within a few feet of the grave.

Then they waited in silence for what seemed a long time. The hooting of a distant owl was all the sound that troubled the dead stillness. Tom's reflections grew oppressive. He must force some talk. So he said in a whisper:

"Hucky, do you believe the dead people like it for us to be here?"

Huckleberry whispered:

"I wisht I knowed. It's awful solemn like, *ain't* it?"

"I bet it is."

There was a considerable pause, while the boys canvassed this matter inwardly. Then Tom whispered:

"Say, Hucky—do you reckon Hoss Williams hears us talking?"

"O' course he does. Least his sperrit does."

Tom, after a pause:

"I wish I'd said *Mister* Williams. But I never meant any harm. Everybody calls him Hoss."

"A body can't be too partic'lar how they talk 'bout these yer dead people, Tom."

This was a damper, and conversation died again.

Presently Tom seized his comrade's arm and said:

"Sh!"

"What is it, Tom?" And the two clung together with beating hearts.

"Sh! There 'tis again! Didn't you hear it?"

"I—"

"There! Now you hear it."

"Lord, Tom, they're coming! They're coming, sure. What'll we do?"

"I dono. Think they'll see us?"

"Oh, Tom, they can see in the dark, same as cats. I wisht I hadn't come."

"Oh, don't be afeared. *I* don't believe they'll bother us. We ain't doing any harm. If we keep perfectly still, maybe they won't notice us at all."

"I'll try to, Tom, but Lord, I'm all of a shiver."

"Listen!"

The boys bent their heads together and scarcely breathed. A muffled sound of voices floated up from the far end of the graveyard.

"Look! See there!" whispered Tom. "What is it?"

"It's devil-fire. Oh, Tom, this is awful."

Some vague figures approached through the gloom, swinging an old-fashioned tin lantern that freckled the ground with innumerable little spangles of light. Presently Huckleberry whispered with a shudder:

"It's the devils, sure enough. Three of 'em. Lordy, Tom, we're goners! Can you pray?"

"I'll try, but don't you be afeared. They ain't going to hurt us. Now I lay me down to sleep, I—"

"Sh!"

"What is it, Huck?"

"They're *humans*! One of 'em is, anyway. One of 'em's old Muff Potter's voice."

"No—tain't so, is it?"

"I bet I know it. Don't you stir nor budge. *He* ain't sharp enough to notice us. . . ."

"All right, I'll keep still. Now they're stuck. Can't find it. Here they come again. Now they're hot. Cold again. Hot again. Red hot! They're p'inted right, this time. Say, Huck, I know another o' them voices; it's Injun Joe."

"That's so—that murderin' [Injun]! I'd druther they was devils a dern sight. What kin they be up to?"

The whispers died wholly out, now, for the three men had reached the grave and stood within a few feet of the boys' hiding place.

"Here it is," said the third voice; and the owner of it held the lantern up and revealed the face of young Dr. Robinson.

Potter and Injun Joe were carrying a handbarrow with a rope and a couple of shovels on it. They cast down their load and began to open the grave. The doctor put the lantern at the head of the grave and came and sat down with his back against one of the elm trees. He was so close the boys could have touched him.

"Hurry men!" he said in a low voice; "the moon might come out at any moment."

They growled a response and went on digging. For some time there was no noise but the grating sound of the spades discharging their freight of mold and gravel. It was very monotonous. Finally a spade struck upon the coffin with a dull woody accent, and within another minute or two the men had hoisted it out on the ground. They pried off the lid with their shovels, got out the body and dumped it rudely on the ground.

"Now the cussed thing's ready, Sawbones, and you'll just out with another five, or here she stays."

"That's the talk!" said Injun Joe.

"Look here, what does this mean?" said the doctor. "You required your pay in advance, and I've paid you."

"Yes, and you done more than that," said Injun Joe, approaching the doctor, who was now standing. "Five years ago you drove me away from your father's kitchen one night, when I come to ask for something to eat, and you said I warn't there for any good; and when I swore I'd get even with you if it took a hundred years, your father had me jailed for a vagrant. Did you think I'd forget? The Injun blood ain't in me for nothing. And now I've *got* you, and you got to *settle*, you know!"

He was threatening the doctor, with his fist in his face, by this time. The doctor struck out suddenly and stretched the ruffian on the ground. Potter dropped his knife, and exclaimed:

"Here, now, don't you hit my pard!" and the next moment he had grappled with the doctor and the two were struggling with might and main, trampling the grass and tearing the ground with their heels. Injun Joe sprang to his feet, his eyes flaming with passion, snatched up Potter's knife, and went creeping, catlike and stooping, round and round about the combatants, seeking an opportunity. All at once the doctor flung himself free, seized the heavy head-board of Williams' grave and felled Potter to the earth with it—and in the same instant the Indian saw his chance and drove the knife . . . and in the same moment the clouds blotted out the dreadful spectacle and the two frightened boys went speeding away in the dark.

Presently, when the moon emerged again, Injun Joe was standing over the two forms, contemplating them. The doctor murmured inarticulately, gave a long gasp or two and was still. The Indian muttered:

"*That* score is settled— . . . ."

After which he put the fatal knife in Potter's open right hand, and sat down on the dismantled coffin. Three—four—five minutes passed, and then Potter began to stir and moan. His hand closed upon the knife; he raised it, glanced at it, and let it fall, with a shudder. Then he sat up, pushing the body from him, and gazed at it, and then around him, confusedly. His eyes met Joe's.

"Lord, how is this, Joe?" he said.

"It's dirty business," said Joe, without moving. "What did you do it for?"

"I! I never done it!"

Potter trembled and grew white.

". . . I'm all in a muddle; can't recollect anything of it, hardly. Tell me, Joe—*honest*, now, old feller—did I do it? Joe, I never meant to —'pon my soul and honor, I never meant to, Joe. Tell me how it was, Joe. Oh, it's awful—and him so young and promising."

"Why, you two was scuffling; and he fetched you one with the head-board and you fell flat; and then up you come, all reeling and staggering, like, and snatched the knife and jammed it into him, just as he fetched you another awful clip—and here you've laid, as dead as a wedge till now."

"Oh, I didn't know what I was a-doing. I wish I may die this minute if I did. . . . I never used a weepon in my life before, Joe. I've fought, but never with weepons. They'll all say that. Joe, don't tell! Say you won't tell, Joe—that's a good feller. I always liked you, Joe, and stood up for you, too. Don't you remember? You *won't* tell, *will* you, Joe?" And the poor creature dropped on his knees before the stolid murderer, and clasped his appealing hands.

"No, you've always been fair and square with me, Muff Potter, and I won't go back on you—There, now, that's as fair as a man can say."

"Oh, Joe, you're an angel. I'll bless you for this the longest day I live." And Potter began to cry.

"Come, now, that's enough of that. This ain't any time for blubbering. You be off yonder way and I'll go this. Move, now, and don't leave any tracks behind you."

Potter started on a trot that quickly increased to a run. The Indian stood looking after him. He muttered:

"If he's as much stunned . . . as he had the look of being, he won't think of the knife till he's gone so far he'll be afraid to come back after it to such a place by himself—chicken-heart!"

Two or three minutes later the murdered man, the blanketed corpse, the lidless coffin, and the open grave were under no inspection but the moon's. The stillness was complete again, too.

THE SOLEMN OATH,
FROM THE ADVENTURES OF TOM SAWYER
by Samuel L. Clemens[18]

This episode offers a rare occasion for children to work in pairs to interpret Tom and Hucks' reaction to fear with spontaneous dialogue.

The two boys flew on and on, toward the village, speechless with horror. They glanced backward over their shoulders from time to time, apprehensively, as if they feared they might be followed. Every stump that started up in their path seemed a man and an enemy, and made them catch their breath; and as they sped by some outlying cottages that lay near the village, the barking of the aroused watch-dogs seemed to give wings to their feet.

"If we can only get to the old tannery before we break down!" whispered Tom, in short-catches between breaths. "I can't stand it much longer."

Huckleberry's hard pantings were his only reply, and the boys fixed their eyes on the goal of their hopes and bent to their work to win it. They gained steadily on it, and at last, breast to breast, they burst through the open door and fell grateful and exhausted in the sheltering shadows beyond. By and by their pulses slowed down, and Tom whispered:

"Huckleberry, what do you reckon'll come of this?"

"If Dr. Robinson dies, I reckon hanging'll come of it."

"Do you though?"

[18] Chapter X from *The Adventures of Tom Sawyer* by Samuel L. Clemens. Reprinted by permission of Harper & Row, Publishers, Inc.

"Why, I *know* it, Tom."

Tom thought awhile, then he said:

"Who'll tell? We?"

"What are you talking about? S'pose something happened and Injun Joe *didn't* hang? Why he'd kill us some time or other, just as dead sure as we're a-laying here."

"That's just what I was thinking to myself, Huck."

"If anybody tells, let Muff Potter do it, if he's fool enough. . . ."

Tom said nothing—went on thinking. Presently he whispered:

"Huck, Muff Potter don't *know* it. How can he tell?"

"What's the reason he don't know it?"

"Because he'd just got that whack when Injun Joe done it. D' you reckon he could see anything? D' you reckon he knowed anything?"

"By hokey, that's so, Tom!"

"And besides, look-a-here—maybe that whack done for *him!*"

"No, 'tain't likely, Tom. . . ."

"Hucky, you sure you can keep mum?"

"Tom, we *got* to keep mum. *You* know that. That Injun . . . wouldn't make any more of drownding us than a couple of cats, if we was to squeak 'bout this and they didn't hang him. Now, look-a-here, Tom, le's take and swear to one another—that's what we got to do—swear to keep mum."

"I'm agreed. It's the best thing. Would you just hold hand and swear that we—"

"Oh, no, that wouldn't do for this. That's good enough for little rubbishy common things—specially with gals, cuz *they* go back on you anyway, and blab if they get in a huff—but there orter be writing 'bout a big thing like this. And blood."

Tom's whole being applauded this idea. It was deep, and dark, and awful; the hour, the circumstances, the surroundings, were in keeping with it. He picked up a clean pine shingle that lay in the moonlight, took a little fragment of "red keel" out of his pocket, got the moon on his work, and painfully scrawled these lines, emphasizing each slow down-stroke by clamping his tongue between his teeth, and letting up the pressure on the up-strokes.

HUCK FINN AND
TOM SAWYER SWEARS
THEY WILL KEEP MUM
ABOUT THIS AND THEY
WISH THEY MAY DROP
DOWN DEAD IN THEIR
TRACKS IF THEY EVER
TELL AND ROT.

Huckleberry was filled with admiration of Tom's facility in writing, and the sublimity of his language. He at once took a pin from his lapel and was going to prick his flesh, but Tom said:

"Hold on! Don't do that. A pin's brass. It might have verdigrease on it."

"What's verdigrease?"

"It's p'ison. That's what it is. You just swaller some of it once— you'll see."

So Tom unwound the thread from one of his needles, and each boy pricked the ball of his thumb and squeezed out a drop of blood. In time, after many squeezes, Tom managed to sign his initials, using the ball of his little finger for a pen. Then he showed Huckleberry how to make an H and an F, and the oath was complete. They buried the shingle close to the wall, with some dismal ceremonies and incantations, and the fetters that bound their tongues were considered to be locked and the key thrown away.

• • •

Then they separated, cogitating. When Tom crept in at his bedroom window, the night was almost spent. He undressed with excessive caution, and fell asleep congratulating himself that nobody knew of his escapade. He was not aware that the gently snoring Sid was awake, and had been so for an hour.

Appendixes

Suggestions for use of materials

Not all children will respond for the same reasons to the same stories, and each teacher will find his own ways of predicting "readiness" for a particular story by a given group of children. Some generalizations may be helpful in this process. For example, seasons of the year, and the age level of children provide general patterns for predicting responses.

Subject Interests by Seasons

All sorts of things and weather
Must be taken in together,
To make up a year
And a Sphere.

RALPH WALDO EMERSON

Poetry and stories appeal particularly to children when they are interested in the subject and aroused by the pervading mood of a particular piece of literature. Children's moods are awakened naturally by environmental, social, and traditional happenings which occur during the various seasons of a year. Mood is aroused also by awareness and reflection on a particular thought or feeling. Interest by subjects and moods within seasons is the point of view from which the following selections have been arranged. These suggestions are to be regarded clearly as *suggestions*. It happens now and then that a story or poem suggested for appeal in springtime may find noticeable response for a group of children in winter or autumn if the children are interested in the subject and tuned in to a particular mood revealed within the literature.

315

AUTUMN INTERESTS

POEMS

Action
Pat-a-Cake ❋ To Market ❋
  ❋ Spring is Showery ❋ Yankee-
  Doodle ❋ Happy Birthday
Sing a Song of Seasons

Afternoon on a Hill
Marching Song
Happy Thought
A Song of Greatness

Characterization
Baby Seeds
Trains
Up in the Air
Eskimo Land
Mexico
Fish
Halloween

Psalm 150
Morning
The Mysterious Cat
Dance of Death
Thanksgiving Day
The Bagpipe Man
Meg Merrilies

Conflict
Five Little Squirrels ❋ I Had a
  Little Nut Tree
Come Little Leaves
Hunting for a Halloween Cat
Women in Moss
Lines from "The New Colossus"
The Country Mouse and the Town
  Mouse
The Turtle and the Rabbit

The New Duckling
Lines from "Hiawatha's Child-
  hood
The Charge of the Light Brigade
Barbara Frietchie
I Saw Three Witches
The Pirate Don Durk of Dowdee
The Creation

STORIES

Action
Home on Sunday
The Hanukkah Dreidle
The Lion and the Mouse
Teeny-Tiny
Little Mouse and Mr. Scare Crow
A First Thanksgiving
The Gingerbread Boy

The Big Spider
Henny-Penny
Adventure in the Orchard
Injun Summer
Wahoo
The Horned Women
Dunis and the Thankful Frog

The Little Rabbit Who Wanted
   Red Wings

Joseph the Dreamer
Twenty Pieces of Silver

WINTER INTERESTS

POEMS

Action
Galoshes
My Shadow
Skating

An Old Christmas Greeting
For Hanukkah

Characterization
Riddle-dee-dee ❋ A Star ❋
   A Candle
Falling Snow
Fog

A Valentine
Jack Frost
From "Snowbound"

Conflict
The North Wind Doth Blow
  ❋ Tom, Tom, the Piper's Son
  ❋ Little Robin Redbreast

Boats in Fog
Long, Long Ago
A Visit from St. Nicholas

STORIES

Where is Christmas
The Story of Christmas
Claire and the Nutcracker
Why the Chimes Rang
Snow-White and Rose-Red

Molly Whuppie
Prometheus
Where Love Is, God Is
King of the Golden River
Jo Meets Apollyn

SPRING INTERESTS

POEMS

Action
Pat-a-Cake ❋ To Market ❋
   Spring is Showery ❋ Yankee-
   Doodle ❋ Happy Birthday

Marching Song
Mud
Picnicking

Sing a Song of Seasons
At the Seaside
Merry-Go-Round
Afternoon on a Hill
The Swing

Happy Thought
My Shadow
If Once You Have Slept on an
Island

Characterization
The Wind
Rain
The Little Plant
Baby Seed Song
The Secret

A Fairy
Lines from "The Song of Solomon"
The Year's at the Spring
Circus

Conflict
Ride a Cock Horse * Humpty
Dumpty * Hey, Diddle,
Diddle * Three Young Rats
Crab-Apple
Women in Moss

Frogs at School
I Saw Three Witches
Pirate Don Durk of Dowdee
Casey at the Bat
The Creation

STORIES

The Little Flower Who Never Got
a Bloom
Cats for Free
Home for a Bunny
The Peddler and the Monkeys
Pua and the Menehunes
The Wolf and the Kids
Fraidy-Cat and the Wise One
Raggylug
The Big Turnip
A Place of Peace
How the Potato Face Blind Man
Enjoyed Himself on a Fine
Spring Morning
The Frog Prince
Boots and His Brothers

Urashima Taro
Rapunzel
The Ugly Duckling
Drakestail
An Ark in the Wilderness
David, the Shepherd Boy
David and the Giant of Gath
Pandora
Demeter and Persephone
The Death of Balder
The Knights of the Silver Shield
Prologue to the Merry Adventures
of Robin Hood
Tragedy in the Graveyard
The Solemn Oath

Age Level Interests

The world stands out on either side
No wider than the heart is wide.
                                    EDNA ST. VINCENT MILLAY

Experience with children suggests the following arrangement of poems and stories according to their maximum age group appeals.

FIVE- AND SIX-YEAR-OLDS—A REAL WORLD AWAITS

POEMS

Action
Pat-a-Cake ✳ to Market ✳
    Spring is Showery ✳ Yankee-
    Doodle ✳ Happy Birthday
Sing a Song of Seasons
At the Seaside
Merry-Go-Round
Afternoon on a Hill
Marching Song

Galoshes
Mud
Picnicking
The Swing
Happy Thought
My Shadow
An Old Christmas Greeting
For Hanukkah

Characterization
Riddle-dee-ldee ✳ A Star ✳ A
    Candle
The Wind
Baby Seeds
Rain
Falling Snow
Trains
Up in the Air

The Little Plant
Baby Seed Song
Fish
Fog
The Secret
A Valentine
Halloween

Conflict
The North Wind Doth Blow ✳
    Five Little Squirrels ✳ Ride a
    Cock Horse ✳ Humpty
    Dumpty ✳ Tom, Tom, the
    Piper's Son ✳ Hey, Diddle,
    Diddle ✳ Little Robin Redbreast

Boats in Fog
Come Little Leaves
Hunting for a Halloween Cat
Long, Long Ago
A Visit from St. Nicholas

STORIES

The Little Flower Who Never Got
  a Bloom
Cats for Free
Home for a Bunny
Home on Sunday
The Hanukkah Dreidle
The Peddler and the Monkeys
The Lion and the Mouse
The Wolf and the Kids
Teeny-Tiny
Little Mouse and Mr. Scare Crow
A First Thanksgiving

Where Is Christmas
The Story of Christmas
Fraidy-Cat and the Wise One
The Gingerbread Boy
Raggylug
The Little Rabbit Who Wanted
  Red Wings
The Big Spider
The Big Turnip
Henny-Penny
Injun Summer

SEVEN-, EIGHT- AND NINE-YEAR-OLDS—IT'S A WONDERFUL WORLD

POEMS

Action

A Market ❋ Spring is Showery
  ❋ Happy Birthday
Sing a Song of Seasons
At the Seaside
Merry-Go-Round
Afternoon on a Hill
Marching Song
Mud
Picnicking

The Swing
Happy Thought
My Shadow
If Once You Have Slept on an
  Island
Skating
An Old Christmas Greeting
For Hanukkah

Characterization

Riddle-dee-dee ❋ A Star ❋ A
  Candle
The Wind
Baby Seeds
Rain
Falling Snow
Trains
Up in the Air
The Little Plant

Fish
Fog
A Valentine
Jack Frost
Halloween
A Fairy
The Year's at the Spring
Circus
The Mysterious Cat

Eskimo Land
Mexico

Thanksgiving Day
The Bagpipe Man

Conflict

The North Wind Doth Blow *
  Five Little Squirrels * Ride a
  Cock Horse * Humpty Dumpty
  * Tom, Tom, the Piper's Son *
  Hey, Diddle, Diddle * Three
  Young Rats * I Had a Little Nut
  Tree * Little Robin Redbreast
Boats in Fog
Crab-Apple
Come Little Leaves

Hunting for a Halloween Cat
Women in Moss
Frogs at School
Long, Long Ago
The Grasshopper and the Ant
The New Duckling
The Turtle and the Rabbit
The Pirate Don Durk of Dowdee
A Visit from St. Nicholas
The Creation

STORIES

The Little Flower Who Never Got
  a Bloom
Cats for Free
Home for a Bunny
Home on Sunday
The Hanukkah Dreidle
The Peddler and the Monkeys
Pua and the Menehunes
The Lion and the Mouse
The Wolf and the Kids
Teeny-Tiny
Little Mouse and Mr. Scare Crow
A First Thanksgiving
Where Is Christmas
The Story of Christmas
Claire and the Nutcracker
Fraidy-Cat and the Wise One
The Gingerbread Boy
Raggylug
The Little Rabbit Who Wanted
  Red Wings

The Big Spider
The Big Turnip
Henny-Penny
A Place of Peace
Adventure in the Orchard
Injun Summer
Wahoo
Snow Maiden
Boots and His Brothers
The Horned Women
Snow-White and Rose-Red
Molly Whuppie
Urashima Taro
Rapunzel
Dunis and the Thankful Frog
The Ugly Duckling
Drakestail
An Ark in the Wilderness
David, the Shepherd Boy
Joseph the Dreamer

TEN-, ELEVEN- AND TWELVE-YEAR-OLDS—THE OPEN ROAD . . . THE
WORLD BEFORE ME

POEMS

Action
Sing a Song of Seasons
Afternoon on a Hill
Happy Thought
If Once You Have Slept on an
    Island

Skating
An Old Christmas Greeting
For Hanukkah
A Song of Greatness

Characterization
The Wind
Fish
Fog
A Valentine
Psalm 150
Lines from "The Song of Solomon"
The Year's at the Spring
Morning

Circus
The Mysterious Cat
Dance of Death
Thanksgiving Day
From "Snowbound"
The Bagpipe Man
Meg Merrilies

Conflict
Tom, Tom, the Piper's Son ✱
    Hey, Diddle, Diddle ✱ Three
    Young Rats
Women in Moss
Long, Long Ago
Lines from "The New Colossus"
The Country Mouse and the Town
    Mouse
The Grasshopper and the Ant
The Turtle and the Rabbit

The New Duckling
Lines from "Hiawatha's Child-
    hood"
The Charge of the Light Brigade
Barbara Frietchie
I Saw Three Witches
The Pirate Don Durk of Dowdee
A Visit from St. Nicholas
Casey at the Bat
The Creation

STORIES

The Peddler and the Monkeys
A First Thanksgiving
The Story of Christmas
Claire and the Nutcracker

Dunis and the Thankful Frog
The Ugly Duckling
Drakestail
An Ark in the Wilderness

Raggylug
A Place of Peace
How the Potato Face Blind Man
  Enjoyed Himself on a Fine
  Spring Morning
Adventure in the Orchard
Injun Summer
Why the Chimes Rang
Wahoo
Snow Maiden
The Frog Prince
Boots and His Brothers
The Horned Women
Snow-White and Rose-Red
Molly Whuppie
Urashima Taro
Rapunzel

David, the Shepherd Boy
David and the Giant of Gath
Joseph the Dreamer
Twenty Pieces of Silver
Prometheus
Pandora
Demeter and Persephone
The Death of Balder
The Knights of the Silver Shield
Where Love Is, God Is
King of the Golden River
Jo Meets Apollyn
Prologue to the Merry Adventures
  of Robin Hood
Tragedy in the Graveyard
The Solemn Oath

Bibliography

This is a selective list of books in the specialized area of creative dramatics and related fields.

CREATIVE DRAMATICS AND
CHILDREN'S THEATRE

Allstrom, Elizabeth, *Let's Play a Story*, Friendship Press, 1957.

Association for Childhood Education International, *Creative Dramatics*, Membership Service Bulletin, No. 2-A, Association for Childhood Education International, 1961.

Brown, Corinne, *Creative Drama in the Lower School*, Appleton-Century-Crofts, Inc., 1929.

Burger, Isabel, *Creative Play Acting*, A. S. Barnes & Co., 1950.

Davis, Jed H. and Mary Jane Watkins, *Children's Theatre*, Harper & Row, Publishers, Inc., 1960.

Durland, Francis Caldwell, *Creative Dramatics for Children*, The Antioch Press, 1952.

Fitzgerald, Burdette, *Let's Act the Story*, Fearon Publishers, 1957.

Fitzgerald, Burdette, *World Tales for Creative Dramatics and Storytelling*, Prentice-Hall, Inc., 1962.

Gillies, Emily P., "Crosses and Knives," *Childhood Education*, May, 1946, pp. 435 ff.; April, 1947, pp. 382 ff.

Gillies, Emily P., "Therapy Dramatics for the Public Schoolroom," *The Nervous Child*, July, 1948, pp. 328 ff.

Haaga, Agnes and Patricia Randles, *Supplementary Materials for Use in Creative Dramatics for Younger Children*, University of Washington Press, 1952.

Hartley, Ruth E., Lawrence K. Frank, and Robert M. Goldenson, *Understanding Children's Play*, Columbia University Press, 1952.

Kase, C. Robert, *Stories for Creative Acting*, Samuel French, Inc., 1961.
Kerman, Gertrude Lerner, *Plays and Creative Ways with Children*, Harvey House, 1961.
Lease, Ruth G. and Geraldine Brain Siks, *Creative Dramatics in Home, School and Community*, Harper & Row, Publishers, Inc., 1952.
Lowndes, Polly, *Creative Assemblies*, T. S. Denison & Co., 1961.
Merrill, John and Martha Fleming, *Playmaking and Plays*, The Macmillan Company, 1930.
Siks, Geraldine Brain and Hazel Brain Dunnington (eds.), *Children's Theatre and Creative Dramatics*, University of Washington Press, 1961.
Siks, Geraldine Brain, *Creative Dramatics: An Art for Children*, Harper & Row, Publishers, Inc., 1952.
Siks, Geraldine Brain, "Creative Dramatics for Children," *Ginn and Company Contributions in Reading No. 26*, Ginn and Company, Publishers, 1961.
Slade, Peter, *Child Drama*, The University of London Press, 1954.
Walker, Pamela Prince, *Seven Steps to Creative Children's Dramatics*, Hill & Wang, 1957.
Ward, Winifred, *Creative Dramatics: For the Upper Grades and Junior High School*, Appleton-Century-Crofts, Inc., 1930.
Ward, Winifred, *Playmaking with Children*, 2nd ed., Appleton-Century-Crofts, Inc., 1957.
Ward, Winifred, *Theatre for Children*, rev. ed., The Children's Theatre Press, 1950.
Ward, Winifred, *Stories to Dramatize*, The Children's Theatre Press, 1952.
Ward, Winifred, *Drama With and For Children*, U.S. Government Printing Office, 1960.
Ward, Winifred and Rita Criste (film eds.), *Creative Drama: The First Steps*, Northwestern University and Gilbert Altschul Productions, Inc., 1962.
Woods, Margaret S., *Thinking, Feeling, Experiencing; Toward Realization of Full Potential*, National Educational Association, 1962.
Wykell, Esther, *Creative Dramatics in the Jewish School*, Board of Jewish Education, 1962.

THEATRE

Baker, George Pierce, *Dramatic Technique*, Houghton Mifflin Company, 1919.

Cheney, Sheldon, *The Theater: Three Thousand Years of Drama, Acting, and Stagecraft*, Longmans, Green & Co., Inc., 1930.

Dean, Alexander, *Fundamentals of Play Directing*, Holt, Rinehart and Winston, Inc., 1941.

Freedley, George and John A. Reeves, A *History of the Theatre*, Crown Publishers, Inc., 1941.

Gassner, John, *Masters of the Drama*, 3rd rev. ed., Dover Publications, Inc., 1954.

Hartnoll, Phyllis (ed.), *The Oxford Companion to the Theatre*, 2nd ed., Oxford University Press, 1957.

Hughes, Glenn, *The Story of the Theatre*, Samuel French, Inc., 1928.

Jones, Robert Edmond, *The Dramatic Imagination*, Theatre Arts Books, 1941.

Matthews, Brander, A *Study of the Drama*, Houghton Mifflin Company, 1910.

Nicoll, Allardyce, *The Development of the Theatre*, Harcourt, Brace & World, Inc., 1945.

Ommanney, Katharine Anne, *The Stage and the School*, 3rd ed., McGraw-Hill Book Company, Inc., 1960.

Wilde, Percival, *The Craftsmanship of the One-Act Play*, Little, Brown, and Company 1923.

CREATIVITY

Anderson, Harold H. (ed.), *Creativity and Its Cultivation*, Harper & Row, Publishers, Inc., 1959.

Barron, Frank, "Creativity," *NEA Journal*, March, 1961, pp. 17 ff.

Getzels, J. W., *Creativity and Intelligence*, John Wiley & Sons, Inc., 1962.

Guilford, J. P., *Personality*, McGraw-Hill Book Company, Inc., 1959.

Lowenfeld, Viktor, *Creative and Mental Growth*, 3rd ed., The Macmil- Company, 1949.

Mearns, Hughes, *Creative Power: The Education of Youth in the Creative Arts*, 2nd rev. ed., Dover Publications, Inc., 1958.

Miel, Alice M., *Creativity in Teaching*, Wadsworth Publishing Co., 1961.

Torrance, E. P. (ed.), *Creativity*, University of Minnesota Center for Continuation Study of the General Extension Division, 1959.

Torrance, E. P., *Guiding Creative Talent*, Prentice-Hall, Inc., 1962.

Torrance, E. P., "Creative Thinking Through the Language Arts," in L. D. Crow and Alice Crow (eds.), *Readings in Human Learning*, David McKay Company, Inc., 1963.

Torrance, E. P., *Education and the Creative Challenge*, University of Minnesota Press, 1963.
Wilt, Miriam E., *Creativity in the Elementary School*, Appleton-Century-Crofts, Inc., 1959.

EDUCATION AND LANGUAGE ARTS

Adshead, Gladys L., *An Inheritance of Poetry*, Houghton Mifflin Company, 1948.
Applegate, Mauree, *Easy is English*, Harper & Row, Publishers, Inc., 1960.
Applegate, Mauree, *Helping Children Write*, International Textbook Company, 1949.
Arbuthnot, May H., *Children and Books*, rev. ed., Scott, Foresman and Company, 1957.
Beauchamp George A., *Basic Dimensions of Elementary Method*, Allyn and Bacon, Inc., 1959.
Brameld, Theodore, *Education for the Emerging Age*, Harper & Row, Publishers, Inc., 1959.
Broudy, Harry S., *Building a Philosophy of Education*, 2nd ed., Prentice-Hall, Inc., 1961.
Course of Study for Teaching the English Language Arts in Elementary, Junior High, and Senior High School, *Guideposts to the English Language Arts*, Seattle Public Schools, 1962.
Dawson, M. A. and Marian Zollinger, *Guiding Language Learning*, World Book Company, 1957.
Fisk, Margaret Palmer, *The Art of the Rhythmic Choir*, Harper & Row, Publishers, Inc., 1950.
Gesell, Arnold and Frances L. Ilg, *The Child from Five to Ten*, Harper & Row, Publishers, Inc., 1946.
Gesell, Arnold, Frances L. Ilg, and Louise Bates Ames, *Youth: The Years from Ten to Sixteen*, Harper & Row, Publishers, Inc., 1956.
Golden Anniversary White House Conference on Children and Youth, *Conference Proceedings*, U.S. Government Printing Office, 1960.
Hayakawa, S. I. (ed.), *Language in Thought and Action*, Harcourt, Brace and Company, 1959.
Hayakawa, S. I., *Our Language and Our World*, Harper & Row, Publishers, Inc., 1959.
Hazard, Paul, *Books, Children and Men*, 2nd ed., The Horn Book, 1947.
Herrick, Virgil E. and L. B. Jacobs (eds.), *Children and the Language Arts*, Prentice-Hall, Inc. 1955.

Meyer, Adolph E., *The Development of Education in the Twentieth Century*, Prentice-Hall, Inc., 1961.

National Council of Teachers of English, Commission on the English Curriculum, *The English Language Arts*, Curriculum Series, Appleton-Century-Crofts, Inc., Vol. I, 1952.

National Council of Teachers of English, Commission on the English Curriculum, *Language Arts for Today's Children*, Curriculum Series, Appleton-Century-Crofts, Inc., Vol. II, 1954.

National Council of Teachers of English, *The National Interest and the Teaching of English*, National Council of Teachers of English, 1961.

Ogilvie, Mardel, *Speech in the Elementary School*, McGraw-Hill Book Company, Inc., 1954.

Phenix, Philip H., *Education and the Common Good*, Harper & Row, Publishers, Inc., 1959.

Sawyer, Ruth, *The Way of the Storyteller*, The Viking Press, 1955.

Strickland, Ruth G., *The Language Arts in the Elementary School*, 2nd ed., D. C. Heath and Company, 1957.

Strunk, William and E. B. White, *Elements of Style*, The Macmillan Company, 1959.

Tidyman, Willard F., and Butterfield, Marguerite, *Teaching the Language Arts*, Prentice-Hall, Inc., 1955.

Van Riper, Charles and Katherine G. Butler, *Speech in the Elementary Classroom*, Harper and Row, Publishers, Inc., 1955.

Weber, Christian O., *Basic Philosophies of Education*, Holt, Rinehart and Winston, Inc., 1960.

Whitehead, Alfred North, *The Aims of Education*, Mentor Books, 1961.

CHILDREN'S LITERATURE—POEMS

Arbuthnot, May H., *Time for Poetry*, Scott, Foresman and Company, 1952.

Asquith, Herbert, *Pillicock Hill*, The Macmillan Company, 1926.

Austin, Mary, *Children Sing in the Far West*, Houghton Mifflin Company, 1928.

Bialik, H. N., *Far Over the Sea*; trans. from Hebrew by Jessie Sampter, Union of American Hebrew Congregations, 1939.

de la Mare, Walter, *Poems for Children*, Holt, Rinehart, and Winston, Inc., 1930.

Field, Rachel, *Taxis and Toadstools*, Doubleday & Company, Inc., 1926.

Fish, Helen Dean, *The Boy's Book of Verse*, J. B. Lippincott Company, 1951.

Holy Bible, King James version.

Lindsay, Vachel, *Collected Poems*, The Macmillan Company, 1942.

Millay, Edna St. Vincent, *Collected Poems*, Harper & Row, Publishers, Inc., 1917.

McFarland, Wilma, *For a Child*, Westminster Press, 1947.

Noyes, Alfred, *Collected Poems in One Volume*, J. B. Lippincott Company, 1948.

Ponst, Marie (trans.), *Fables of La Fontaine*, Grossett and Dunlap, Inc., 1957.

Read, Herbert, *This Way, Delight*, Pantheon Books, Inc., 1956.

Sandburg, Carl, *Chicago Poems*, Holt, Rinehart and Winston, Inc., 1944.

Sechrist, Elizabeth, *One Thousand Poems for Children*, Macrae Smith Company, 1946.

Shakespeare, William, *The Complete Works of William Shakespeare.*

Smith, William Jay, *Laughing Time*, Little, Brown and Company, 1955.

Stevenson, Robert Louis, *A Child's Garden of Verses*, Rand McNally and Company, 1900.

The Tenggren Mother Goose, illus. by Gustaf Tenggren, Little, Brown & Company, 1940.

Tippett, James S., *I Go A-Traveling*, Harper & Row, Publishers, Inc., 1929.

Turner, Nancy Byrd, *Magpie Lane*, Harcourt, Brace & World, Inc., 1955.

Whitman, Walt, *There Was a Child Went Forth*, Harper & Row, Publishers, Inc., 1943.

CHILDREN'S LITERATURE—STORIES AND ANTHOLOGIES

Alcott, Louisa May, *Little Women*, Grossett & Dunlap, Inc., 1947.

Alden, Raymond Macdonald, *Why the Chimes Rang and Other Stories*, The Bobbs-Merrill Company, Inc., 1954.

Andersen, Hans Christian, *Fairy Tales*, The World Publishing Co., 1946.

Arbuthnot, May H. (compiler), *The Arbuthnot Anthology*, Scott, Foresman and Company, 1954.

Bacmeister, Rhoda W., *Stories to Begin On*, E. P. Dutton and Co., Inc., 1940.

Brown, Margaret Wise, *Home for a Bunny*, Golden Press, Inc., 1956.

Bullfinch, Thomas, *A Book of Myths; Selections from Bullfinch's "Age of Fable,"* The Macmillan Company, 1942.

Curry, Charles and Erle Elsworth Clippinger, *Children's Literature*, Rand McNally & Company, 1920.

Grimm's Fairy Tales, Pantheon Books, Inc., 1944.

Hamilton, Edith, *Mythology*, Little, Brown & Co., 1954.

Harper, Wilhelmina (ed.), *The Gunniwolf and Other Merry Tales*, David McKay Company, Inc., 1936.
Harris, Joel Chandler, *Uncle Remus: His Songs and Sayings*, Appleton-Century-Crofts, 1921.
Hawthorne, Nathaniel, *The Wonder Book and Tanglewood Tales*, Houghton Mifflin Company, n.d.
Hollowell, Lillian (ed.), *A Book of Children's Literature*, 2nd ed., Holt, Rinehart and Winston, Inc., 1950.
Holy Bible, King James version.
Huber, Miriam B., *Story and Verse for Children*, The Macmillan Company, 1940.
Jacobs, Joseph (ed.), *English Fairy Tales*, 3rd ed. rev., G. P. Putnam's Sons, 1892.
Johnson, Edna, Evelyn R. Sickels, and Frances Clarke Sayers (eds.), *Anthology of Children's Literature*, 3rd ed. rev., Houghton Mifflin Company, 1959.
Lang, Andrew (ed.), *The Blue Fairy Books*, new ed., Longmans, Green & Co., 1948.
Lang, Andrew (ed.), *The Red Fairy Book*, new ed., Longmans, Green & Co., 1948.
Pyle, Howard, *Merry Adventures of Robin Hood of Great Renown in Nottinghamshire*, Charles Scribner's Sons, 1953.
Ruskin, John, *King of the Golden River*, J. B. Lippincott Company, 1932.
Sandburg, Carl, *Rootabaga Stories*, Harcourt, Brace & World, Inc., 1922.
Seton, Ernest Thompson, *Wild Animals I Have Known*, Charles Scribner's Sons, 1898.
Thorne-Thomsen, Gudrun (ed.), *East o' the Sun and West o' the Moon with Other Norwegian Folk Tales*, rev. ed., Harper & Row, Publishers, Inc., 1946.
Uchida, Yoshiko, *The Dancing Kettle, and Other Japanese Folk Tales, Retold*, Harcourt, Brace & World, Inc., 1948.

RELATED CREATIVE ARTS

Andrews, Gladys, *Creative Rhythmic Movement for Children*, Prentice-Hall, Inc., 1954.
Batchelder, Marjorie, and Virginia Lee Comer, *Puppets and Plays: A Creative Approach*, Harper & Row, Publishers, Inc., 1956.
Beaton, Mabel, and Les Beaton, *Marionettes: A Hobby for Everyone*, Thomas Y. Crowell Company, 1948.

Cole, Natalie R., *The Arts in the Classroom*, The John Day Company, Inc., 1940.

Dixon, C. Madeleine, *The Power of the Dance*, The John Day Company, Inc., 1939.

Hughes, Langston, *The First Book of Rhythms*, Franklin Watts, Inc., 1954.

Joseph, Helen Haiman, *A Book of Marionettes*, B. W. Huebsch and Co., 1927.

Lowenfeld, Viktor, *Your Child and His Art*, The Macmillan Company, 1954.

McPharlin, Paul, *The Puppet Theatre in America: A History 1524 to Now*, Harper & Row, Publishers, Inc., 1949.

Robertson, S. M., *Creative Crafts in Education*, Robert Bentley, Inc., 1953.